VERMONT COLLEGE
MONTPELIER,
WITHDRAWN
D0562508

BASIC PRINCIPLES OF
MOLECULAR GENETICS

Basic Principles of Molecular Genetics

IRWIN H. HERSKOWITZ
Hunter College, The City University of New York

Little, Brown and Company • Boston

Copyright © 1967 by Little, Brown and Company (Inc.)

ALL RIGHTS RESERVED. NO PART OF THIS BOOK MAY BE REPRODUCED IN ANY FORM OR BY ANY ELECTRONIC OR MECHANICAL MEANS INCLUDING INFORMATION STORAGE AND RETRIEVAL SYSTEMS WITHOUT PERMISSION IN WRITING FROM THE PUBLISHER, EXCEPT BY A REVIEWER WHO MAY QUOTE BRIEF PASSAGES IN A REVIEW.

Library of Congress Catalog Card No. 67-18000

First Printing

Published simultaneously in Canada
by Little, Brown & Company (Canada) Limited

Printed in the United States of America

575.21
H572b

Preface

The present time seems appropriate for a textbook designed to present the basic facts and principles of molecular genetics. Such an attempt has been made possible by our newly-acquired wealth of knowledge of the subject, and has been made necessary by the unifying role of molecular genetics in the entire field of biology. In this book the properties of genetic material – its physics and chemistry, replication, function, mutation, recombination, regulation, and evolution – are discussed at the molecular level whenever possible. The most essential information is presented as a series of conclusions or postulates, each of which is individually proved, supported, or discussed. Also included are questions and points which promise to be areas for future investigation.

Each chapter begins with a brief introduction and ends with a series of discussion questions and problems followed by a bibliography.

Much of the text material can be covered in fifteen to twenty periods of an undergraduate college course which has been preceded by a course in biological science at the college or secondary school level.

25757

Acknowledgments

I wish to thank my wife, Reida Postrel Herskowitz, for preparing the typescript, and my present and former students for numerous suggestions. I also wish to express special appreciation to Joel Herskowitz and Ira Herskowitz, my sons, for the clarity of the presentation is due largely to their extensive revision of the manuscript.

Contents

*The book is respectfully
and affectionately dedicated to the memory of
Hermann Joseph Muller*

CHAPTER 1

Genetic Material

All organisms contain information for their self-maintenance and self-reproduction. This book is devoted to a consideration of the molecular basis of this information and its use in organisms. Let us investigate first the general nature of this informational material and then its specific form in several simple organisms. In the next chapter we will deal further with its chemical and physical properties.

1·1 *The genetic material of an organism contains the information for the formation of a unique set of proteins and for the organism's self-maintenance and self-reproduction.*

Common to every organism on earth today are two properties – the abilities to maintain its individuality for a period of time and to produce offspring of the same kind. This self-preservation and self-reproduction in the face of an ever-changing environment depends at the molecular level upon the presence and arrangement of essentially three types of giant molecules, or *macromolecules* – namely, *carbohydrates, proteins,* and *nucleic acids.* Lipids, which are involved in membrane structure and energy storage, are another important class of molecules. Simpler chemical substances – water, for example, which makes up the greatest bulk of most organisms – are usually also needed for structure, maintenance, and reproduction.

The carbohydrates and their derivatives store chemical energy that can be used for maintenance and reproduction. Thus these substances serve to prolong the period of time an organism can exist. Although most organisms contain a significant amount of carbohydrates, some viruses (the simplest organisms) contain none at all. Composed entirely of protein combined with nucleic acid, such viruses persist, and may under appropriate conditions reproduce, in the absence of carbohydrates.

The proteins, on the other hand, play a somewhat more integral role in structure, maintenance, and reproduction; for all organisms contain these macromolecules. Moreover, the uniqueness of each kind of organism is

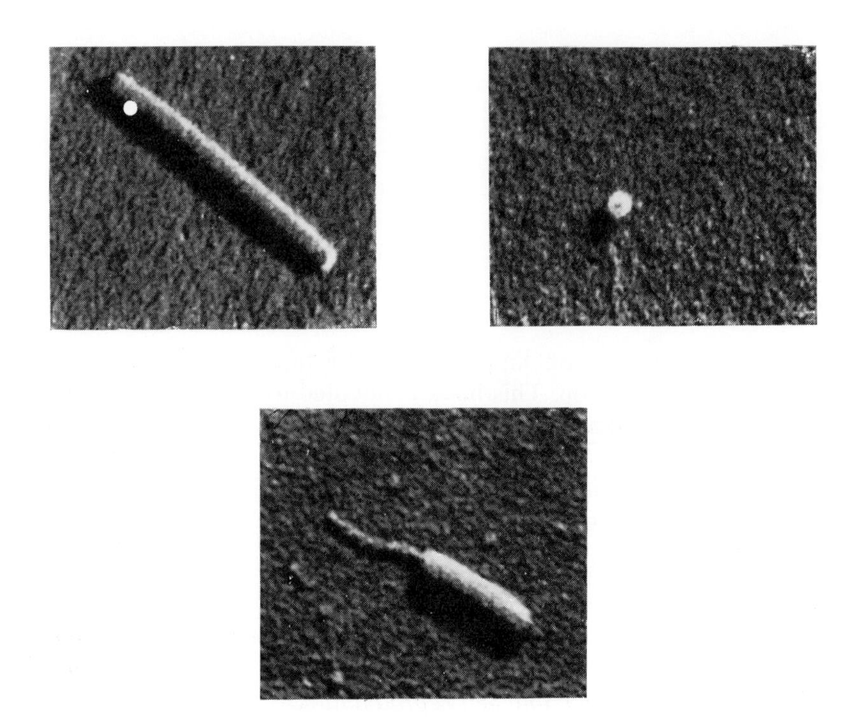

Figure 1-1. Electron micrographs of tobacco mosaic virus (TMV) showing its general configuration (top, left) and its hollow core (top, right). The bottom photo shows a particle whose protein has been partially removed by treatment with detergent, leaving a thinner strand of RNA. (Courtesy of R. G. Hart)

associated with a unique set of protein molecules. Proteins are an essential part of membranes, which maintain the physical integrity of organisms, and are also enzymes, which catalyze their metabolic reactions. Although the structure and metabolic activities of a cell are organized for its preservation, the protein components are continually being destroyed and replaced throughout the cell's existence. Therefore, an organism must possess initially and must retain during its life instructions for producing proteins of correct kinds and amounts. Such information must also be transmitted to and maintained in its offspring.

The two properties common to all organisms thus have a common basis: a store of preserved, replicable, and transmissible information – the *genetic material.* We can rule out carbohydrates as the usual genetic material because of their absence from a number of viruses. Such viruses can be used to study whether proteins, nucleic acids, or both constitute the genetic material.

1·2 *Ribonucleic acid (RNA) is the genetic material of some viruses.*

Tobacco mosaic virus (TMV) (Figure 1-1) is composed entirely of a characteristic protein complexed with a specific type of nucleic acid, *ribonucleic acid (RNA)*. After a TMV particle enters a host tobacco cell and a suitable incubation period has elapsed, hundreds of TMV progeny are formed. Since uninfected tobacco cells do not synthesize the characteristic protein of TMV, the virus particle must contain the information required for its synthesis.

The RNA of TMV particles can be isolated by extracting the protein with a phenol and water mixture, a procedure which leaves the RNA in the aqueous phase. When tobacco cells are exposed to the protein fraction, they do not synthesize more viral protein. Cells exposed to the RNA fraction, however, produce hundreds of TMV progeny whose protein and RNA composition is identical to that of the infecting virus. Different strains of TMV and different strains of tobacco have been tested with the same result: viral progeny identical to the parent type were produced when the nucleic acid (RNA) fraction was used. We conclude therefore that the RNA of TMV contains the information required for synthesis of both viral protein and more RNA – that RNA is the genetic material of the tobacco mosaic virus.

Poliomyelitis, influenza, and encephalitis viruses as well as some *bacteriophages,* or *phages* (viruses that attack bacteria) are other organisms composed solely of RNA and protein. RNA isolated from such viruses, as with TMV, gives rise to progeny of the same kind. Thus RNA is the genetic material of these organisms, too.

1·3 *Deoxyribonucleic acid (DNA) is the genetic material of other viruses.*

Some viruses consist only of a characteristic protein combined with *deoxyribonucleic acid (DNA)* rather than RNA. As before, we can obtain pure viral nucleic acid by phenol treatment. When DNA from ϕX174 (ϕ = phage) – a rather simple, spherical phage – is mixed with *Escherichia coli* bacteria (with cell walls removed to facilitate penetration of certain chemicals), ϕX174 progeny are produced. Since the protein fraction of the virus transfers no such information, we conclude that DNA is its genetic material.

Other phages of *E. coli* (those of the T series) also contain DNA. Larger and structurally more complex than ϕX174, T phages contain their nucleic acid within a protein "head" (Figure 1-2). Since DNA contains no sulfur and T-phage protein contains no phosphorus, we can carry out the following experiment. We label the DNA of one phage sample by

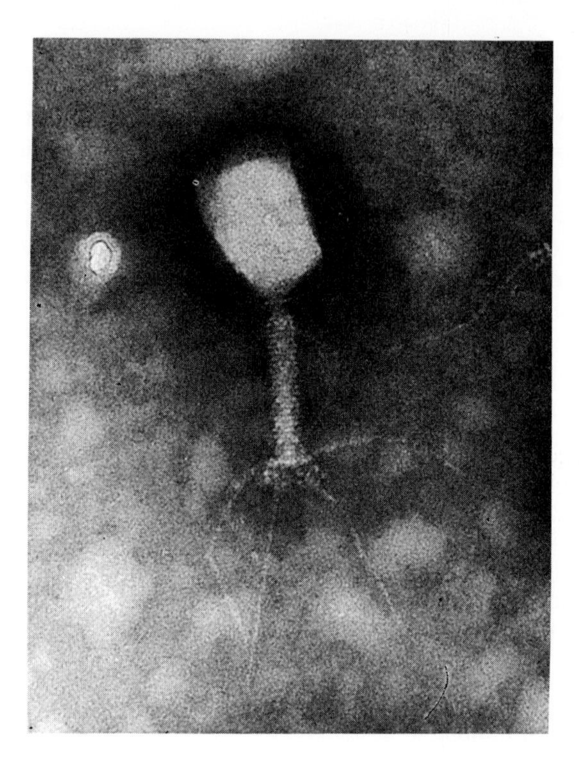

Figure 1-2. A. Electron micrograph of bacteriophage T4 (magnification 300,000 ×). (Courtesy of T. F. Anderson)

growing the viruses in bacteria containing radioactive phosphorus, P^{32}; we label the protein of another sample by growing the phage in bacteria containing radioactive sulfur, S^{35}. Labeled phage are then permitted to infect "cold," that is, unradioactive, *E. coli.* In one sample all the P^{32} (hence all of the DNA) enters the bacterium; in the other only about 3% of the S^{35} (thus only a small fraction of the protein) enters. Even if 80% of the phage protein attached to the outside of the host cells is removed by the shearing action of a blender, a full yield of progeny phage results. Such findings prove that DNA is the genetic material of T phages.

1·4 *Before the DNA or RNA of a cell organelle can be considered genetic material, it must be shown to contain information that is used for its own replication.*

DNA and RNA occur in various cell organelles. Most DNA occurs in threadlike bodies, *chromosomes,* found in the nuclear areas of bacteria

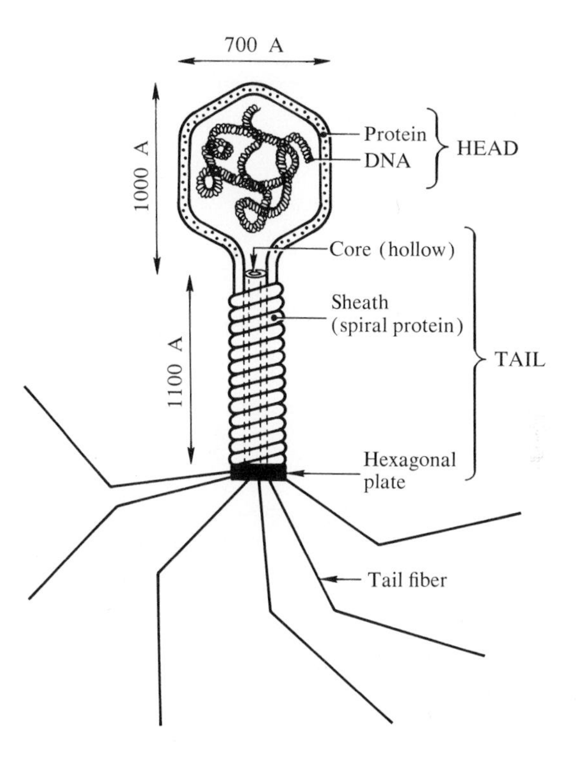

Figure 1-2. B. Diagrammatic representation of the structures observed in intact and triggered T-even phages of *E. coli.*

and blue-green algae and in the nuclei of cells of higher organisms (Figure 1-3). When stained with certain dyes, such chromosomal DNA is called *chromatin.* DNA is also found in mitochondria, chloroplasts, centrioles, and basal granules of cilia and flagella. DNA is attached to or present in the cell membrane in bacteria and is reported to occur in the cell membrane of red blood corpuscles which do not contain nuclei.

More than three-quarters of the RNA in a cell is located in *ribosomes,* small particles found in great numbers in the cytoplasm (in plastids, and free or attached to the endoplasmic reticulum) and in the nucleus (inside and outside the nucleolus). RNA is also present in mitochondria and in chromosomes.

Since replicability is the property of genetic material most intimately involved with informational continuity, we can consider it the most essential property. Hence, we must show that the nucleic acid of an organelle contains information for its own replication before we can regard it as genetic material. Earlier, in identifying as genetic material the nucleic acid of several viruses, we followed this procedure.

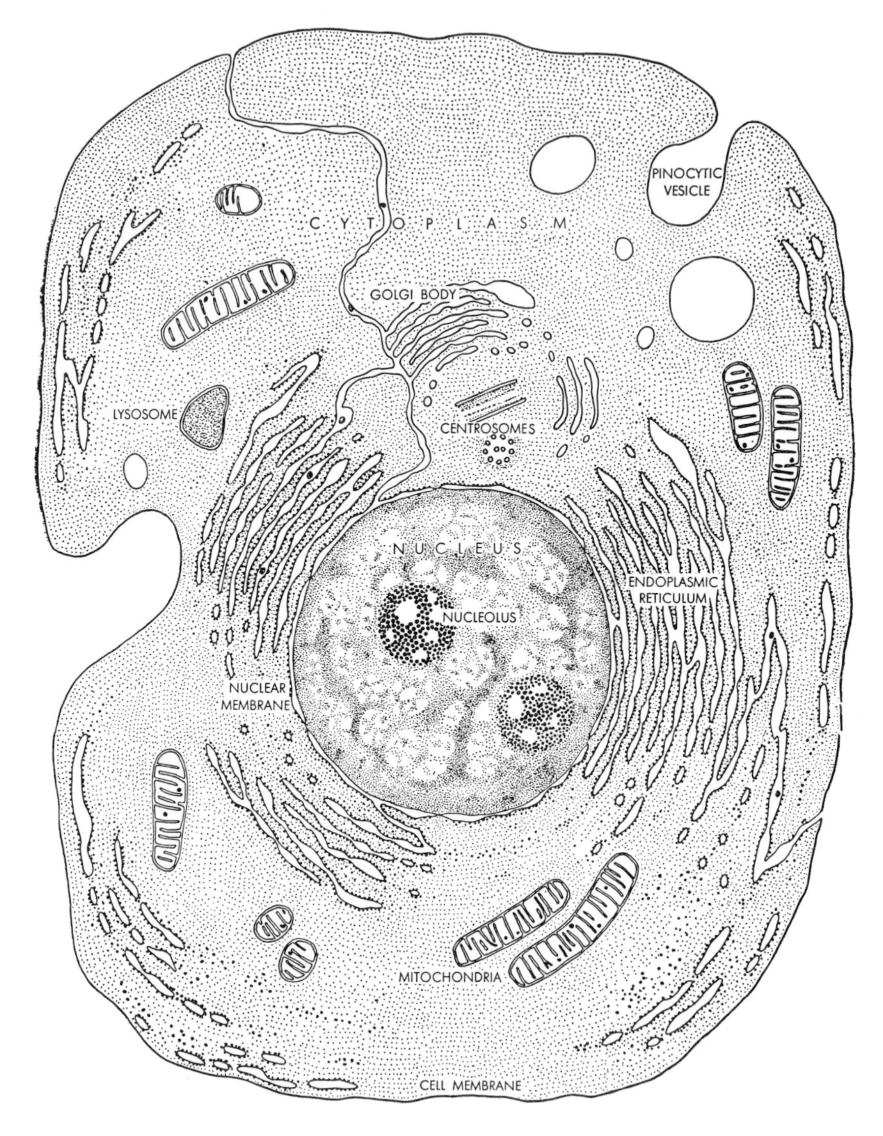

Figure 1-3. Diagrammatic cross-section of a cell. (Reprinted with permission. Copyright 1961 by Scientific American, Inc. All rights reserved.)

1·5 *Molecular genetics is the study of the properties of genetic material at the molecular level.*

A mature virus particle neither metabolizes nor replicates outside of its host cell. Within a host, however, the virus preserves its information by utilizing its environment for the replication of its own nucleic acid, for the formation of its characteristic protein, and for the assembly of these molecules into viral progeny. For a more complete understanding of a virus's life activities, we would like to answer the following questions about genetic material:

> What are the chemical and physical characteristics of DNA and RNA? Where and how do nucleic acids store information? How are DNA and RNA replicated? In what way does genetic material direct the synthesis of proteins? Do DNA and RNA contain other information? Once replicated, how is genetic material distributed? What are the consequences of chemical changes in genetic material and of errors in distribution and in replication? How did genetic material originate? How did it evolve?

Answers to such questions pertain not only to viruses but to the entire spectrum of living things. In the following chapters we will consider properties of genetic material at the molecular level whenever possible and, in so doing, seek to clarify basic principles of molecular genetics.

Questions and Problems

1·1 A growing crystal of table salt that can "reproduce" after fragmentation is not considered an organism. Why?

1·2 Does an organism that fails to reproduce contain genetic material? Explain.

1·3 How would you identify the genetic material of an organism from another planet?

1·4 If nucleic acid is the sole carrier of information of some viruses, why is their transmissive form not simply nucleic acid?

1·5 What can you conclude about the genetic material of T phages from the experiment described in Section 1·3?

1·6 Discuss the functional specialization of different kinds of macromolecules.

1·7 Give a definition of molecular genetics.

References

General – Journals

Cold Spring Harbor Symposia on Quantitative Biology
Journal of Molecular Biology
Nature (London)
Proceedings of the National Academy of Sciences (United States)
Science

General – Books

Adelberg, E. A. (Editor) 1966. *Papers on Bacterial Genetics, Second Edition.* Boston: Little, Brown and Co.

Haggis, G. H., Michie, D., Muir, A. R., Roberts, K. B., and Walker, P. M. B. 1964. *Introduction to Molecular Biology.* New York: J. Wiley & Sons, Inc.

Herskowitz, I. H. 1965. *Genetics, Second Edition.* Boston: Little, Brown and Co. (A supplement contains Nobel Prize Lectures through 1962 dealing with genetics.)

Ingram, V. M. 1966. *The Biosynthesis of Macromolecules.* New York: W. A. Benjamin, Inc.

Kennedy, D. (Editor) 1965. *The Living Cell.* San Francisco: W. H. Freeman & Co. (Readings from *Scientific American.*)

Ravin, A. W. 1965. *The Evolution of Genetics.* New York: Academic Press.

Steiner, R. F. 1965. *The Chemical Foundations of Molecular Biology.* Princeton: D. Van Nostrand Co., Inc.

Stent, G. S. (Editor) 1965. *Papers on Bacterial Viruses, Second Edition.* Boston: Little, Brown and Co.

Taylor, J. H. (Editor) 1963. *Molecular Genetics, Part I.* New York: Academic Press.

Taylor, J. H. (Editor) 1965. *Selected Papers on Molecular Genetics.* New York: Academic Press.

Vogel, H. J., Bryson, V., and Lampen, J. O. (Editors) 1963. *Informational Macromolecules.* New York: Academic Press.

Watson, J. D. 1965. *Molecular Biology of the Gene.* New York: W. A. Benjamin, Inc.

Specific

Gierer, A. 1960. Ribonucleic acid as genetic material of viruses, in *Microbial Genetics,* Hayes, W., and Clowes, R. C. (Editors), Cambridge: Cambridge University Press, 1960, pp. 248–271.

Hershey, A. D., and Chase, M. 1952. Independent functions of viral protein and nucleic acid in growth of bacteriophage. J. Gen. Physiol., 36: 39–54. Reprinted in *Papers on Bacterial Viruses, Second Edition.* Stent, G. S. (Editor), Boston: Little, Brown and Co., 1965, pp. 87–104.

Philipson, L., and Zetterqvist, Ö. 1964. The presence of DNA in human erythrocyte membranes. Biochim. Biophys. Acta, 91: 171–173.

Randall, J., and Disbrey, C. 1965. Evidence for the presence of DNA at basal-body sites in *Tetrahymena pyriformis.* Proc. Roy. Soc., B, 162: 473–491.

CHAPTER 2

Primary Structure of Nucleic Acids

To determine what part of a nucleic acid contains information, what this information is, and how it is used, we will consider first the *primary structure* of nucleic acids, that is, the organization of component parts into single strands.

2·1 *A nucleic acid is a polymer of nucleotides. Its monomeric units consist of a phosphate, a pentose, and an organic base.*

DNA and RNA are made up of many similar units, *nucleotides,* and are thus polymers of nucleotide monomers, or *polynucleotides.* Each nucleotide consists of one *phosphate* (PO_4) group, one *pentose* (a five-carbon sugar), and one *organic base* in which nitrogen and carbon atoms are arranged in one or two aromatic rings. The average molecular weight (MW) of a nucleotide is 330.

2·2 *The usual pentose of RNA is D-ribose (ribose); in DNA it is 2′-deoxy-D-ribose (deoxyribose).*

Four of the five carbons in a pentose plus a single atom of oxygen can form a five-membered ring (Figure 2-1). (By convention, ring carbons are often omitted in structural diagrams, as in Figure 2-1a′ and b′.) The pentose usually found in RNA is *D-ribose,* commonly called *ribose* (Fig-

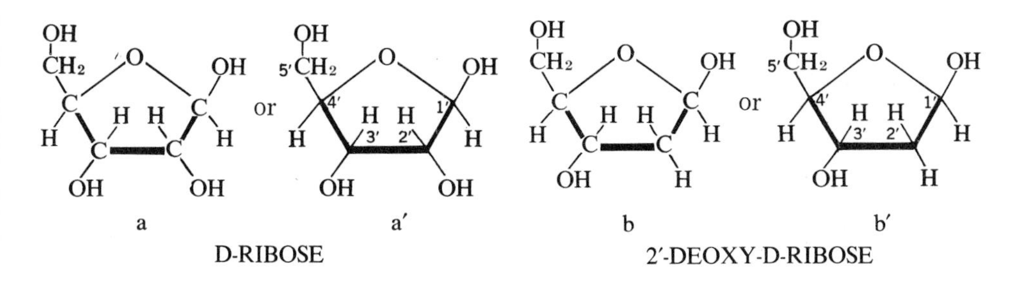

Figure 2-1. Pentoses found in nucleic acids.

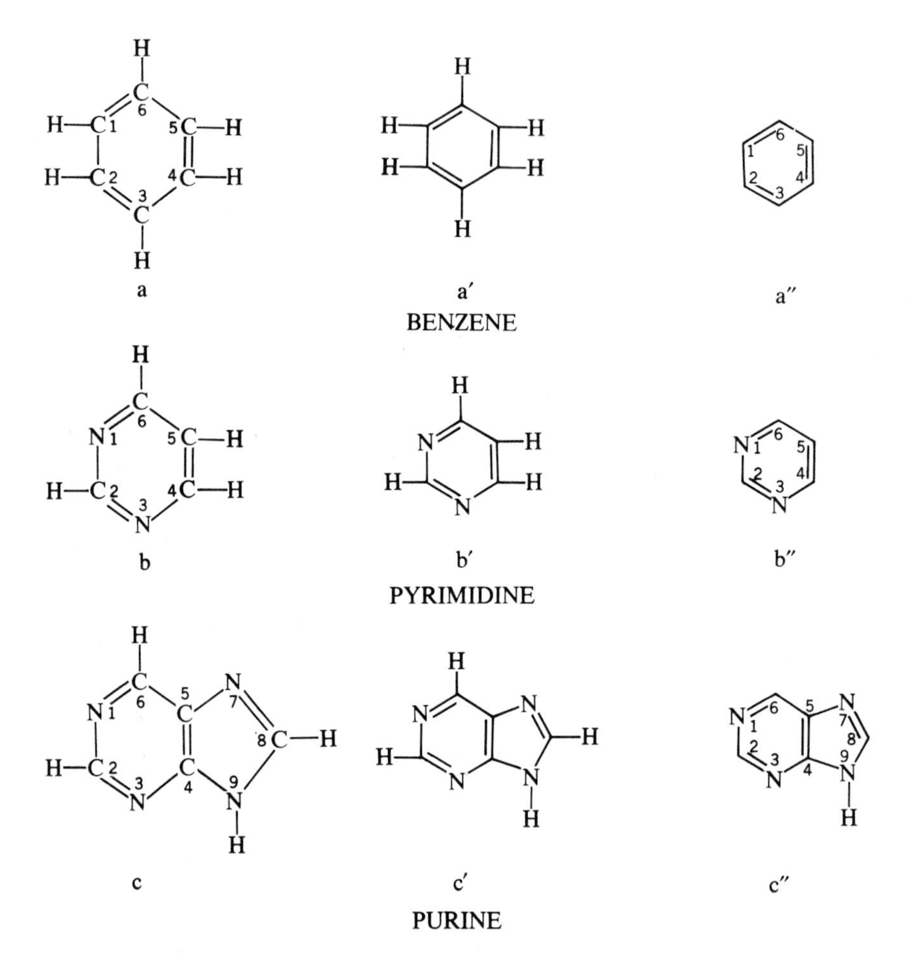

Figure 2-2. Relationship between certain ring compounds.

ure 2-1a and a′), which has a hydroxyl (OH) group at positions 1′, 2′, 3′, and 5′. (The positions of carbon atoms in the pentose are primed so they can be distinguished from the positions of carbons in an organic base.) Since the pentose usually found in DNA is a ribose which lacks oxygen at the 2′ position, it is called *2′-deoxy-D-ribose*, or *deoxyribose* (Figure 2-1b and b′).

2·3 *The organic base of a nucleotide is either a pyrimidine or a purine. The most common pyrimidines are cytosine (C) and uracil (U) in RNA, and cytosine and thymine (T) in DNA. The most common purines in RNA and DNA are adenine (A) and guanine (G).*

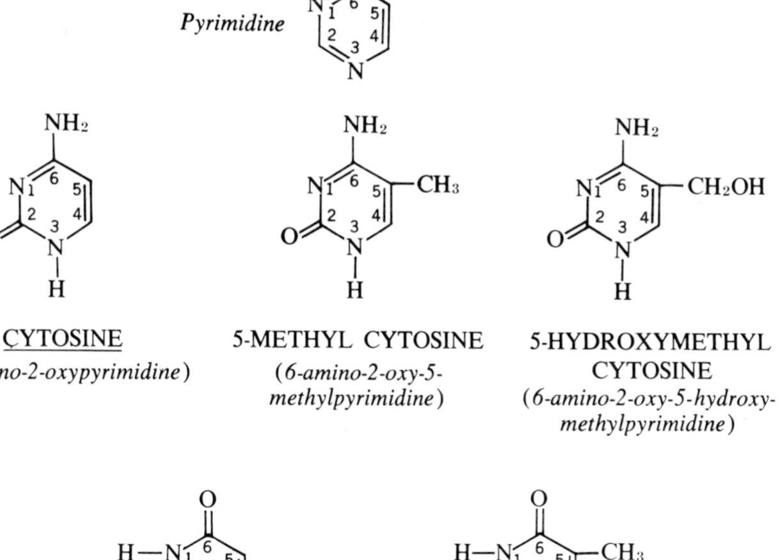

URACIL
(*2,6-oxypyrimidine*)

THYMINE
(*2,6-oxy-5-methylpyrimidine*)
(*5-methyl uracil*)

Figure 2-3. Pyrimidines. Names of pyrimidines occurring most often in DNA are underlined.

The structure of an organic base in a nucleotide is related to that of benzene, an aromatic hydrocarbon with a six-membered ring (Figures 2-2a, a′, and a″). The fundamental ring of the organic base is a *pyrimidine* ring, in which N replaces CH at positions 1 and 3 in the benzene ring (Figure 2-2b). Figures 2-2b′ and 2b″ are successive abbreviations of this formula corresponding to those used for benzene.

The other kind of organic base in nucleotides is a *purine,* which is closely related to a pyrimidine. A purine molecule consists of a pyrimidine ring joined to a 5-membered imidazole ring at positions 4 and 5 (Figures 2-2c, c′, and c″). Hereafter, we will use the most abbreviated of these structural representations for pyrimidines and purines.

Figure 2-3 gives structural formulas for the most common pyrimidines in nucleic acids. All the derivatives shown have an oxygen at position 2

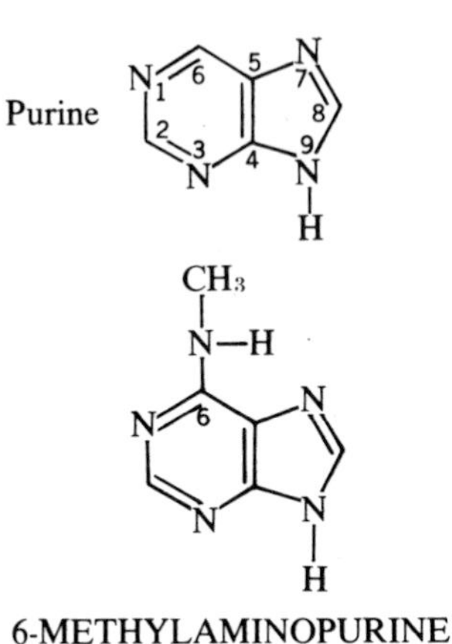

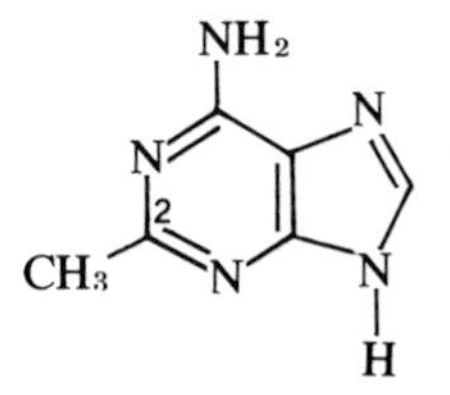

ADENINE
(*6-aminopurine*)

6-METHYLAMINOPURINE

2-METHYL ADENINE
(*2-methyl-6-aminopurine*)

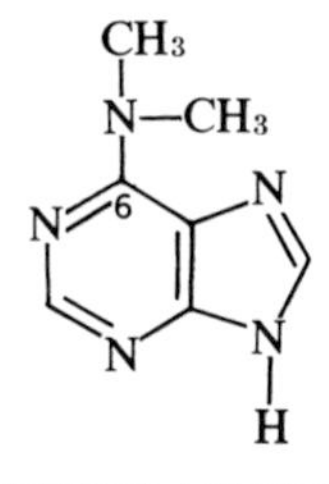

6-DIMETHYLAMINOPURINE

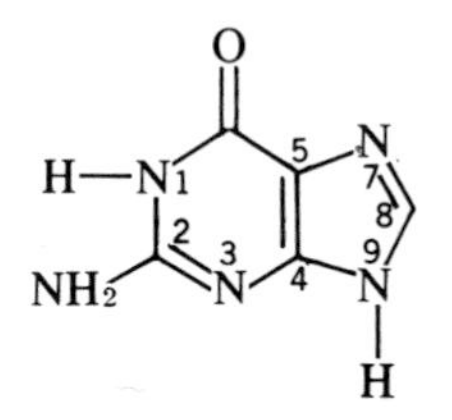

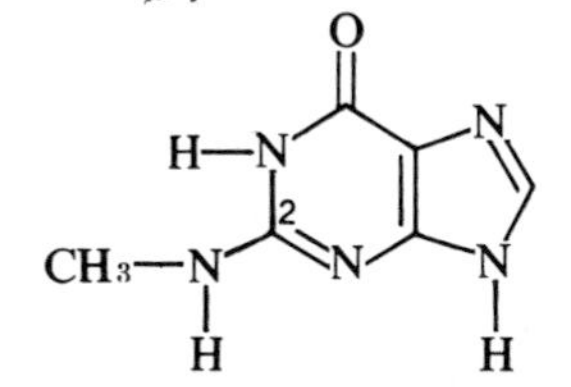

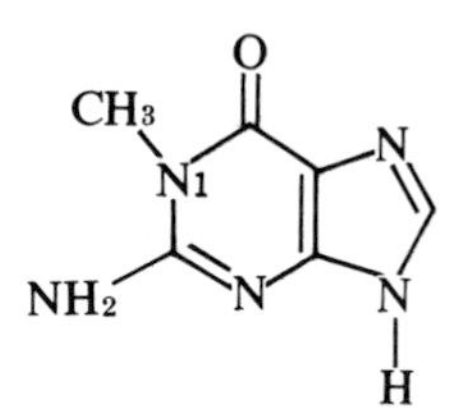

GUANINE
(*2-amino-6-oxypurine*)

2-METHYLAMINO GUANINE

1-METHYL GUANINE

Figure 2-4. Purines. Names of purines occurring most often in RNA and DNA are underlined.

in the keto form (O=C$\lessgtr$). The two pyrimidines found most often in RNA are *cytosine* (C) and *uracil* (U). Cytosine has an amino (NH_2) group at position 6, whereas uracil has a keto oxygen at this position. Cytosine and *thymine* (T) are the two pyrimidines usually found in DNA. Since thymine is uracil with a methyl (CH_3) group at position 5, we can also call it 5-methyl uracil. The pyrimidines differ primarily in the groups attached at the 5 and 6 positions.

In Figure 2-4 are structural formulas for several purines occurring in nucleic acids. The two most common purines in RNA and DNA are *adenine* (A) and *guanine* (G). Adenine has an NH_2 group at position 6, whereas guanine has an O in keto form at this position and an NH_2 group at position 2. Purines differ most significantly in the groups at the 2 and 6 positions.

2·4 *The combination of a pentose and an organic base is a nucleoside. Those in DNA are deoxyribonucleosides and those in RNA are ribonucleosides.*

A purine or pyrimidine linked with a pentose is a *nucleoside*. The usual nucleosides in DNA, *deoxyribonucleosides,* are deoxycytidine, deoxythymidine, deoxyadenosine, and deoxyguanosine (Figure 2-5). In RNA

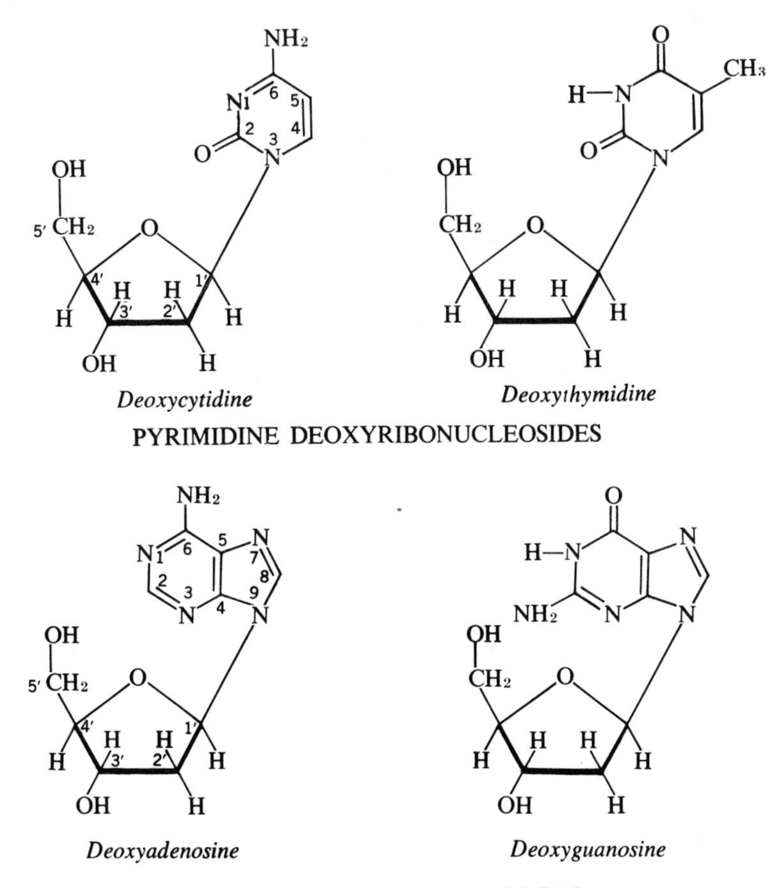

Figure 2-5. Common deoxyribonucleosides.

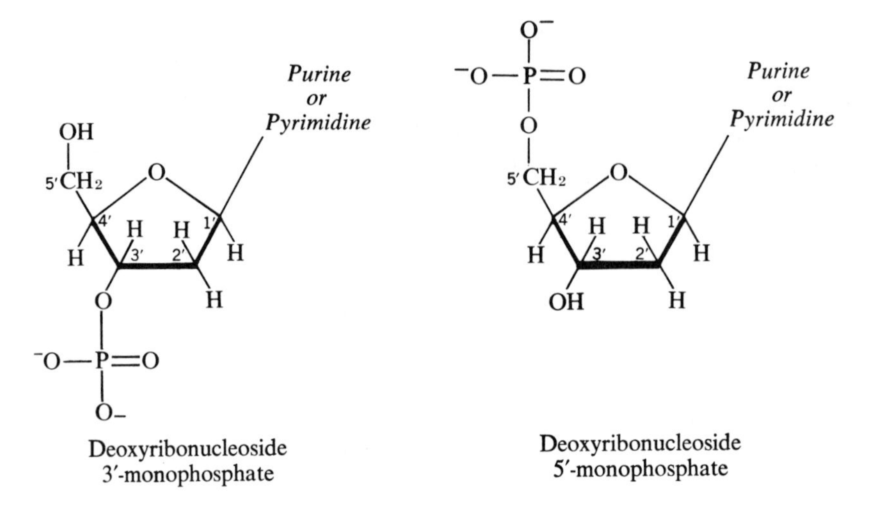

Figure 2-6. Deoxyribonucleotides.

the usual nucleosides are cytidine, uridine, adenosine, and guanosine – *ribonucleosides*. The linkage that forms a nucleoside is between the 1′ position of the pentose and position 3 of pyrimidines or position 9 of purines.

2·5 *A nucleoside and a phosphate make up a nucleotide. Those in DNA are deoxyribonucleotides and those in RNA are ribonucleotides.*

A *nucleotide* consists of a phosphate group joined to either the 3′ or 5′ carbon of the sugar in a nucleoside. The nucleotides in DNA are *deoxyribonucleotides* (Figure 2-6), or deoxyribonucleoside monophosphates. Deoxyribonucleoside 5′-monophosphates of C, T, A, and G are deoxycytidylic acid, deoxythymidylic acid, deoxyadenylic acid, and deoxyguanylic acid.

The nucleotides in RNA are *ribonucleotides;* the ribonucleoside 5′-monophosphates of C, U, A, and G are cytidylic acid, uridylic acid, adenylic acid, and guanylic acid.

2·6 *Nucleic acids are linear, polarized polymers with a pentose-phosphate backbone. This primary structure imposes no restrictions upon the sequence of organic bases nor any limit to the length of the nucleic acid molecule.*

DNA is a *polydeoxyribonucleotide* – a chain in which deoxyribonucleotides comprise the links. We can see how the links join by examining the

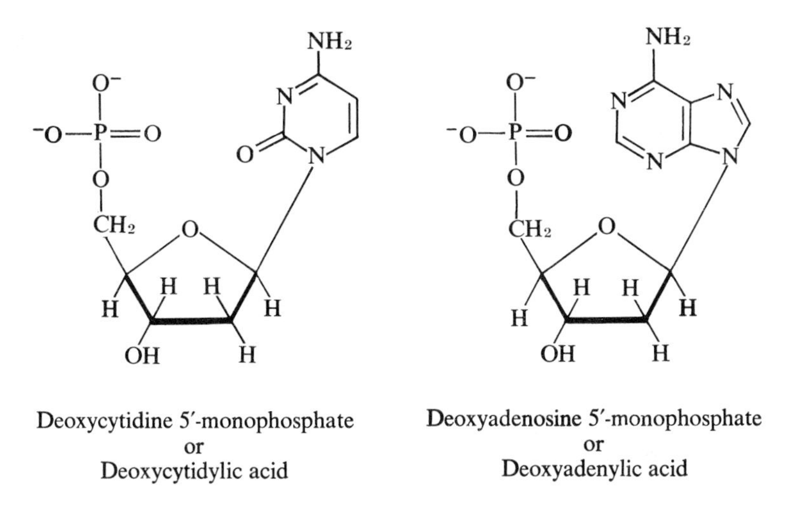

Figure 2-7. Specific deoxyribonucleotides.

two separate deoxyribonucleoside 5′-monophosphates shown in Figure 2-7. They can join if the topmost O of the right compound replaces the OH at position 3′ of the sugar in the left compound. Since deoxyribonucleoside 5′-monophosphates can join by means of phosphate linkage to the 3′ position, polydeoxyribonucleotide chains of great length are possible (Figure 2-8). Linear, unbranched macromolecules, polydeoxyribonucleotides are of indefinite length, with a backbone of sugar-phosphate linkages and with a linearity independent of the particular bases present at any point. In other words, the primary structure of the chain is uninfluenced by the sequence of the bases, and vice versa. We notice further that this polymer of deoxyribonucleotides does not read the same in both directions. As indicated by the arrows, the phosphate to sugar linkages are in a 3′5′ sequence; in the opposite direction, however, the order is 5′3′. Because of this difference, the DNA molecule is said to be *polarized.*

Ribonucleosides of RNA are linked by phosphates joined both at the 3′ and 5′ positions of the sugar, just as are the deoxyribonucleosides of DNA. Consequently, Figure 2-8 can represent a *polyribonucleotide* if we add an O at each 2′ position (making each sugar D-ribose) and substitute U for T.

In summary, the nucleic acids DNA and RNA occur as *polynucleotides* (polydeoxyribonucleotides or polyribonucleotides). Each polynucleotide is made up of *mononucleotides* (deoxyribo- or ribonucleotides), which in turn are composed of phosphates joined to the 5′ carbon of *nucleosides* (deoxyribo- or ribonucleosides). These nucleosides consist of a *pentose* (deoxyribose or ribose) joined to a *pyrimidine* (usually C or T for DNA; C or U for RNA) or to a *purine* (usually A or G).

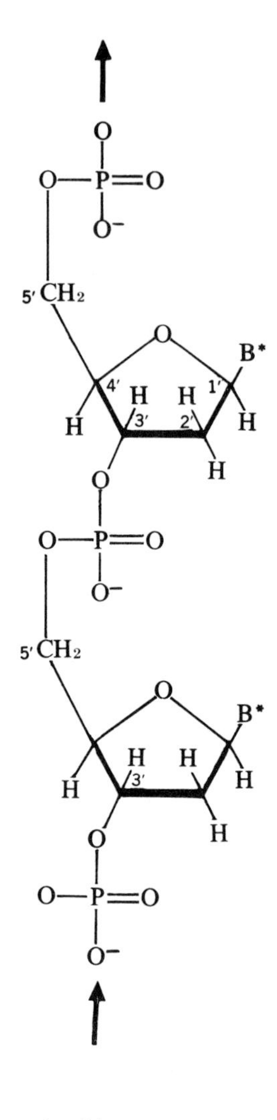

* Pyrimidine or purine base of appropriate type (usually cytosine, thymine, adenine or guanine).

Figure 2-8. Polydeoxyribonucleotide.

2·7 *Nucleic acids are of finite length. Their termination may involve specific amino acid sequences.*

Although a nucleic acid is theoretically of indefinite length, it does of course have an end, and may have a particular way of ending. Evidence indicates that in *E. coli,* proteins link DNA segments of 2.5×10^8 molecular weight. Small amounts of amino acids – some 0.1% by weight – have been found in association with "purified" DNA extracted from human sperm and may be involved in nucleic acid termination. Amino acids are also reported to occur in the DNA of human leucocytes, calf thymus cells, and the vaccinia virus.

2·8 *The DNA of certain phages is a single polynucleotide ring.*

TMV RNA and sRNA (see p. 54), as well as DNA of certain viruses, are single polynucleotides with two ends. The DNA of mature ϕX174, however, has no ends. It is a single polynucleotide ring, a polymer of nearly 4500 deoxyribonucleotides. Each nucleotide is approximately 10A in diameter and contributes about 3.4A to the length of the chain.

2·9 *Naturally-occurring DNA and RNA vary considerably in the types of bases they contain. Two factors can account for this variation: the types of bases incorporated when the polynucleotide is formed, and chemical changes occurring after polynucleotide formation.*

In the DNA of some viruses, one of the usual pyrimidines is replaced completely by another pyrimidine. In ϕPBS1 and ϕPBS2, for example, uracil occurs in place of thymine. The infectious bovine rhinotracheitis virus contains thymine modified by substitution of a bromo group for the methyl group at position 5. And in T-even phages – T2, T4, T6 – the hydrogen at position 5 of cytosine is replaced by a hydroxymethyl (CH_2OH) group. The result is 5-hydroxymethyl cytosine ($\overline{\text{HMC}}$). A further variation occurs when glucose is added to some $\overline{\text{HMC}}$ in phage DNA.

Still other pyrimidines are found in DNA. 5-methyl cytosine occurs in higher organisms such as mammals, fish, insects, and cereal grains but not in many microorganisms – e.g., bacteria, actinomycetes, yeasts, algae, and protozoans.

DNA likewise contains a variety of purines. 6-methyl adenine occurs with a frequency of up to 0.7% of all bases in some bacteria and their phages, but is not found in DNA of actinomycetes, yeast, and higher plants and animals. Trace amounts of 2-methyl A, 1-methyl G, 2-methylamino G, and 6-dimethylaminopurine are also reported to occur in DNA.

In contrast to the pyrimidines, the usual purines (A and G) are not known to be replaced completely or in appreciable quantity by other purines when DNA is made under ordinary conditions in living organisms. For example, several molecules structurally similar to adenosine occur naturally, but none of these analogs has been found in polyribonucleotides of living organisms. Thus the cell must have a way to produce these ribonucleosides yet keep them out of nucleic acid polymers.

Many variations of C, A, and G found in DNA can be considered the result of methylation. In the presence of appropriate enzymes, DNA can be methylated to form 5-methyl C (from cytosine) and 6-methylaminopurine (from adenine). The DNA of different organisms is methylated to different extents.

In one type of RNA (sRNA) some 2% of the purine and pyrimidine bases are methylated. The amino acid methionine (Figure 6-1) serves as donor of the methyl groups. Some bases of another kind of RNA (rRNA) may also be methylated. Bases that are already part of a polyribonucleotide seem capable of methylation. Several different enzymes, *RNA methylases,* take part in the synthesis of 1-methyl G, thymine (5-methyl U), 5-methyl C, 2-methyl A, 6-methylaminopurine, and 6-dimethylaminopurine. These RNA methylases are found in the nucleolus and differ from species to species.

2·10 *The complete base sequence is known for several sRNA molecules. A number of bases other than A, U, C, and G are present.*

The primary structure of several naturally-occurring RNA molecules has been completely determined; the base sequence of one is given in Figure 2-9. This polyribonucleotide is an sRNA molecule (in the form of a sodium salt) with a molecular weight of 26,600; it consists of 77 ribonucleotides. Although most nucleotide residues contain the common bases A, U, C, and G, some contain such bases as the following (Figure 2-10): hypoxanthine, 1-methylhypoxanthine, pseudouracil, 5-methyl uracil (thymine), 5,6-dihydrouracil, 1-methyl guanine and N^2-dimethylguanine.

2·11 *The four most common bases occur in different proportions in the DNA of different species.*

Percentages of A, T, G, and C in DNA extracted from organisms of various species are given in Figure 2-11. We see a considerable variation in the relative frequencies of these bases – ranging from an organism relatively rich in A and T and poor in C and G (sea urchin) to one in which A and T are much less abundant than C and G (tubercle bacillus).

The chicken, salmon, and locust – certainly very different genetically – have very similar base ratios. Roughly the same relative frequencies of bases are also found in different members of a single species, when the total DNA in cells with large DNA content is analyzed. Likewise, the base ratios of normal (and neoplastic) tissues from different human beings are essentially identical. In order to give rise to the great variation within and among species, therefore, a set of chromosomes in one individual must contain many DNA molecules which differ not only in base content but also in sequence from the DNA molecules of another.

2·12 *Different species differ in quantity of DNA per cell.*

We expect that genetic differences among species can be correlated with differences in nucleic acid quantity and base content. Figure 2-12 gives the DNA content per set of chromosomes in various types of organisms.

5′ End
G-G-G-C-G-U-G-U-MeG-G-C-G-C-G-U-A-G-DiHU-C-G-G-DiHU-A-G-
1 10 20

C-G-C-DiMeG-C-U-C-C-C-U-U-hX-G-C-MehX-Ψ-G-G-G-A-G-A-G-U-C-
30 40 *3′ End*

U-C-C-G-G-T-Ψ-C-G-A-U-U-C-C-G-G-A-C-U-C-G-U-C-C-A-C-C-A
50 60 70 77

Figure 2-9. The base sequence of an RNA (alanyl-sRNA). The structure of the unusual bases are shown in Figure 2-10.

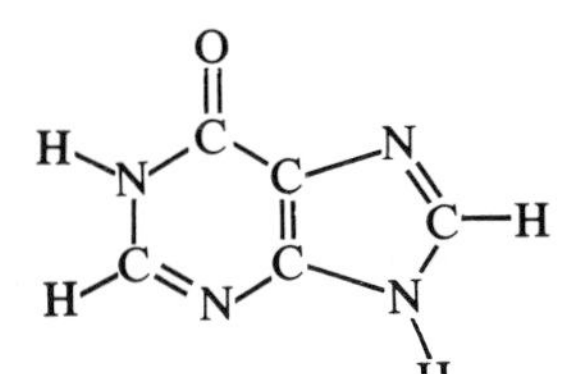

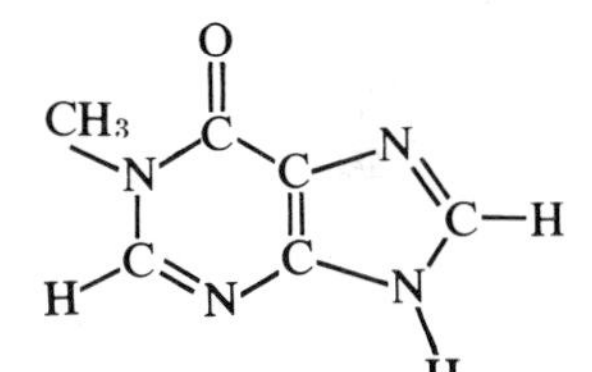

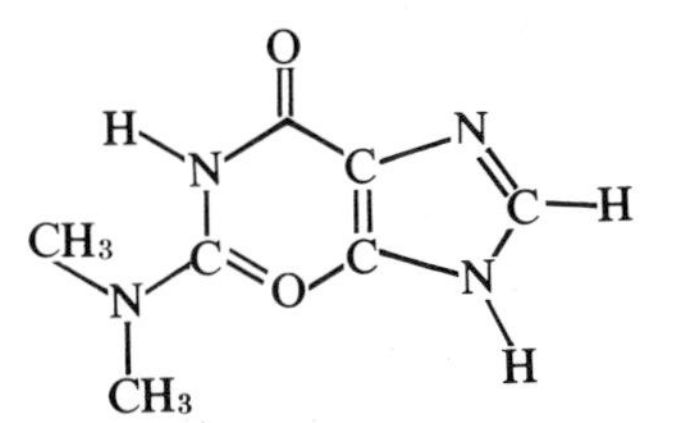

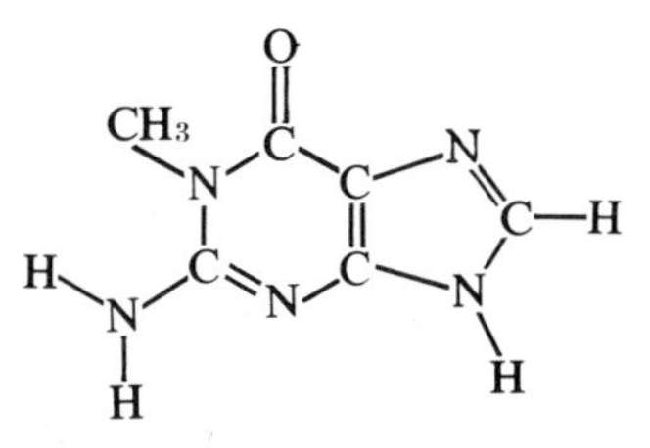

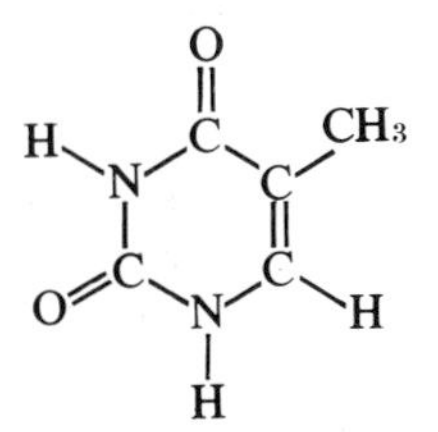

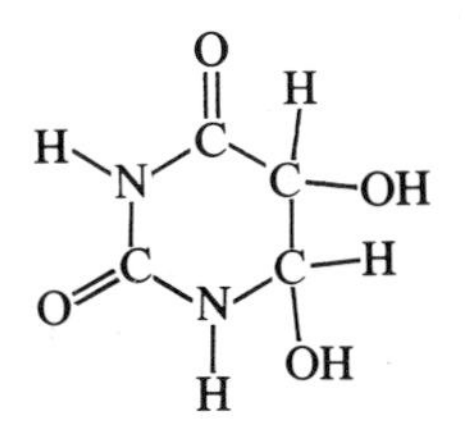

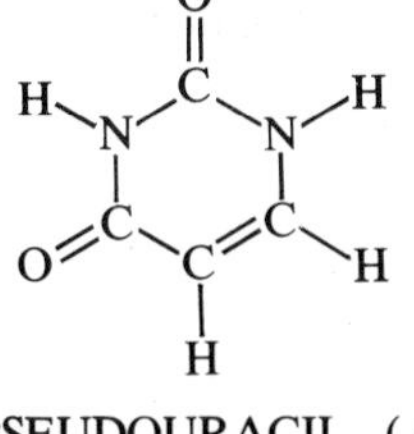

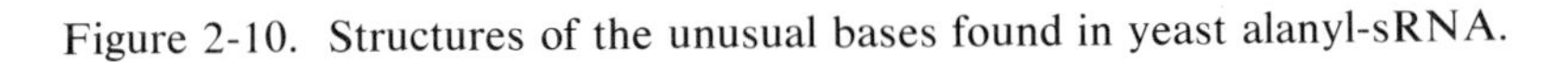
Figure 2-10. Structures of the unusual bases found in yeast alanyl-sRNA.

	Adenine	Thymine	Guanine	Cytosine
Man (sperm)	31.0	31.5	19.1	18.4
Chicken	28.8	29.2	20.5	21.5
Salmon	29.7	29.1	20.8	20.4
Locust	29.3	29.3	20.5	20.7
Sea urchin	32.8	32.1	17.7	17.7
Yeast	31.7	32.6	18.8	17.4
Tuberculosis bacillus	15.1	14.6	34.9	35.4
Escherichia coli	26.1	23.9	24.9	25.1
Vaccinia virus	29.5	29.9	20.6	20.3
E. coli bacterio-phage T_2	32.6	32.6	18.2	16.6*

Figure 2-11. Base composition of DNA from various organisms. (*5-hydroxy-methyl cytosine)

Man, Mouse, Corn	$1\text{-}1.4 \times 10^{10}$
Drosophila	1.6×10^{8}
Aspergillus	8×10^{7}
Escherichia	2×10^{7}
Bacteriophage T4	4×10^{5}
Bacteriophage λ	1×10^{5}
Polyoma virus	1×10^{4}
Bacteriophage X174	4.5×10^{3}

Figure 2-12. DNA nucleotides per chromosome set in various organisms.

Although it is generally true that the higher an organism is on the evolutionary scale, the larger is its DNA content; it is perhaps more meaningful to say that DNA content increases as the amount of information needed for growth, maintenance, and reproduction increases.

2·13 *The information content of a nucleic acid lies in its organic bases.*

Since some nucleic acids are genetic material, we expect successive portions of these molecules to be different and thus to contain different pieces of information. This linear differentiation cannot be due either to the pentose or phosphate, since one of each is present in every nucleotide. Therefore, all differences in information – genetic information – along the length of the polynucleotide strand must be due to the organic bases present.

2·14 *A gene is the smallest informational unit of genetic material. The size of the gene depends upon what kind of information is stored.*

As we have noted, the information for an organism's growth, maintenance, and continuity is contained in genetic material. Let us define the smallest informational unit of this genetic material as a *gene*. Thus the nucleotide, the smallest informational unit of a nucleic acid macromolecule, may be considered a gene. We cannot, however, specify the size of a "typical" gene without a knowledge of the particular tasks which the genetic material carries out and the ways in which it does so. We can expect that different tasks will require different amounts of information and, hence, genes of different sizes.

Questions and Problems

2·1 What is meant by the primary structure of a polymer such as a nucleic acid?

2·2 List similarities and differences between DNA and RNA.

2·3 Can one characterize DNA or RNA by molecular weight? Explain.

2·4 Discuss the ways DNA molecules end.

2·5 List specific features of the primary structure of a nucleic acid which might carry information.

2·6 What parts of a nucleotide are not factors in the polarization of a nucleic acid? What parts do polarize the polymer? Explain.

2·7 Discuss the variation in the organic bases which occur in DNA and RNA.

References

Chargaff, E., and Davidson, J. N. (Editors) 1955 (Vol. 1 and Vol. 2). *The Nucleic Acids;* 1960 (Vol. 3). New York: Academic Press.

Davidson, J. N., and Cohn, W. E. (Editors) 1963. *Progress in Nucleic Acid Research;* 2 Vols. New York: Academic Press.

Holley, R. W. 1966. The nucleotide sequence of a nucleic acid. Scient. Amer., 214 (No. 2) 30–39, 138.

Madison, J. T., Everett, G. A., and Kung, H. 1966. Nucleotide sequence of a yeast tyrosine transfer RNA. Science, 153: 531–534.

Massie, H. R., and Zimm, B. H. 1965. Molecular weight of the DNA in the chromosomes of *E. coli* and *B. subtilis*. Proc. Nat. Acad. Sci., U.S., 54: 1636–1641.

Roscoe, D. H., and Tucker, R. G. 1964. The biosynthesis of a pyrimidine replacing thymine in bacteriophage. Biochem. Biophys. Res. Commun., 16: 106–110.

Srinivasan, P. R., and Borek, E. 1964. Species variation of the RNA methylases. Biochemistry, 3: 616–619.

Stevens, J. G., and Groman, N. B. 1963. A nucleic acid analogue dependent animal virus. Biochem. Biophys. Res. Commun., 10: 63–66.

Takahashi, I., and Marmur, J. 1963. Replacement of thymidylic acid by deoxyuridylic acid in the deoxyribonucleic acid of a transducing phage for *Bacillus subtilis*. Nature, Lond., 197: 794–795.

CHAPTER 3

Secondary, Tertiary, and Quaternary Structures of Nucleic Acids

Because of their chemical and physical properties, polynucleotides interact with themselves and with other strands. The double coil which is formed when one strand winds on itself or when two strands wind about each other is the *secondary structure* of a nucleic acid. The result of a regular twisting and folding of a single strand or a double coil is its *tertiary structure*. And the interaction of two or more double coils gives rise to a *quaternary structure*. In later chapters we will see how these levels of organization are related to the function of genetic material.

3·1 *The DNA of most organisms contains an equal number of A and T nucleotides as well as an equal number of C and G nucleotides.*

Since, as we have noted, the primary structure of a DNA strand imposes no restrictions upon either the types or the frequencies of the bases present along the length of the strand, the base ratio, $\frac{A + T}{G + C}$, can vary greatly from species to species. The numbers of A and T nucleotides in the DNA of organisms within a single species are, however, remarkably similar, as are the numbers of G and C (Figure 2-11). Since $A = T$ and $G = C$ in such species, $A + G = T + C$ by simple algebraic addition. In other words, the total number of DNA purines equals the total number of DNA pyrimidines. We must note carefully, though, that the primary structure of DNA does not account for this genetically significant regularity.

3·2 *DNA usually does not occur as a single strand.*

The basis for the $A = T$ and $G = C$ relationships becomes clear from X-ray diffraction studies of DNA. A beam of X rays is bent or diffracted when it passes through matter. If this matter is completely heterogeneous in structure and orientation, the emergent beam will not form a regular diffraction pattern. But if the material is composed of molecules spatially arranged in a regular manner, then the entering rays will be bent to form a characteristic pattern. From such patterns as those shown in Figure 3-1, crystallographers are able to "work backwards" and recreate the object which scattered the X-rays. Symmetrical patterns in diffraction pictures indicate a repeating unit structure in the sample. For instance, the black spots located symmetrically near the upper and lower edges in both photographs of Figure 3-1 correspond to nucleotides regularly spaced along the DNA chain.

X-ray diffraction patterns also show that most cellular RNA is single-stranded but that DNA, on the other hand, is often composed of more than one strand. Thus in addition to its primary structure, a nucleic acid may have a higher level of organization.

3·3 *DNA usually has a secondary structure as a double-stranded helix. In general, adenine in one strand is hydrogen-bonded to thymine in the other strand; and cytosine in one strand is similarly linked to guanine in the other. Thus A:T and C⁝G pairing accounts for the usual equivalences of these bases.*

A simple model for the *secondary structure* of DNA, consistent with X-ray diffraction findings, was proposed by J. D. Watson and F. H. C. Crick in 1953 and has since been verified. They hypothesized that DNA usually contains two strands (Figure 3-2) which are coiled around each other like the strands in a rope and which, therefore, cannot be separated unless one strand has two free ends. According to their explanation, a pentose-phosphate chain (corresponding to the ribbon in the illustration) forms the backbone of each strand on the outside of the double spiral. The rather flat organic bases (shown as horizontal bars) project into the center and lie perpendicular to the long axis of the fiber (the vertical interrupted line). Coiled right-handedly, i.e., clockwise, the backbone completes a turn each 34A. Each nucleotide occupies 3.4A along the length of a strand. Consequently there are ten nucleotides per complete turn, with each successive nucleotide turning 36° in the horizontal plane.

Two DNA strands can form such a double coil, a *double helix,* with a uniform diameter of about 20A if a pyrimidine base on one strand is paired with a purine base on the other. A pair of pyrimidines (each a single ring) would be too short to bridge the gap between backbones, whereas two purines (each a double ring) would take up too much space. If cytosine (a pyrimidine) is paired with guanine (a purine) and adenine with thymine, the number of stabilizing bonds between each *base pair* is at a maximum.

Hydrogen bonds or *H bonds,* weak electrostatic interactions, can hold members of a base pair together. In order for three H bonds to form between cytosine and guanine (Figure 3-3), C⁝G, we should note that one

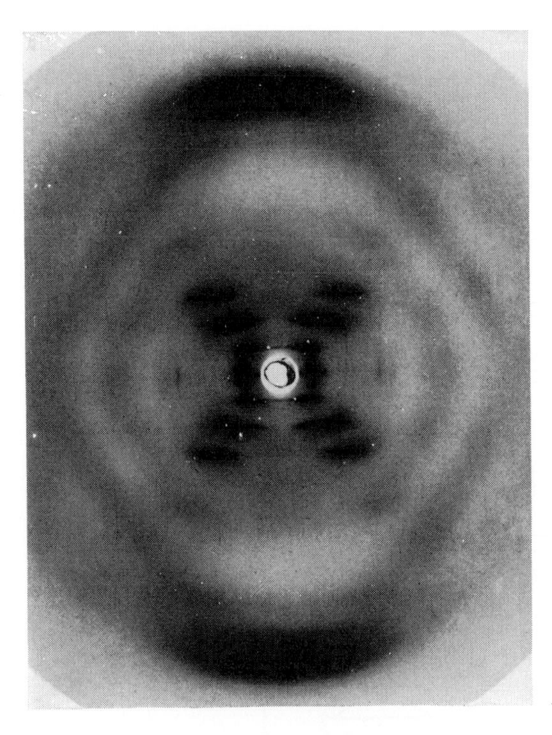

A

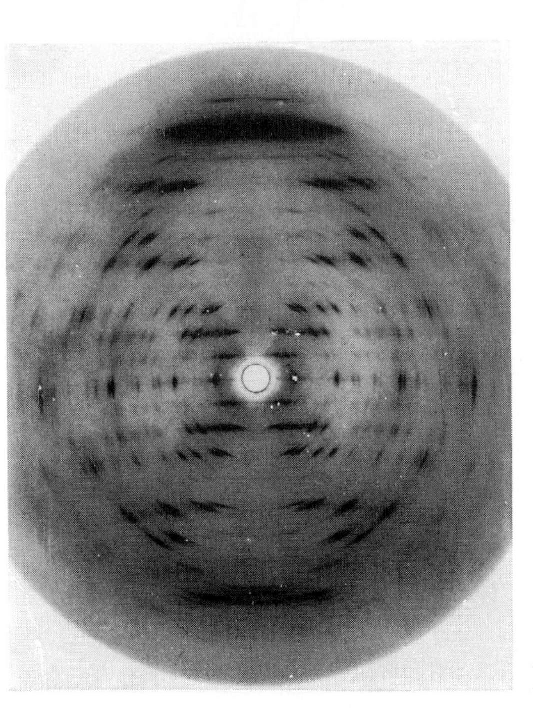

B

Figure 3-1. X-ray diffraction photographs of suitably hydrated fibers of DNA, showing the so-called B configuration. (A) Pattern obtained using the sodium salt of DNA. (B) Pattern obtained using the lithium salt of DNA. Analysis of these patterns gives details of nucleic acid structure. (Courtesy of Biophysics Research Unit, Medical Research Council, King's College, London)

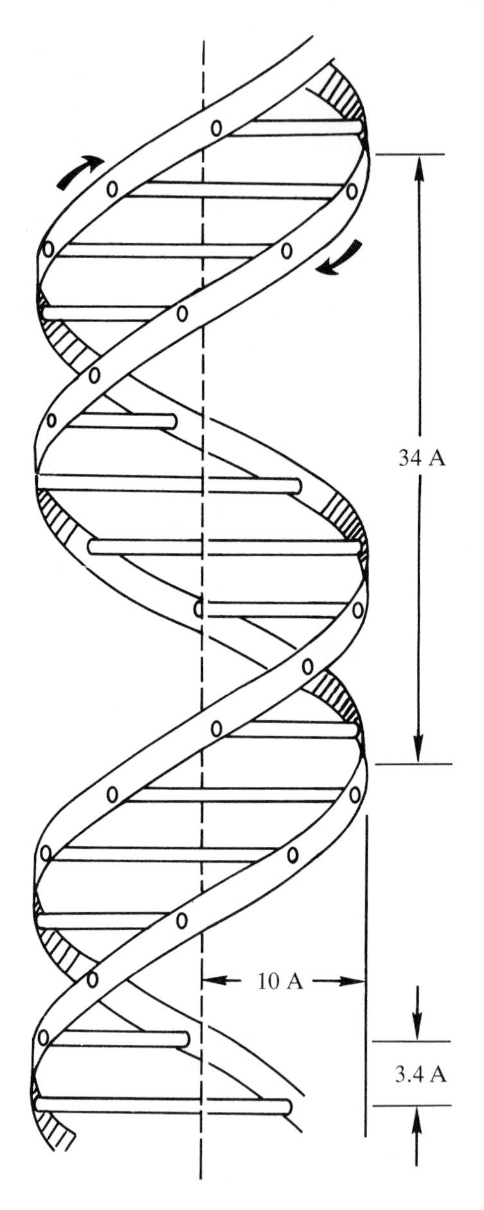

Figure 3-2. The double-stranded helix of DNA.

base must be turned over relative to the other if we represent them initially as in Figure 2-3. The resulting bonds will involve the 6-NH_2 of C and the 6-O of G, the 2-O of C and 2-NH_2 of G, and the 1-N of C and the 1-NH of G. The A:T base pair, joined by only two hydrogen bonds, is represented in the bottom half of Figure 3-3.

Although the hydrogen bond is weak as compared with the covalent

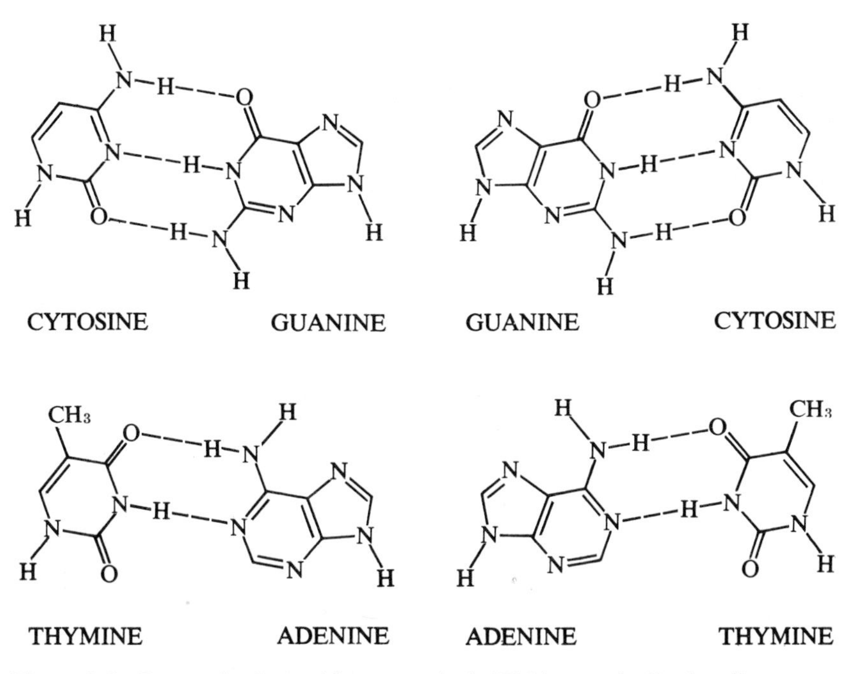

Figure 3-3. Base pairs formed between single DNA strands. Broken lines represent hydrogen bonds.

C-C bond, the great number of H bonds present along a double helix makes the structure as a whole rather rigid even when moderately hydrated. Another structural characteristic involves the relationship between backbone and bases. We can see in Figure 3-4 that the region surrounding two base-paired nucleosides is separated into two areas by the point of attachment of each organic base to its respective pentose. If we were able to look "down" on a nucleic acid, i.e., perpendicular to its long axis, we would see that the combination of larger areas determined by successive nucleoside pairs constitutes a *major groove* and the combination of smaller areas a *minor groove.*

According to the Watson-Crick model, all the sugars of one strand face in one direction and all those of the second face in the other (Figure 3-5). Furthermore, phosphate linkages to sugar in the right chain read 3′5′, 3′5′, and so on, from top to bottom; whereas the left chain reads 5′ to 3′. Thus we can say that the chains of a double helix run in opposite directions (as indicated by the arrows).

3·4 *The two strands in double-helix DNA are complementary.*

For DNA whose secondary structure is a double-helix, we can consider one strand the complement of the other. Thus if we know the sequence of

Figure 3-4. The major and minor areas surrounding base-paired nucleosides. A succession of these areas forms major and minor grooves.

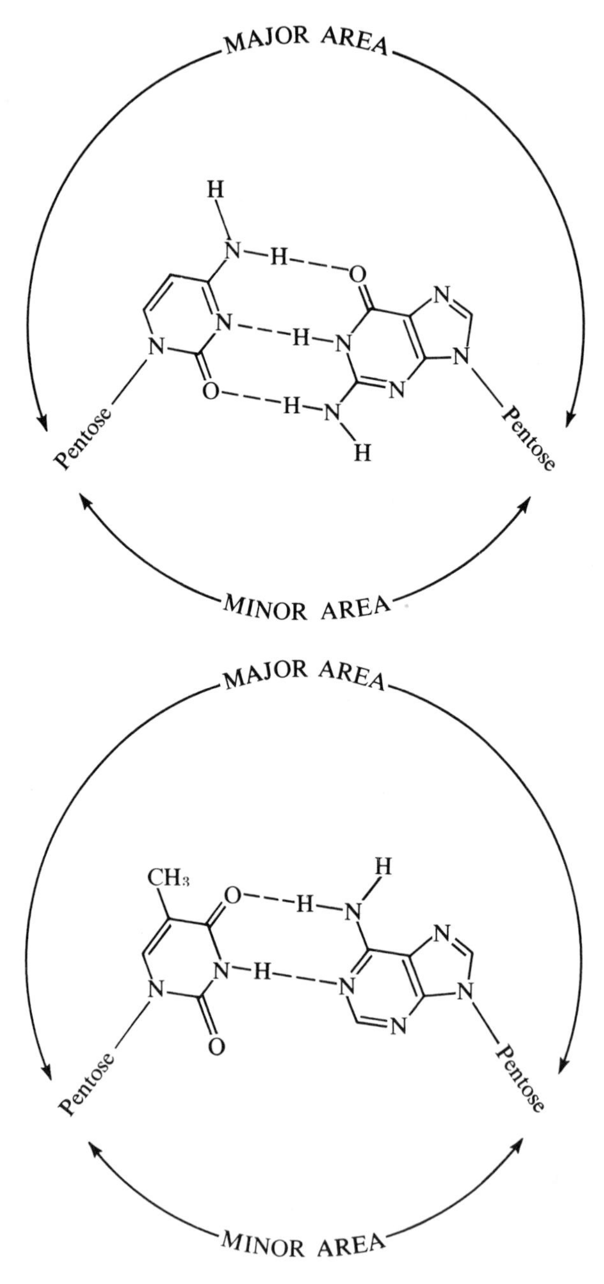

bases in one strand, we know the base composition of the other. For example, if one strand contains the base sequence ATTGC, the other strand will have TAACG in a corresponding region. The information in DNA is therefore redundant, since the base sequence of one strand necessarily implies the base sequence, hence, the information, of the complementary strand.

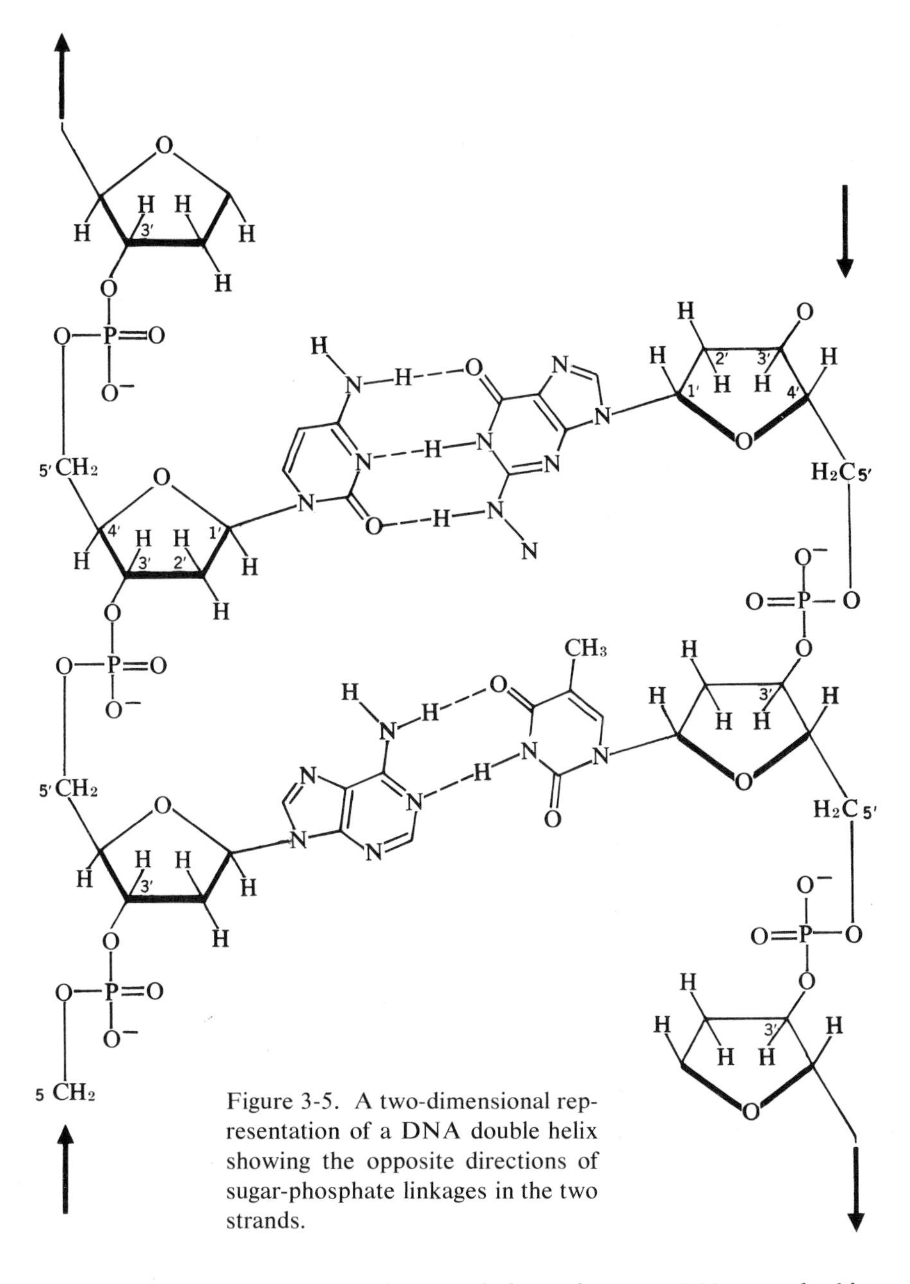

Figure 3-5. A two-dimensional representation of a DNA double helix showing the opposite directions of sugar-phosphate linkages in the two strands.

3·5 *Some DNA is single-stranded, and some RNA is double-stranded.*

X-ray diffraction results which led to the double-helix hypothesis did not tell us that all DNA is two-stranded. Nor did they rule out the possibility that a double-stranded nucleic acid may be single-stranded at certain places or at certain times. What they did show was that an appreciable part of the DNA of a wide variety of organisms is double-stranded. The DNA of ϕT2 and ϕT7, for example, is found to occur in the Watson-Crick double helix configuration. But the DNA of mature ϕX174 is single-stranded, as proved by the nonequivalence of A and T and of C and G and by X-ray diffraction photographs.

In contrast to TMV and many other viruses which contain single-stranded RNA as their genetic material, the infective forms of a wound virus obtained from sweet clover and a reovirus associated with the respiratory and enteric tracts of animals have double-stranded RNA as their genetic material. The RNA of these organisms is in a double-helix configuration (like that of double-stranded DNA) in which A = U and C = G.

3·6 *Double-stranded nucleic acids can be denatured and renatured.*

Heating a double-stranded nucleic acid for ten minutes at 100°C breaks all hydrogen bonds between base pairs, so that the two complementary strands usually separate. This process is one of melting, or *denaturation.* Naturally-occurring double-stranded DNA with a high $\frac{A + T}{G + C}$ ratio becomes single-stranded, that is, it denatures, at a lower temperature than double-stranded DNA with a lower ratio. We should not be surprised by this difference, for G and C are linked by three hydrogen bonds but A and T by only two. Consequently, less energy is needed to break the hydrogen bonds of a DNA double helix rich in adenine and thymine than for one with high G-C content.

When the heated mixture is cooled quickly, the chains remain single as *denatured DNA.* Loss of the characteristic X-ray diffraction pattern of double-helix DNA confirms the single-strandedness of the denatured polymer. Denaturation, whether brought about by chemical or physical means, is accompanied by an increase of up to 40% in absorption of ultraviolet light of 2600A – the so-called *hyperchromic effect.* A single strand of denatured DNA can base pair with itself if folding brings together complementary parts of the strand.

When the hot mixture of denatured DNA is cooled slowly, however, base pairing occurs between complementary strands, and double-stranded DNA is formed. This *renatured DNA* is similar to the original DNA in ultraviolet absorption, X-ray diffraction pattern, molecular weight, density, and appearance under the electron microscope.

Denaturation and renaturation occur similarly for double-stranded RNA. Denatured RNA likewise shows a hyperchromic effect and can form a partial double helix by base-pairing with itself under certain conditions.

3·7 *Double-stranded nucleic acid hybrids can form if the two strands are sufficiently complementary.*

Hybrid DNA-RNA duplexes (each composed of one DNA strand and one RNA strand) can be made by filtering single-stranded RNA through agar which contains denatured DNA from the same organism. This hybridization shows that at least some RNA from a given organism is complementary to some of its own DNA. Hybrid DNA-DNA duplexes made up of single DNA strands from two different species can also be formed, if the genetic material of these species contains similar base sequences. We see therefore that hybridization can be a particularly useful technique in determining the similarity of RNA and DNA from the same or from different organisms.

3·8 *DNase may cause breaks in one or two strands of double-stranded DNA.*

When certain preparations of naturally-occurring double-stranded DNA are heated, the single strands obtained have a molecular weight of *less than half* that of the duplex. This reduction in molecular weight is due to the digestive action of an enzyme – a *deoxyribonuclease,* or *DNase* – present as a contaminant. DNA exposed to dilute concentrations of DNase first incurs single-strand breaks. Only later, when both strands have been attacked at reasonably nearby positions, is the duplex severed.

3·9 *Some double-helix DNA molecules are twisted in a regular manner, thus giving the nucleic acid a tertiary structure.*

In boar sperm, bacteria, the polyoma virus, and several phages, double-stranded DNA occurs in ring form. In this form, we recall, the two complements cannot separate completely because of the absence of free ends. Superimposed on the right-handed coils of the polyoma duplex are additional coils which cause the double-stranded ring to fold back on itself (Figure 3-6A). The additional turns thus determine the *tertiary structure* of polyoma DNA. When DNase induces single-strand breaks in such DNA, a site on the unbroken complementary strand opposite the break acts as a "swivel" and permits the unbroken strand to rotate and release the tertiary turns. Consequently the duplex assumes an untwisted or unfolded ring configuration (Figure 3-6B).

That DNA has a tertiary structure in other organisms is indicated by the packing of long DNA molecules into containers of relatively small size – e.g., phage heads, bacterial cells, and nuclei – and by the coiling

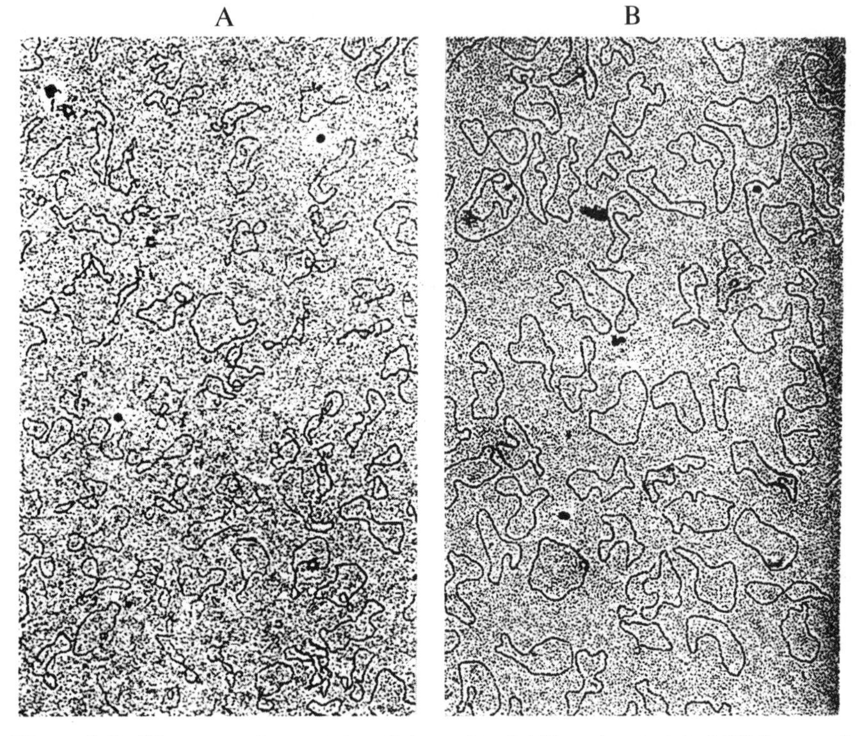

Figure 3-6. Electron micrographs of the twisted (A) and untwisted (B) forms of polyoma DNA (× 18,400). The period of treatment with pancreatic DNase was relatively short in A and relatively long in B. (Courtesy of J. Vinograd)

and uncoiling of chromosomes during nuclear division cycles without producing knots which would interfere with replication and strand movement.

Evidence indicates that sRNA also has a tertiary structure.

3·10 *Native nucleic acids often occur in combination with proteins.*

Nucleic acids are often found in combination with proteins. Such combinations are called *nucleoproteins*. In nucleated cells the DNA is usually combined with basic proteins such as *histone* or *protamine*. The amino groups of these basic proteins probably bond electrostatically to the phosphates of DNA. In some sperm the chromosome appears to contain a unit fibril about 40A in diameter composed of protamine and a single DNA duplex. In other nucleated cells, two DNA double helixes and histone form a chromosomal fibril about 100A thick.

3·11 *The nucleic acid in chromosomes containing more than one DNA double helix has a quaternary structure.*

In cell nuclei of higher organisms, chromosomes that have replicated but not yet separated into daughter chromosomes contain at least two DNA double helixes. The cells of several larval tissues of Dipteran organisms have giant nuclei whose chromosomes are highly *polynemic,* or *polytene;* that is, they contain many DNA duplexes – sometimes over a thousand – lying side by side. The organization of two or more duplexes within a chromosome is the *quaternary structure* of the nucleic acids involved.

Questions and Problems

3·1 State two phenomena associated with DNA that cannot be explained on the basis of its primary structure.

3·2 What is meant by the primary, secondary, tertiary, and quaternary structures of a polymeric molecule?

3·3 Name four different compounds that can be attached to the backbone (1) of RNA; (2) of DNA.

3·4 Is a double helix containing only A and G or C and T possible? Explain.

3·5 State three ways to determine whether a sample contains only single-stranded or only double-stranded nucleic acid.

3·6 What are the consequences of heating polyoma virus DNA for 10 minutes at 100°C?

3·7 Suppose you have three unlabeled cultures, two of one bacterial species and one of a distant relative. How can you tell which is which if all three cultures are accidentally killed by boiling?

3·8 Suggest a taxonomic use of the finding that the base ratio of a double-stranded nucleic acid can be determined by measuring its melting point.

3·9 A detective has the problem of identifying whether some blood found in a steam bath is human or canine. Suggest how he might determine its origin.

3·10 Suppose 1000 bases in a double-stranded nucleic acid are uracil. If this RNA consists of 10,000 nucleotides, determine the approximate molecular weight of the duplex and the percentages of all the bases present.

References

Abelson, J., and Thomas, C. A., Jr. 1966. The anatomy of the T5 bacteriophage DNA molecule. J. Mol. Biol., 18: 262–291. (The complementary strands are interrupted at different positions.)

Bautz, E. K. F., and Hall, B. D. 1962. The isolation of T4-specific RNA on a DNA-cellulose column. Proc. Nat. Acad. Sci., U.S., 48: 400–408.

Cole, A., and Langley, R. 1963. Study of the radiosensitive structure of T2 bacteriophage using low energy electron beams. Biophysical J., 3: 189–197. (How DNA is packed in the phage head.)

Crick, F. H. C. 1957. Nucleic acids. Scient. Amer., 197: 188–200.

Eigner, J., and Doty, P. 1965. The native, denatured and renatured states of deoxyribonucleic acid. J. Mol. Biol. 12: 549–580.

Gomatos, P. J., and Tamm, I. 1963. Animal and plant viruses with double-helical RNA. Proc. Nat. Acad. Sci. U.S., 50: 878–885.

Sarin, P. S., Zamecnick, P. C., Bergquist, P. L., and Scott, J. F. 1966. Conformational differences among purified samples of transfer RNA from yeast. Proc. Nat. Acad. Sci., U.S., 55: 579–585. (Similar types of RNA differ in their secondary and tertiary structures.)

Sinsheimer, R. L. 1962. Single-stranded DNA. Scient. Amer., 207 (No. 1): 109–116. (Studies of ϕX174.)

Spiegelman, S. 1964. Hybrid nucleic acids. Scient. Amer., 210 (No. 5): 48–56, 150.

Vinograd, J., and Lebowitz, J. 1966. Physical and topological properties of circular DNA. J. Gen. Physiol., 49 (Suppl.) (No. 6, Part 2): 103–125; and *Macromolecular Metabolism,* Boston: Little, Brown and Co.

Vinograd, J., Lebowitz, J., Radloff, R., Watson, R., and Laipis, P. 1965. The twisted circular form of polyoma viral DNA. Proc. Nat. Acad. Sci., U.S., 53: 1104–1110.

Watson, J. D., and Crick, F. H. C. 1953. Molecular structure of nucleic acids. A structure for deoxyribose nucleic acid. Nature, Lond., 171: 737–738. Reprinted in *Classic Papers in Genetics,* Peters, J. A. (Editor). Englewood Cliffs, N.J.: Prentice-Hall, Inc., 1959, pp. 241–243.

Watson, J. D., and Crick, F. H. C. 1953. Genetical implications of the structure of deoxyribonucleic acid. Nature, Lond., 171: 964–969. Reprinted in *Papers on Bacterial Genetics, Second Edition.* Adelberg, E. A. (Editor). Boston: Little, Brown and Co., 1966, pp. 127–132.

Watson, J. D., and Crick, F. H. C. 1953. The structure of DNA. Cold Spring Harb. Sympos. Quant. Biol., 18: 123–131. Reprinted in *Papers on Bacterial Viruses, Second Edition.* Stent, G. S. (Editor). Boston: Little, Brown and Co., 1965, pp. 230–245.

CHAPTER 4

Transcription of Nucleic Acids

Since the genetic information of viral progeny is identical to that of their parent, a *transcription* of information must have taken place. This process involves the copying of information that is contained in the sequence of organic bases and results in a transcription of information from DNA to DNA or from RNA to RNA. Since uracil and thymine are, in a sense, equivalent (both being complements of adenine) transcription can also occur from DNA to RNA and from RNA to DNA. A transcript which is itself transcribed is genetic material.

4·1 *Replication* in vivo *of double-stranded DNA results in two duplexes, each containing a parental strand and a newly-synthesized complementary strand.*

Let us consider an experiment designed to test the hypothesis that replication of double-stranded bacterial DNA *in vivo* involves the complete separation of parental strands and the formation of two duplexes, each containing a parental strand and a newly-synthesized strand that is complementary to the parental strand. We recall that each pyrimidine normally found in DNA contains two, and each purine four, nitrogen atoms. Most of these atoms are ordinary "light" nitrogen, N^{14}. Thus, if we grow bacteria in a culture medium whose only nitrogen is the "heavy" isotope N^{15}, these bacteria will contain heavy DNA. We can actually see the difference between heavy and light DNA by means of a process called *density gradient ultracentrifugation.*

When a solution of cesium chloride is centrifuged for about twenty hours at great speed, a gradient of densities is established in the centrifuge tube such that the concentration of cesium chloride is greatest at the bottom and least at the top. DNA ultracentrifuged in such a tube assumes the position that corresponds to its own density. We expect, therefore, that heavy and light DNA will form different bands in the centrifuge tube. The nucleic acid can then be detected by its absorption of ultraviolet light of 2600A.

To test the hypothesis, we grow bacteria on heavy nitrogen medium for several generations so we can be certain that all DNA is heavy. Then, after synchronizing their multiplication, we allow the bacteria to grow for a single generation on a light nitrogen medium. DNA isolated from these bacteria forms a band exactly intermediate between the bands that heavy and light DNA would take in the density gradient. If we allow bacteria to grow for two generations on the light medium, isolated DNA takes two positions in the centrifuge tube – one intermediate between light and heavy, and a second at the light position. Results of these and other generation times are shown in Figure 4-1.

These findings are consistent with our hypothesis; for a duplex of heavy DNA must strand-separate at some time in its replication if it is to form a hybrid duplex containing light nitrogen. Similar results have been obtained with DNA from the unicellular alga Chlamydomonas, man, and other higher organisms.

4·2 *The* E. coli *chromosome is a circular duplex of DNA, both strands of which are transcribed in parallel starting at one point.*

Electron micrographs reveal that the single chromosome in the nuclear area of *E. coli* is a ring of double-stranded DNA. If we label DNA precursors radioactively to detect the position of newly synthesized DNA, we find that replication begins at the same point in both strands (Figure 4-2) – only one starting point per chromosome – and that synthesis of both strands proceeds in the same direction. The starting point of replication in some *E. coli* strains appears to be random. In other strains, however, replication always starts at the same position.

Electron micrographs of *E. coli* confirm the conclusion of Section 4·1 – that duplex replication involves the separation of parental strands and the formation of two duplexes, each with one parental strand and a newly synthesized complement. This replication necessarily involves not only the unwinding of the parental duplex but also the rewinding of strands to form two new duplexes in ring form at the completion of replication. Since the parental duplex is in ring form and cannot completely strand-separate, it has been suggested that the point in the parental duplex where DNA synthesis starts serves as a "swivel" whose rotation permits uncoiling.

4·3 *Double-stranded DNA is transcribed* in vivo *to double-stranded or single-stranded DNA (by DNA polymerase) or to single-stranded RNA (by DNA-dependent RNA polymerase).*

The transcription of double-stranded nucleic acid to double-stranded nucleic acid (as occurs in the replication of the DNA of the *E. coli* chromo-

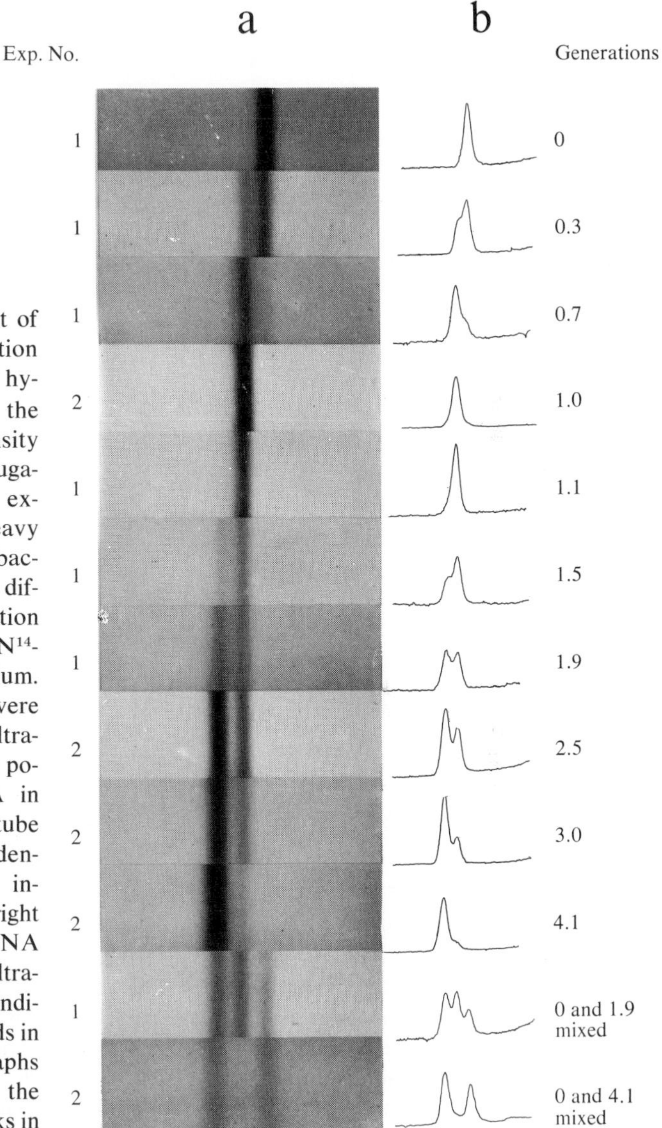

Figure 4-1. Test of the "chain separation after replication" hypothesis, using the technique of density gradient centrifugation. DNA was extracted from heavy (N^{15}-labeled) bacteria grown for different generation times on light (N^{14}-containing) medium. The extracts were subjected to ultracentrifugation to position the DNA in the centrifuge tube according to its density. (Density increases to the right of the figure.) DNA absorption of ultraviolet light is indicated by the bands in different photographs under *a* and the height of the peaks in the corresponding densitometer tracings under *b*. The rightmost band in the bottom two frames and the band in the top frame represent heavy DNA. The leftmost band, seen clearly in all generation times after 1.5 generations, represents light DNA. The only other clear band is between the heavy and light ones. This band, which is the only one present after 1.0 generations, represents DNA which is hybrid in density. Note that at 1.9 generations, half the DNA is light and half is hybrid in density (see row showing 0 and 1.9 mixed). (Courtesy of M. Meselson and F. W. Stahl, Proc. Nat. Acad. Sci., U.S., 44: 675, 1958.)

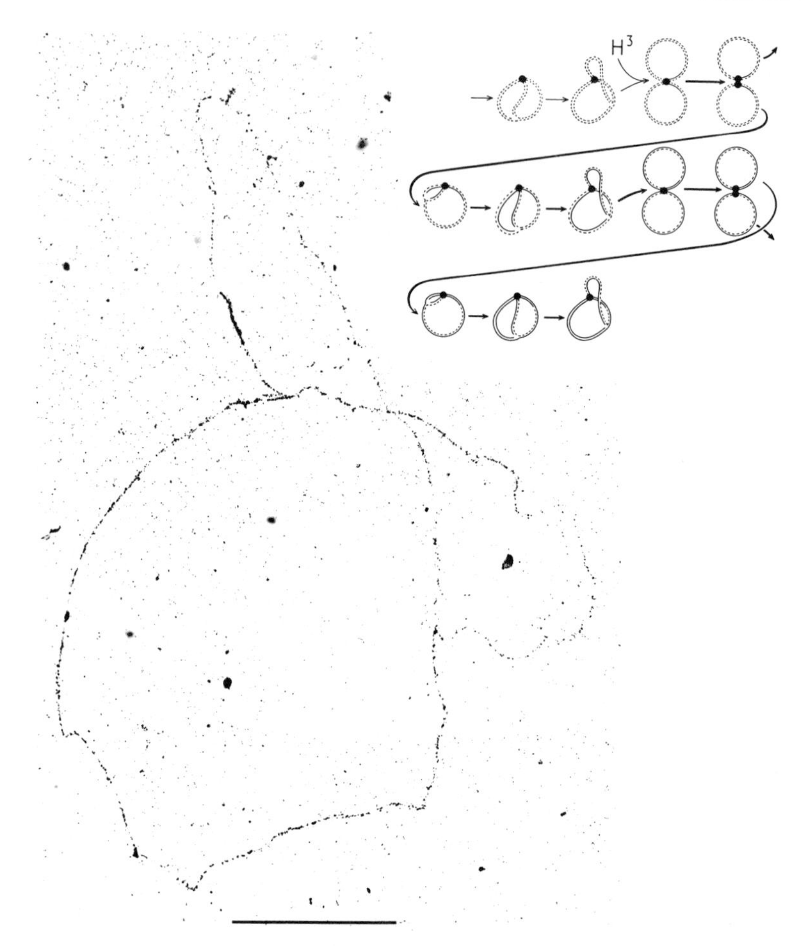

Figure 4-2. Replication of the *E. coli* chromosome.

Autoradiograph of the circular chromosome labeled with tritiated thymidine for two generations. Exposure time 2 months. The scale shows 100μ.

Inset is a diagrammatic representation of the chromosome, based on the assumption that each cycle of replication begins at the same place and proceeds in the same direction. ----- = nonlabeled single DNA strand; ——— = labeled single DNA strand; ● = swivel; H^3 = tritiated thymidine. (Courtesy of J. Cairns and the Cold Spring Harbor Laboratory of Quantitative Biology)

some) is called a *two-complement transcription* (Figure 4-3A). The DNA of mature ϕX174 is, we recall, in the form of a single-stranded ring. Once the phage enters an *E. coli* host, a *DNA polymerase* synthesizes a "minus" strand which is complementary to the "plus" parental strand (Figure 4-3B). Thus, the parental strand undergoes a *one-complement*

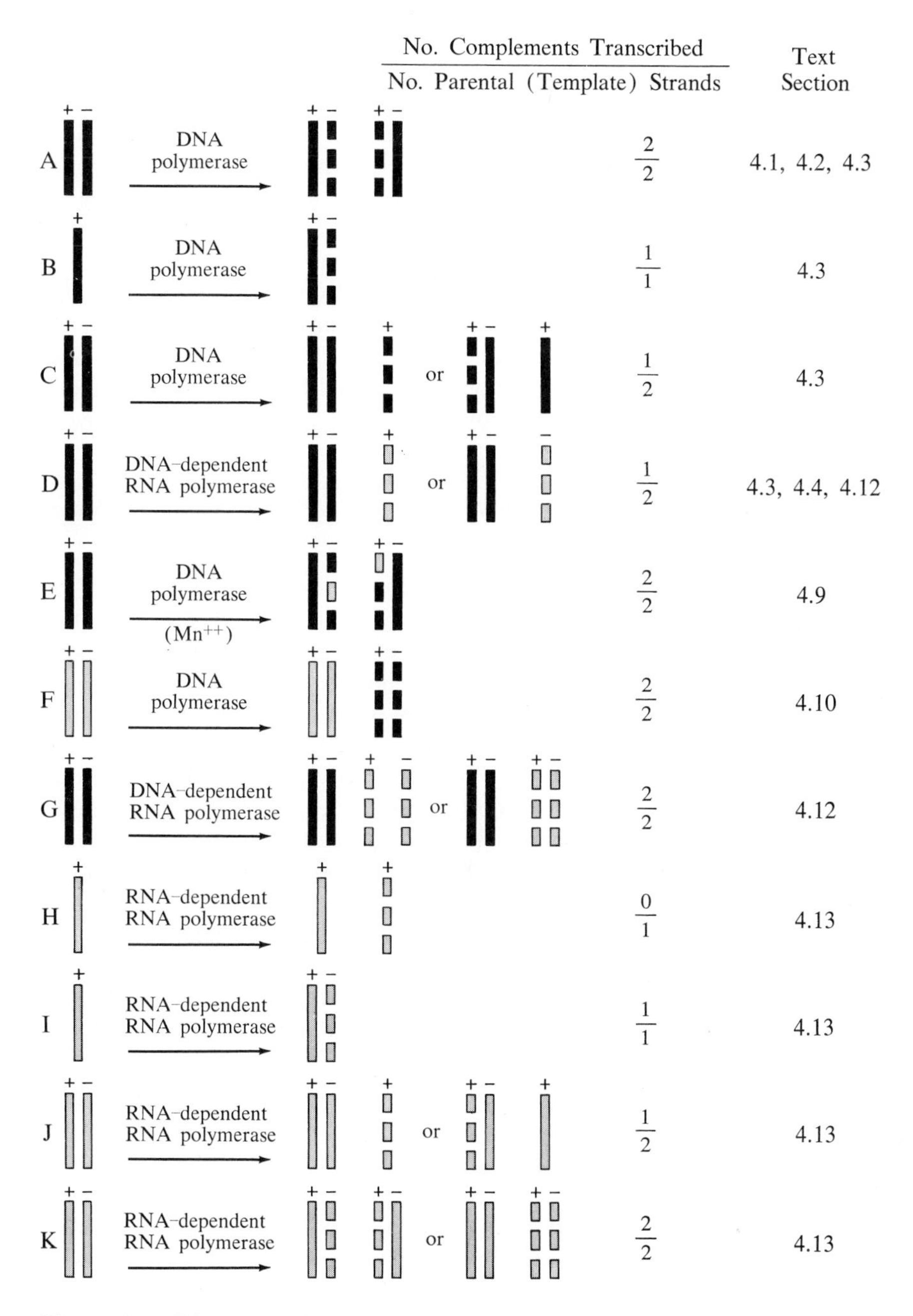

Figure 4-3. Diagrammatic representation of transcription. ▬▬ and ■ ■ ■ = old and new single DNA strands; ▭▭ and ▭ ▭ ▭ = old and new single RNA strands.

transcription. (This synthesis does not replicate the DNA.) As a result, a "plus-minus" DNA helix (double-stranded and circular) is produced. This duplex first replicates new duplexes, by two-complement transcription, each composed of one old and one new strand. Then the "plus-minus" duplexes are used to synthesize, by one-complement transcription, "plus" DNA strands which are used in forming ϕX174 progeny (Figure 4-3C).

DNA replication is not involved when normal cellular DNA is transcribed to RNA. Base ratio and DNA-RNA hybridization studies show that in bacteria and other cells all normal cellular RNA is complementary to only one strand of double-stranded DNA. This finding is due to one-complement transcription, from double-stranded DNA to single-stranded RNA (Figure 4-3D), catalyzed by *DNA-dependent RNA polymerase.*

4·4 *Transcription can occur from genetic DNA to genetic RNA* in vivo.

Mate-killer (*mu*), *lambda,* and *kappa* (Figure 4-4) are the names of related bacterial symbionts which can exist in the cytoplasm of certain strains of Paramecium. Although these particles contain double-stranded DNA, have the ability to self-replicate, and are infective, each depends upon the DNA genetic material of its host for maintenance. For example, in Paramecium the presence of an *M* gene is required for growth and replication of mu particles. Paramecia are not able to generate these particles *de novo,* however, even if they do have *M* genes. Furthermore, if the *M* genes in paramecia with mu particles are replaced by alternative *m* genes, the particles disappear some 8 to 18 cell divisions later. From these facts we hypothesize that the *M* gene controls mu particle existence by producing a substance which is not made by the *m* gene. This substance has been shown to be single-stranded RNA of the host.

The protozoon Didinium can acquire both this RNA and mu particles by eating paramecia containing them. The amount of ingested RNA, as well as the number of mu particles, subsequently increases in Didinium. Since this RNA can hybridize with denatured DNA from paramecia containing *M* genes or (to a lesser extent) *m* genes but not with denatured DNA from Didinium, we conclude that the RNA is a transcript of the *M* genes of Paramecium and that Didinium contains no such genes. Nevertheless, this RNA not only persists in Didinium but it also multiplies. In summary, it behaves in Paramecium like RNA virus genetic material which is made but cannot subsequently be replicated; whereas in Didinium, where it is ingested but not made, this RNA acts like virus genetic material capable of being replicated. Such evidence indicates that transcription of genetic DNA *in vivo* can produce genetic RNA.

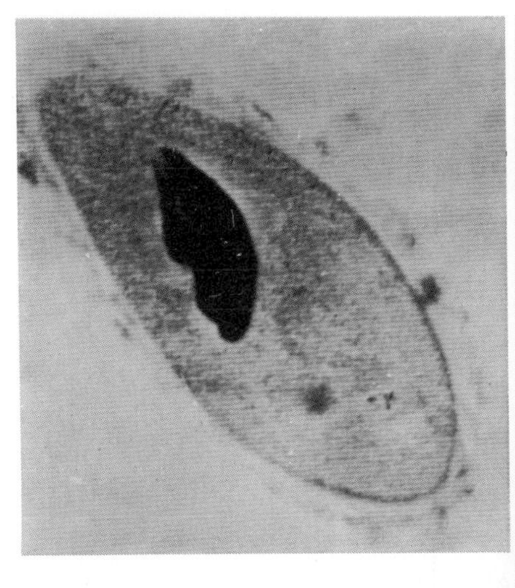

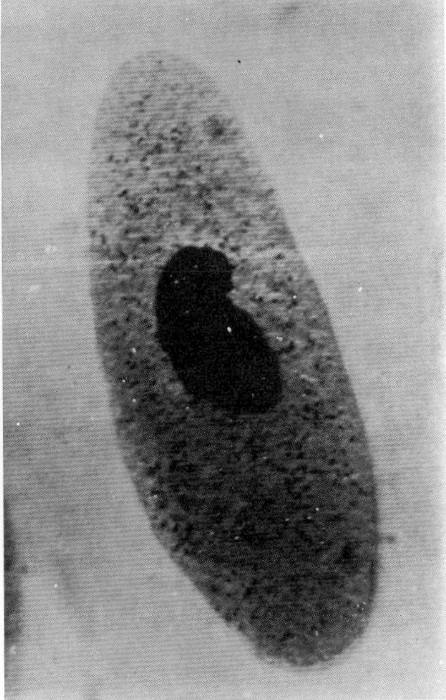

Figure 4-4. Normal (above) and kappa-containing (right) Paramecium. (Courtesy of T. M. Sonneborn)

4·5 *Transcription apparently can also occur from genetic RNA to genetic DNA* in vivo.

The following evidence indicates that DNA can be transcribed from RNA *in vivo*. The *Rous sarcoma virus* (*RSV*), whose genetic material is single-stranded RNA, infects chick embryo cells. RNA-DNA hybridization experiments reveal that only after infection does the chick cell contain DNA which can base-pair with the viral RNA. This "new" DNA appears to be a transcript of RSV RNA and to contain information needed for replication of the virus. For if DNA synthesis is inhibited soon after the chick cells are exposed to the virus, no RSV progeny result. Transcription may perhaps occur in the reverse direction also (from genetic DNA to genetic RNA) when RSV progeny are made.

4·6 In vitro *studies of nucleic acid transcription help us to understand its molecular mechanism* in vivo.

Studies of nucleic acid transcription *in vitro* provide useful information for the construction of models of mechanisms by which transcription occurs *in vivo*. We must recognize, however, that *in vitro* mechanisms may be a biased sample of ways that nucleic acids are replicated *in vivo*. But

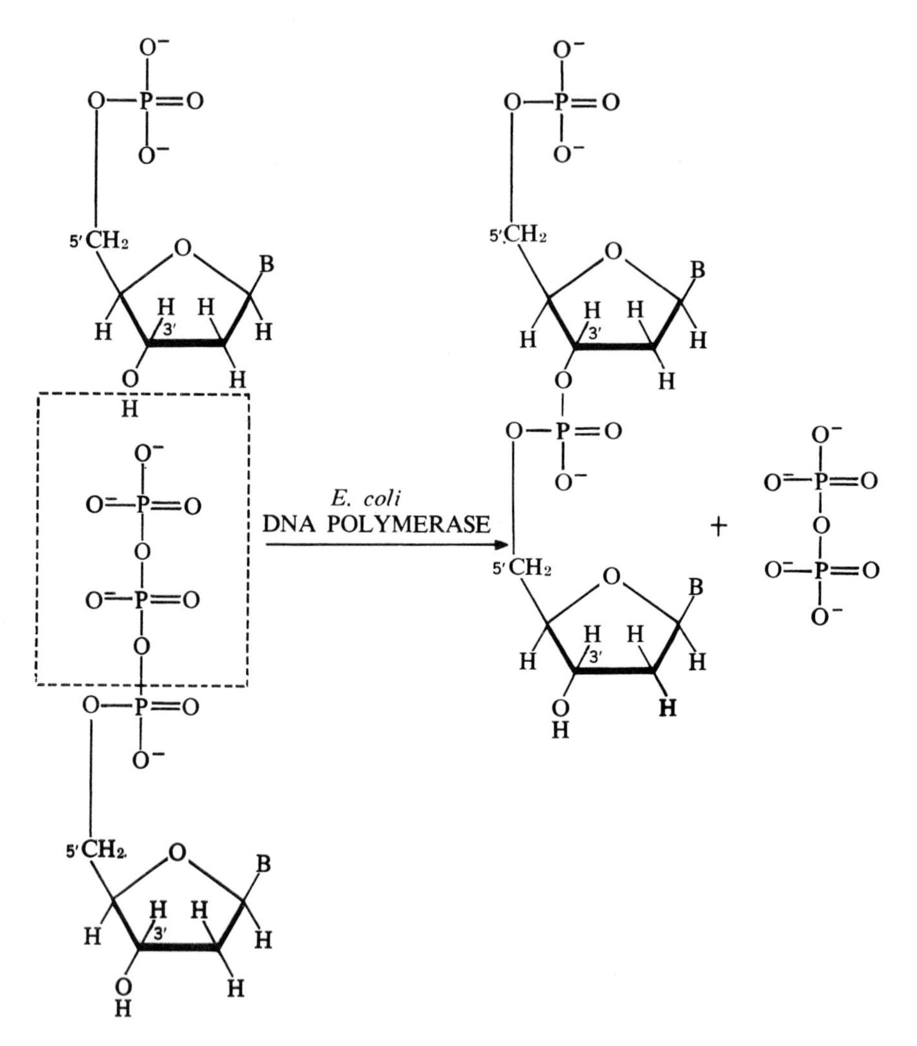

Figure 4-5. Union of deoxyribonucleotides catalyzed by *E. coli* DNA polymerase.

whether or not *in vitro* studies closely reflect the conditions *in vivo*, they are (at the very least) valuable in helping us to understand the origin of such mechanisms and to formulate hypotheses subject to experimental test.

4·7 *Short strands of DNA that are synthesized* de novo *can serve as templates for further synthesis.*

DNA can be synthesized *in vitro* from suitable precursors in the presence of DNA polymerase isolated from *E. coli*. This enzyme splits off the two

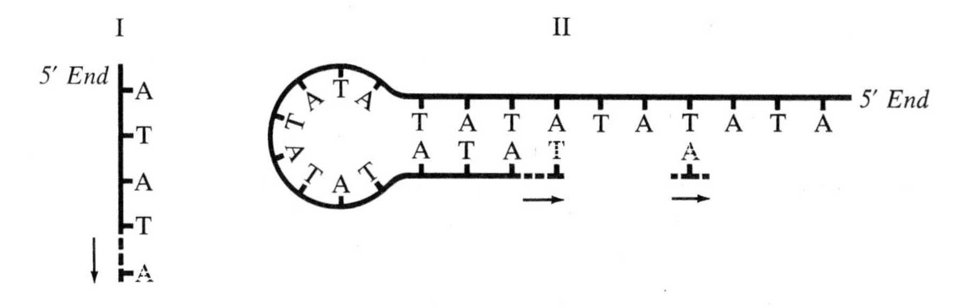

Figure 4-6. Synthesis of dAT. Arrows show direction of growth.
I. *De novo*
II. Template base-pairing synthesis.
T is lengthening the strand;
A is initiating a new strand.

terminal phosphates of a deoxyribonucleoside 5′-triphosphate (Figure 4-5) as *pyrophosphate* (*PP*), and the remaining monophosphate joins by its phosphate to the free 3′ position of another deoxyribonucleoside 5′-monophosphate. Thus in the absence of DNA, short strands of the nucleic acid can be formed after several hours of incubation in a system which contains deoxyadenosine 5′-triphosphate (dAPPP), deoxythymidine 5′-triphosphate (dTPPP), Mg^{++} ion, and *E. coli* DNA polymerase. A and T occur in perfect alternation in such strands – called *copolymers* of AT, or dAT. The mechanism for this *de novo* synthesis of DNA is not yet completely understood.

When a dAT strand becomes long enough to fold, it often base-pairs with itself. A single strand folded back on itself so that its free 3′ end is paired with an internal (rather than terminal) complement can grow by a *base-pairing synthesis* (Figure 4-6). In such a synthesis the unpaired portion of the strand serves as a mold, or *template,* which attracts complementary precursors. As implied above, *E. coli* DNA polymerase can catalyze the addition of a single nucleotide to the free 3′ position of DNA and thereby lengthen the polymer. Hence, the polymerase lengthens the dAT strand at its free 3′ position, this already-formed DNA serving as a *primer* for its own lengthening. A portion of dAT that is not base-paired with itself can serve as template for the synthesis of a completely new complementary strand.

Discovery of a "natural dAT" polymer in the sperm of a certain crab indicates clearly the important role such polymers may play *in vivo.* Comprising nearly 30% of the total nuclear DNA content, this crab polymer consists mostly of A and T in strict alternation. G and C occur with a frequency of about 3%.

DNA polymerase isolated from calf thymus, in contrast to the *E. coli*

DNA polymerase, cannot form dAT *de novo*. Just like the *E. coli* enzyme, however, the calf thymus DNA polymerase can use dAT as template for making complementary DNA.

4·8 *DNA synthesized* in vitro *is very similar to the DNA used as template. The* in vitro *process does, however, differ from that* in vivo *in several important ways.*

E. coli DNA polymerase can synthesize large quantities of DNA *in vitro* by the base-pairing, template mechanism in the presence of double-stranded DNA from any of several organisms, Mg^{++} ions, and appropriate deoxyribonucleoside 5′-triphosphates. The resulting DNA is a replica of the "parental" template in the following ways: (1) the numbers of its purines and pyrimidines are equal; (2) A = T and C = G; and (3) its $\frac{A+T}{G+C}$ ratio is essentially identical to that of the template. Furthermore, DNA synthesized *in vitro* has physical properties similar to naturally-occurring double-stranded DNA. Sedimentation rate and viscosity indicate that the *in vitro* product, like that *in vivo*, is of high molecular weight. Heating the *in vitro* product for ten minutes at 100°C destroys its secondary structure (just as in native double-stranded DNA); and upon denaturation, it collapses to form compact, randomly-coiled single strands. An extensive *in vitro* synthesis of primarily double-stranded DNA can also be carried out starting with single-stranded DNA from ϕX174 as template. These and other studies indicate that most of the DNA product of *in vitro* synthesis is two-stranded.

Several significant differences, however, do exist between *in vitro* and *in vivo* synthetic processes. *E. coli* DNA polymerase seems to work more slowly *in vitro* than in the bacteria, and calf thymus DNA polymerase *in vitro* only doubles the amount of DNA initially present. Both enzymes synthesize DNA which does not strand-separate completely after prolonged heating and which therefore renatures more readily than native DNA. Electron microscope studies show that DNA made *in vitro* by the *E. coli* enzyme is branched.

Another difference involves a fact noted earlier – that in *E. coli* there seems to be only one starting point in a template DNA strand for the synthesis of new strands *in vivo*. *In vitro*, several positions in a single DNA strand can be used as template starting points for the synthesis of new strands. An especially significant difference is that synthesis proceeds *in vivo* in a parallel manner with the addition of nucleotides at the free 3′ end of one strand and the 5′ end of the other; *in vitro*, however, synthesis occurs in an antiparallel manner with strands growing only at the 3′ end. Such differences may be the result of *in vivo* factors that are missing *in vitro* and from contaminants that are not present *in vivo,* as well as from changes incurred by DNA when it is isolated for use as a template in an *in vitro* synthesis.

4·9 *Strands which contain both DNA and RNA nucleotides can be synthesized* in vitro.

In the presence of Mn^{++} (not Mg^{++}) ions, a mixture of ribo- and deoxyribonucleoside 5′-triphosphates, and some template DNA, *E. coli* DNA polymerase can synthesize complementary strands *in vitro* that contain both ribo- and deoxyribonucleotides (Figure 4-3E). The biological or genetic significance of such RNA-DNA strands is yet to be shown.

4·10 *Double-stranded RNA can be transcribed to double-stranded DNA* in vitro *apparently without complete strand separation of the template RNA.*

Poly (A + U) is a double-stranded RNA in which one strand contains only A and the other only U. Poly A and poly U base pair to form poly (A + U). An *in vitro* system of poly (A + U), *E. coli* DNA polymerase, Mg^{++} ions, dAPPP, and dTPPP produces double-stranded DNA. One strand of this DNA contains only deoxyadenylic acids and is, accordingly, poly dA. Poly dA base-pairs with a strand containing only deoxythymidylic acids, poly dT, to make up the double-stranded poly (dA + dT). Clearly, then, poly (A + U) has served as a template.

Experimental evidence indicates that in this system no hybrid duplexes of DNA and RNA (one strand DNA, the other RNA) are formed. Hence, complete strand separation of poly (A + U) apparently does not occur in the synthesis of poly (dA + dT); and both DNA strands may need to be synthesized simultaneously (Figure 4-3F). In a similar manner, poly (G + C) probably can act as template for synthesis of poly (dG + dC).

4·11 *RNA can be synthesized* de novo *in a nontranscriptional synthesis.*

Polynucleotide phosphorylase synthesizes RNA *de novo* from ribonucleoside *diphosphates* in an *in vitro* system. When different ribonucleoside diphosphates are involved, the final polymer contains ribonucleotides in a random linear array. Polynucleotide phosphorylase may serve *in vivo* to digest rather than synthesize RNA.

We should keep in mind that since the *de novo* synthesis of nucleic acids replicates no previous information, it is a *nontranscriptional* process.

4·12 *Under some* in vitro *conditions double-stranded DNA can be transcribed to single-stranded RNA.*

In the presence of preformed DNA and the ribonucleoside 5′-triphosphates of A, U, C, and G, DNA-dependent RNA polymerase can catalyze the synthesis of RNA *in vitro*. Double-stranded DNA is a more effective template than single-stranded DNA. Under certain conditions the synthesized RNA has the same base ratio as the double-stranded primer-template DNA (we are considering T equivalent to U), indicating that a two-complement transcription has occurred from a two-stranded template (Figure 4-3G).

If we extract the "plus-minus" duplex ring DNA of ϕX174 from its host carefully so that the duplex ring is not broken and then put it into an *in vitro* system with DNA-dependent RNA polymerase, we find that the RNA synthesized is complementary to only the "minus" DNA strand. From this result we conclude that a one-complement transcription from a two-stranded template has taken place (Figure 4-3D, first alternative only).

4·13 *RNA can be transcribed to RNA* in vitro *by RNA-dependent RNA polymerase.*

E. coli does not normally contain an enzyme which catalyzes the transcription of RNA from an RNA template. The bacterium does possess it, however, after infection by $\phi Q\beta$ or ϕMS2, single-stranded RNA viruses. In a system of Mg^{++} ions and the ribonucleoside 5′-triphosphates of A, U, C, and G, the polymerase from cells infected with $\phi Q\beta$ will not synthesize RNA with a template of (1) fragmented $\phi Q\beta$ RNA, (2) carefully-extracted RNA from ϕMS2, or (3) unbroken TMV RNA. If, however, the $\phi Q\beta$ ("plus") RNA to be used as template is not fragmented, the polymerase synthesizes ("plus") RNA that is just as infective as the template (Figure 4-3H). The *RNA-dependent RNA polymerase* isolated from *E. coli* infected with ϕMS2 shows a similar requirement for unfragmented ϕMS2 RNA as template for RNA synthesis.

These experiments indicate that there is a kind of specificity between the RNA-dependent RNA polymerase and the RNA it uses as template. The entire genetic RNA of a virus has been synthesized *in vitro*, but we lack many details of the mechanism of this process.

In another RNA phage, ϕf2, replication of its genetic material seems to involve an enzyme that synthesizes a "minus" strand complementary to the parental "plus" strand (Figure 4-3I) and a second enzyme that synthesizes "plus" strands from the "plus-minus" duplex (Figure 4-3J). Also in contrast to the $\phi Q\beta$ and ϕMS2 enzymes, another RNA-dependent RNA polymerase can use poly A, poly U, and poly C as templates in the *in vitro* synthesis of complementary RNA. In TMV, complementary strand formation also takes place *in vivo* during the replication of RNA genetic material. Apparently, both complementary strands are synthesized when mature viruses containing double-stranded RNA reproduce (Figure 4-3K).

4·14 *The mechanisms of transcription are not yet fully known.*

We have seen that transcription of nucleic acids is a process which results in more copies of the information they contain. Let us now take a closer look at this process. When single-stranded genetic material (for example, the DNA of ϕX174 or the RNA of TMV) is transcribed to its complement, polymerases make use of instructions contained in the template to produce a double-stranded helix. Since single-stranded nucleic acids usually are randomly-coiled macromolecules with no regular helical structure, the template (through the hydrogen-bonding characteristics of its bases) and the polymerases (through their surface and configurational properties) must be primarily responsible for the ordering of complementary nucleotides into a strand which forms a duplex with the template.

Transcription may result, however, in more copies of a strand without first producing a complementary strand (as perhaps occurs in $\phi Q\beta$ and ϕMS2). In such instances, the polymerase or some agent attached to it might function as an adapter which accepts for incorporation into the new strand those nucleotides with the same bases as the template.

As in the replication of *E. coli* DNA, double-stranded nucleic acid can be transcribed to form two duplexes, each containing a parental strand and a new strand. This event might occur by one of at least two possible mechanisms. The parental duplex may first denature, with the single strands then acting separately as templates; or replication may occur while the nucleotide pairs of the parent are still hydrogen-bonded to each other, the major or minor areas surrounding a base pair constituting a mold or template. Afterwards, the H-bonds between parental strands break and reform to link parental strands with their newly-synthesized complements.

Likewise, we can propose two hypotheses to explain how transcription of a double-stranded nucleic acid can give two duplexes, one of which is the original and the other all newly-made. We have seen that such a process occurs *in vitro* when poly (A + U) is used to synthesize poly (dA + dT). Without separating, the H-bonded base pair of a parental duplex may act as the template for both complementary nucleotides. Alternatively, the template might denature at the point of synthesis so that the separated bases can act as templates which bring complementary nucleotides of the new duplex close together. Hydrogen bonds would then form between the members of the new duplex and also reform between the strands of the parental duplex.

When only one complement is transcribed from a double-stranded nucleic acid (as in transcription of "plus-minus" DNA of ϕX174 to "plus" RNA), several types of template are possible. For instance, if the duplex does not denature, the base pair can serve as the template for the synthesis of one complement; or, the parental duplex may denature a piece at a time, followed by one-complement synthesis and renaturation.

The site of polymerase activity is indicated by studies dealing with the effect of *actinomycin D* on transcription. At low concentrations this drug binds to G-containing sites in double-stranded DNA (and probably in double-stranded RNA as well) and suppresses the synthesis of RNA by DNA-dependent RNA polymerase. Interference with DNA synthesis also occurs but at much higher concentrations. Experimental evidence suggests that actinomycin D lies in the minor groove of DNA, hypothesized to be the site of DNA-dependent RNA polymerase activity. The major groove may be the site for DNA polymerase action.

Questions and Problems

4·1 Name two enzymes which synthesize nucleic acids nontranscriptionally; transcriptionally.

4·2 When is transcription also replication? When is it not?

4·3 After a lag period during which dCPPP and dGPPP are incubated in the presence of Mg^{++} and *E. coli* DNA polymerase, a double-stranded DNA is synthesized *de novo*. How can you prove that such duplexes are poly (dG + dC)?

4·4 Name a mature virus whose genetic material is
(a) single-stranded DNA.
(b) double-stranded DNA.
(c) single-stranded RNA.
(d) double-stranded RNA.

4·5 State specific different kinds of nucleic acid syntheses each of the following can catalyze.
(a) *E. coli* DNA polymerase.
(b) calf thymus DNA polymerase.
(c) polynucleotide phosphorylase.
(d) DNA-dependent RNA polymerase.
(e) RNA-dependent RNA polymerase.

4·6 Give two pieces of evidence that the parental strands of double-stranded DNA are separated after *E. coli* DNA has replicated.

4·7 Defend the statement that genetic DNA and genetic RNA are intertranscribable.

4·8 What is the functional significance of the grooves of double-stranded DNA?

4·9 The two complementary strands of the DNA in a phage (SP8) that attacks *Bacillus subtilis* have distinctly different base compositions. Describe an experiment to test whether the phage DNA is used in the host for a one-complement transcription to RNA.

4·10 State the role of one-complement transcription of a double-stranded template in the replication of the following viruses: ϕf2, ϕX174, TMV.

4·11 In reoviruses, actinomycin D inhibits RNA-directed incorporation of deoxyribonucleotides into DNA with DNA polymerase as catalyst to a lesser extent than the RNA-directed incorporation of ribonucleotides into RNA with RNA polymerase as catalyst. How does this result compare with that expected from use of this drug on nucleic acid templates?

4·12 After transcription the members of a parental duplex may 1) remain together (*conservative replication*); 2) separate to form old-new hybrid duplexes (*semiconservative replication*); 3) have their contents dispersed among strands that contain both old and new sections (*dispersive replication*); or 4) both be destroyed (*nonconservative replication*).

Place each transcription of a double-stranded template diagrammed in Figure 4-3 into one of these categories.

4·13 Compare the raw materials you expect are needed *in vitro* and *in vivo* for transcriptional DNA synthesis by *E. coli* DNA polymerase.

References

Baldwin, R. L. 1964. Molecular aspects of the gene: replication mechanisms, in (Vol. 5) *The Bacteria,* Gunsalis, I. C., and Stanier, R. Y. (Editors). New York: Academic Press, pp. 327–372.

Cairns, J. 1964. The chromosome of *Escherichia coli.* Cold Spring Harb. Sympos. Quant. Biol., 28: 43–46. Reprinted in *Papers on Bacterial Genetics, Second Edition.* Adelberg, E. A. (Editor). Boston: Little, Brown and Co., 1966, pp. 397–402. (Replication photographed.)

Colvill, A. J. E., Kanner, L. C., Tochhini-Valentini, G. P., Sarnat, M. T., and Geiduschek, E. P. 1965. Asymmetric RNA synthesis *in vitro:* Heterologous DNA-enzyme systems; *E. coli* RNA polymerase. Proc. Nat. Acad. Sci., U.S., 53: 1140–1146.

Francke, B., and Hofschneider, P. H. 1966. Infectious nucleic acids of *E. coli* bacteriophages, IX. Sedimentation constants and strand integrity of infectious M12 phage replicative-form RNA. Proc. Nat. Acad. Sci., U.S., 56: 1883–1890.

Gibson, I., and Sonneborn, T. M. 1964. Is the metagon an m-RNA in Paramecium and a virus in Didinium? Proc. Nat. Acad. Sci., U.S., 52: 869–876.

Gomatos, P. J., Krug, R. M., and Tamm, I. 1965. Reovirus RNA-directed synthesis of DNA. I. The reaction catalyzed by DNA polymerase from *Escherichia coli*. J. Mol. Biol., 13: 802–816. (Duplex RNA serves *in vitro* as template for synthesis of complementary, often double-stranded, DNA.)

Haruna, I., and Spiegelman, S. 1965. Specific template requirements of RNA replicases. Proc. Nat. Acad. Sci., U.S., 54: 579–586.

Haruna, I., and Spiegelman, S. 1965. Recognition of size and sequence by an RNA replicase. Proc. Nat. Acad. Sci., U.S., 54: 1189–1193.

Haruna, I., and Spiegelman, S. 1966. A search for an intermediate involving a complement during synchronous synthesis by a purified RNA replicase. Proc. Nat. Acad. Sci., U.S., 55: 1256–1263. (Using $\phi Q\beta$ RNA.)

Hayashi, M. N., and Hayashi, M. 1966. Participation of a DNA-RNA hybrid complex in *in vivo* genetic transcription. Proc. Nat. Acad. Sci., U.S., 55: 635–641. (Evidence that a DNA-RNA hybrid complex is involved in transcribing one complement of RNA from double-stranded DNA.)

Hirt, B. 1966. Evidence for semiconservative replication of circular polyoma DNA. Proc. Nat. Acad. Sci., U.S., 55: 997–1004. (See Question 4·12.)

Hotta, Y., and Bassel, A. 1965. Molecular size and circularity of DNA in cells of mammals and higher plants. Proc. Nat. Acad. Sci., U.S., 53: 356–361.

Hurwitz, J., and August, J. T. 1963. The role of DNA in RNA synthesis, in *Progress in Nucleic Acid Research,* Davidson, J. N., and Cohn, W. E. (Editors). New York: Academic Press, Vol. 1, pp. 59–92.

Jehle, H. 1965. Replication of double-strand nucleic acids. Proc. Nat. Acad. Sci., U.S., 53: 1451–1455.

Karkas, J. D., and Chargaff, E. 1966. Template functions in the enzymic formation of polyribonucleotides, I. Integrity of the DNA template. Proc. Nat. Acad. Sci., U.S., 56: 664–671. (The role of the template in transcription.)

Kornberg, A. 1962. *Enzymatic Synthesis of DNA*. New York: J. Wiley & Sons.

Kornberg, A., Bertsch, L. L., Jackson, J. F., and Khorana, H. G. 1964. Enzymatic synthesis of deoxyribonucleic acid, XVI. Oligonucleotides as templates and the mechanism of their replication. Proc. Nat. Acad. Sci., U.S., 51: 315–323.

Kubitschek, H. E., and Henderson, T. R. 1966. DNA replication. Proc. Nat. Acad. Sci., U.S., 55: 512–519. (One strand of the parental duplex may specify both complements of the progeny duplex.)

Lee-Huang, S., and Cavalieri, L. F. 1963. Polyribonucleotides as templates for polydeoxyribonucleotides. Proc. Nat. Acad. Sci., U.S., 50: 1116–1122.

Lodish, H. F., and Zinder, N. D. 1966. Replication of the RNA of bacteriophage f2. Science, 152: 372–378. (Evidence supporting the involvement of two enzymes.)

Margolin, P., and Mukai, F. H. 1966. A model for mRNA transcription suggested by some characteristics of 2-aminopurine mutagenesis in Salmonella. Proc. Nat. Acad. Sci., U.S., 55: 282–289. (The DNA base-pair as the template for one-complement transcription to RNA.)

Meselson, M., and Stahl, F. W. 1958. The replication of DNA in *Escherichia coli*. Proc. Nat. Acad. Sci., U.S., 44: 671–682. (Density-gradient ultracentrifugation studies showing semiconservative replication. See Question 4·12.)

Pitts, J. D., and Sinsheimer, R. L. 1966. Effect of phleomycin upon replication of bacteriophage ϕX174. J. Mol. Biol., 15: 676–680. (The drug probably binds to AT-rich DNA, inhibiting DNA polymerase but not DNA-dependent RNA polymerase action.)

Plaut, W., Nash, D., and Fanning, T. 1966. Ordered replication of DNA in polytene chromosomes of *Drosophila melanogaster*. J. Mol. Biol., 16: 85–93. (Evidence for a longitudinal array of starting points for DNA synthesis.)

Reich, E. 1964. Actinomycin: Correlation of structure and function of its complexes with purines and DNA. Science, 143: 684–689.

Richardson, C. C., Schildkraut, C. L., and Kornberg, A. 1964. Studies on the replication of DNA by DNA polymerases. Cold Spring Harb. Sympos. Quant. Biol., 28: 9–19.

Smith, M. 1963. Deoxyribonucleic acids in crabs of the genus Cancer. Biochem. Biophys. Res. Commun., 10: 67–72.

Spiegelman, S., and Haruna, I. 1966. A rationale for an analysis of RNA replication. Proc. Nat. Acad. Sci., U.S., 55: 1539–1554.

Spiegelman, S., Haruna, I., Holland, I. B., Beaudreau, G., and Mills, D. 1965. The synthesis of a self-propagating and infectious nucleic acid with a purified enzyme. Proc. Nat. Acad. Sci., U.S., 54: 919–927.

Temin, H. M. 1964. Homology between RNA from Rous sarcoma virus and DNA from Rous sarcoma virus-infected cells. Proc. Nat. Acad. Sci., U.S., 52: 323–329.

Weismann, C., and Feix, G. 1966. Replication of viral RNA, XI. Synthesis of viral "minus" strands *in vitro*. Proc. Nat. Acad. Sci., U.S., 55: 1264–1268. (Using $\phi Q\beta$ RNA.)

CHAPTER 5

Translation of Nucleic Acids

As we have seen, the genetic material of a virus carries information both for the replication of this genetic material and for the production of the organism's characteristic protein. The copying of DNA or RNA information into more nucleic acid (a process of transcription) involves a single language whose alphabet consists of organic bases. The formation of proteins from genetic information, however, requires a *translation* from the language of nucleic acids into the language of polypeptides, with an alphabet of some twenty amino acids. The present chapter describes the machinery and mechanism of translation.

5·1 *A ribosome consists of a small ribonucleoprotein subunit joined to a larger one. Ribosomal RNA (rRNA) is a transcript of chromosomal DNA.*

Translation occurs on the ribosome (see p. 5). Ribosomes can be characterized by their rate of sedimentation, measured in an ultracentrifuge and expressed in terms of sedimentation units, s. The number of s units for a particle is directly proportional to its size, although the relationship is not linear. An *E. coli* ribosome is a 70s particle consisting of a 30s subunit joined to a 50s subunit. Both subunits are ribonucleoproteins, and each contains about 64% RNA and 36% protein by weight.

Ribosomal RNA (*rRNA*) is single-stranded and has a rather high molecular weight: $0.55 \pm 0.10 \times 10^6$ for the 16s RNA component of the 30s subunit and $1.15 \pm 0.20 \times 10^6$ for the 23s RNA of the 50s subunit. The 16s and 23s RNA components consist of approximately 1000 and 2000 nucleotides. The 23s RNA is not merely two units of 16s RNA, though; for evidence indicates that 16s and 23s RNA are transcripts of different segments of chromosomal DNA. Mammals contain ribosomes that are somewhat larger than those of *E. coli:* 40s and 60s subunits make up 80s particles which contain 18s and 28s RNA components.

Whereas TMV and other viruses are ribonucleoproteins whose protein portion consists of a large number of identical polypeptide subunits (Fig-

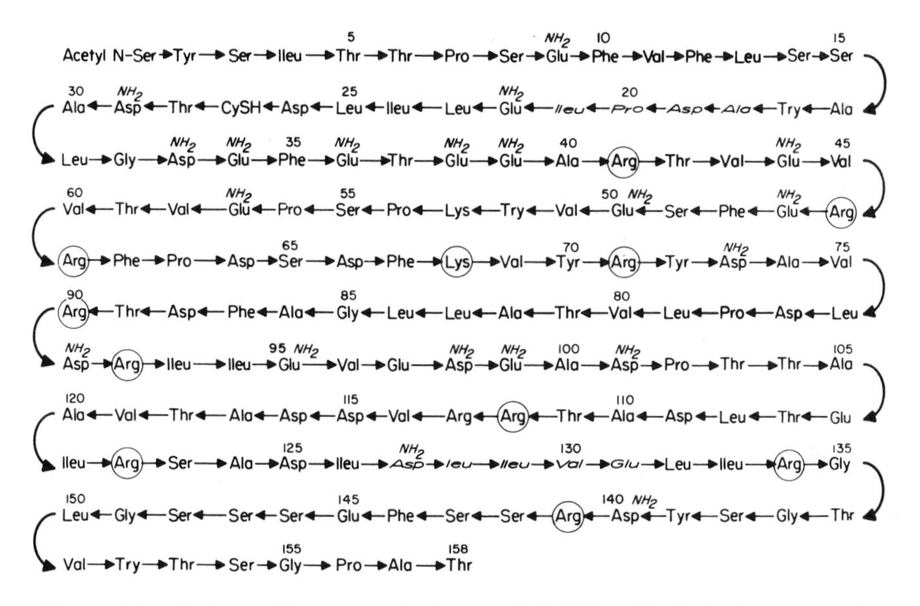

Figure 5-1. Amino acid sequence in the protein building block of tobacco mosaic virus (TMV). There are 158 amino acids in the subunit; the encircled residues indicate the points of digestion by trypsin. (Courtesy of A. Tsugita, D. T. Gish, J. Young, H. Fraenkel-Conrat, C. A. Knight, and W. M. Stanley, Proc. Nat. Acad. Sci., U.S., 46: 1465, 1960.)

ure 5-1), a 30s ribosomal subunit contains ten polypeptide chains, each with a molecular weight of about 30,000 – many or all of them thought to differ from one another. Clearly, the protein structure of ribosomes is more complicated than that of RNA viruses.

5·2 *In cells with nucleoli, rRNA is a transcript of genes in the nucleolus organizer region of a chromosome.*

Like many other sexually-reproducing organisms, the toad *Xenopus laevis* normally has two nucleoli in each nucleus of its somatic (body) cells. Each nucleolus is attached to a *nucleolus organizer region,* which occurs in both members of one chromosome pair. An abnormal Xenopus may have an "anucleolate" chromosome, apparently defective in the nucleolus organizer region, since organisms with one or two such chromosomes lack one or both nucleoli.

When no nucleoli are present, no cells of the developing individual synthesize rRNA. (Some RNA – including a 4s particle – and DNA continue to be made, however.) As we expect, such individuals die early in development because of their inability to make the needed ribosomes. An individual with one nucleolus, however, does produce 28s and 18s rRNA (in fact, as much as an individual with two nucleoli). It appears, therefore, that ribosomal RNA is a transcript of the DNA in the nucleolus organizer region. rRNA-DNA hybridization studies show that most if not all of the nucleolus organizer region is missing from anucleolate chromosomes.

Because rRNA is complementary to about 0.3% of the total DNA in bacteria and mice, it appears that many genes are involved in its synthesis. Since neither 18s nor 28s rRNA is made when both chromosomes in Xenopus are anucleolate, the genes for these types of RNA appear to be close together in a single chromosome. Experiments involving the fruit fly, Drosophila, give similar results.

5·3 *Transfer, or soluble, RNA (sRNA) is another transcript of DNA. A relatively short, single-stranded molecule which base-pairs internally by folding back on itself, an sRNA carries a specific amino acid to the ribosome.*

In addition to rRNA, cells contain another kind of single-stranded RNA, one which is 4s, consists of some 77 nucleotides and has a relatively low MW of about 26,600. Since this RNA is soluble in a solution of approximately 1M NaCl whereas rRNA is not, it is called *soluble RNA*, or *sRNA*. Radioactive labeling of amino acids reveals that an sRNA molecule has an amino acid attached to it when the sRNA arrives at a ribosome. In fact, sRNA transports amino acids to the ribosomes and, hence, is also called *transfer RNA*.

All sRNA molecules terminate at the 3′ end with the base sequence -C-C-A and usually start at the 5′ end with guanine. X-ray diffraction studies indicate that at least part of an sRNA molecule is double-helical. Since each sRNA is single-stranded, the molecule must be bent back on itself in order to base-pair internally and form a double helix. The sRNA molecules whose sequences are known contain some twenty base pairs and seem to have three folds that give them the shape of a clover leaf. Each fold requires at least three unpaired nucleotides. The ends of the sRNA terminate unevenly.

All of the different sRNA's are thought to differ in the sequence and types of bases and to comprise twenty different groups, each one capable of carrying a different amino acid. Since sRNA can base-pair with denatured chromosomal DNA from the same individual, it must be a transcript of DNA. Base-pairing is best when the sRNA and DNA are from the same species – a fact which indicates that different species contain different sets of sRNA's. All sRNA molecules, however, apparently contain the sequence GTΨCG (Ψ = pseudouracil) internally, which may serve as point of attachment to the ribosome.

5·4 *When the base sequence of an sRNA is known, so is all, or almost all, the base sequence of its gene.*

The complete base sequence of an sRNA for alanine in yeast is given in Figure 2-9, p. 19 (see also Section 2·8). Since this nucleic acid is a transcript of DNA, we know essentially the entire order of nucleotides in the gene which specified it. Studies of alanyl-sRNA were the first to give us the base sequence of a natural polyribonucleotide and of its gene. Base sequences are now also known for sRNA's that transport tyrosine (78 nucleotides long) and serine.

5·5 *Activation of an amino acid precedes its attachment to a specific sRNA. A single enzyme (a different one for each kind of amino acid) catalyzes both processes.*

Before attachment to a specific sRNA, an amino acid must be activated. This process involves linkage of the amino acid at its carboxyl $\left(-\mathrm{C}\begin{matrix} /\!\!/ \mathrm{O} \\ \diagdown \mathrm{OH} \end{matrix}\right)$ end to the 2′ or 3′ hydroxyl group of adenosine 5′-triphosphate (APPP or ATP) and the removal of pyrophosphate (PP). We may summarize this reaction as follows: amino acid + ATP $\rightleftharpoons$ amino acyl-AMP + PP, where AMP is adenosine monophosphate. Subsequently, the amino acid joins at its carboxyl end to the A-containing end of an sRNA: sRNA + amino acyl-AMP $\rightleftharpoons$ amino acyl-sRNA + AMP. Both the activation of an amino acid and its attachment to an sRNA are catalyzed by the same enzyme, *amino acyl-sRNA synthetase,* a different one for each kind of amino acid.

5·6 *Messenger RNA (mRNA) is a single-stranded transcript of double-stranded DNA and serves as a carrier of information from the genetic material to the ribosome.*

After a T phage infects *E. coli,* the double-stranded DNA of the phage undergoes a one-complement transcription to RNA. Soon afterwards, this RNA is found attached to a number of preexisting ribosomes. Since it carries information transcribed from phage DNA, it is called *messenger RNA,* or *mRNA*. Messenger RNA is transcribed from DNA of cellular organelles also (see Section 4·3). Although rRNA and sRNA usually are used directly, as we have seen, mRNA functions indirectly, as a message carrier.

5·7 *A ribosome with mRNA attached also has sites for attachment of two amino-acyl-sRNA molecules. These sRNA's function as adapters, since a portion of each base pairs with mRNA, in the stepwise synthesis of a polypeptide.*

Each subunit of a 70s ribosome has a specific function in polypeptide synthesis. The 30s subunit binds to a short segment of messenger RNA and apparently makes sure that the bound segment is single-stranded and has its bases properly exposed for hydrogen-bonding with sRNA. The 50s subunit is thought to contain both sites in the ribosome for holding amino acyl-sRNA molecules (Figure 5-2). The two amino acyl-sRNA's that attach to these sites carry exposed, unpaired bases complementary to those of mRNA bound to the ribosome.

Thus we see that sRNA functions not only as a carrier of amino acids to the ribosome but as an *adapter* molecule which orders amino acids according to instructions of the mRNA. When mRNA and the corresponding amino acyl-sRNA's are attached to a ribosome (Figure 5-2A), the -C-C-A-amino acid end of the sRNA at site 2 of the 50s subunit is free to reach the -C-C-A end of the amino acyl-sRNA at site 1. An enzyme (or two) then catalyzes the formation of a peptide bond $(-\overset{\overset{\displaystyle O}{\|}}{C}-\overset{\overset{\displaystyle H}{|}}{N}-)$ between the carboxyl group of the amino acid at site 2 and the free amino group of the amino acid at site 1. (For every peptide bond formed, a phosphate is apparently liberated from guanosine triphosphate, GTP, by a ribosome-dependent GTPase.) No longer carrying an amino acid, the sRNA at site 2 is liberated from the ribosome and is free to accept another amino acid for transport.

The mRNA molecule then moves along or through the 30s subunit so that more of its message can be translated; the sRNA-dipeptide moves from site 1 to site 2 in the same direction. We should note that the first dipeptide synthesized will have a free *N-terminal end* (the nitrogen of an amino group) and a bound *C-terminal end* (the carbon of the carboxyl group linked to sRNA). Directed by the bases of mRNA, an appropriate amino acyl-sRNA can now attach to vacant site 1, and a peptide bond be formed as before. The result is a tripeptide. By this stepwise addition of amino acids a polypeptide chain is formed which begins at the N-terminal end of its first amino acid and ends at the C-terminal end of the last. In a sense sRNA functions as the dictionary by which the "language" of nucleic acids is translated into that of proteins. We should note further that since the growing polypeptide chain appears attached to the 50s ribosomal subunit (not to the messenger) only at its growing end, the polypeptide may fold to attain part of its three-dimensional configuration before synthesis is complete.

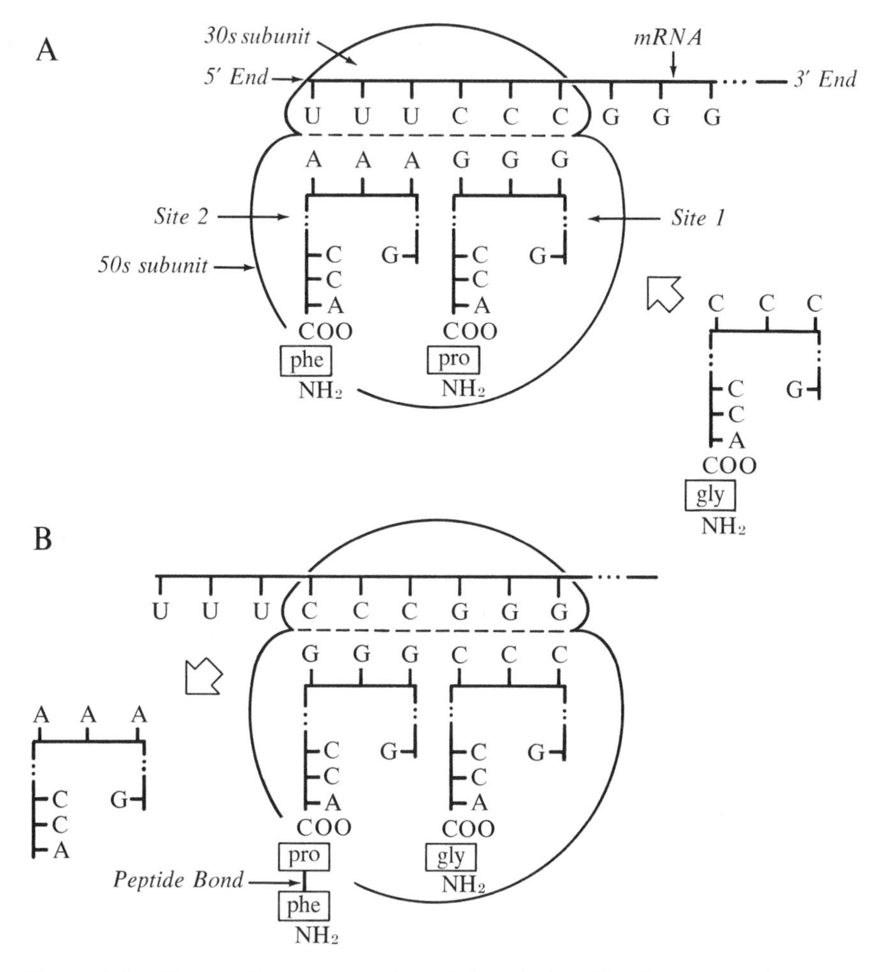

Figure 5-2. Schematic representation of the relationships between amino acyl-sRNA's and mRNA at the ribosome in the formation of peptide linkages. The mRNA moves in the 5′ direction with respect to the ribosome; the mRNA and amino acyl-sRNA's pair in an antiparallel manner.

5·8 *Each ribosome attaches to the 5′ end of an mRNA and moves toward its 3′ end. If the mRNA molecule is long enough, several ribosomes can join to the same messenger. The successive ribosomes of such a polyribosome each bear a polypeptide chain at a successive stage of synthesis.*

A 70s ribosome, with a diameter of approximately 230A, can receive only one mRNA and can make only one polypeptide chain at a given time. The 5′ end of the messenger, the part synthesized first, is also the first to become attached to the ribosome (sometimes, apparently, before the mRNA molecule has been completely synthesized). Since some mRNA molecules contain more than 1500 nucleotides, each an average of 3.4A in length, such RNA is more than 50,000A long. It seems reasonable, therefore, that several ribosomes can use the same RNA molecule simultaneously. Since translation begins at only one end of a messenger, we would expect ribosomes along the mRNA to carry polypeptides at successive stages of completion (Figure 5-3). In support of this hypothesis is evidence that protein synthesis occurs among aggregates of five to eight ribosomes in some organisms. Such aggregates, called *polyribosomes* or *polysomes,* are visible in electron micrographs (Figure 5-4) and may contain dozens of ribosomes when a long mRNA is being read. Those ribosomes that have completely traversed an mRNA are freed and can translate the same message or others several times.

5·9 *Different mRNA's survive for various lengths of time.*

As noted earlier, transcription from DNA to RNA is blocked by actinomycin D. Studies of bacteria treated with this drug show that mRNA exists for about two minutes, on the average, and is available as a template ten to twenty times before being degraded. The mRNA for hemoglobin, on the other hand, is among those which persist for a longer period. The mechanism by which the nucleic acid is degraded is still unknown, but *ribonuclease* (*RNase*) is thought to be involved, for much, if not all, of a bacteria's RNase is found in latent form attached to the 30s particle. Moreover, in reticulocytes (immature red blood corpuscles), where mRNA shows little turnover, no latent RNase has been found on ribosomes. Some evidence indicates that polynucleotide phosphorylase also is able to degrade mRNA (see Section 4·11).

5·10 *Apparently all polypeptides synthesized by organisms are translations of nucleic acids in a ribosome-amino acyl-sRNA system.*

The genetic material of all RNA viruses functions as messenger RNA by binding to ribosomes. Subsequently the characteristic protein of a virus (including coat protein and usually RNA-dependent RNA polymerase) is produced. Under special conditions *in vitro,* and perhaps *in vivo* as well, single-stranded DNA can act like mRNA and be translated into protein in the presence of ribosomes and amino acyl-sRNA's.

Tryptophan synthetase, an enzyme found in *E. coli,* can be treated so that its two polypeptide chains dissociate *in vitro.* Neither chain by itself has the usual catalytic ability of the enzyme; but when the two chains are reassociated, normal enzymatic activity is restored. Since the polypeptides which make up this protein are different, we can hypothe-

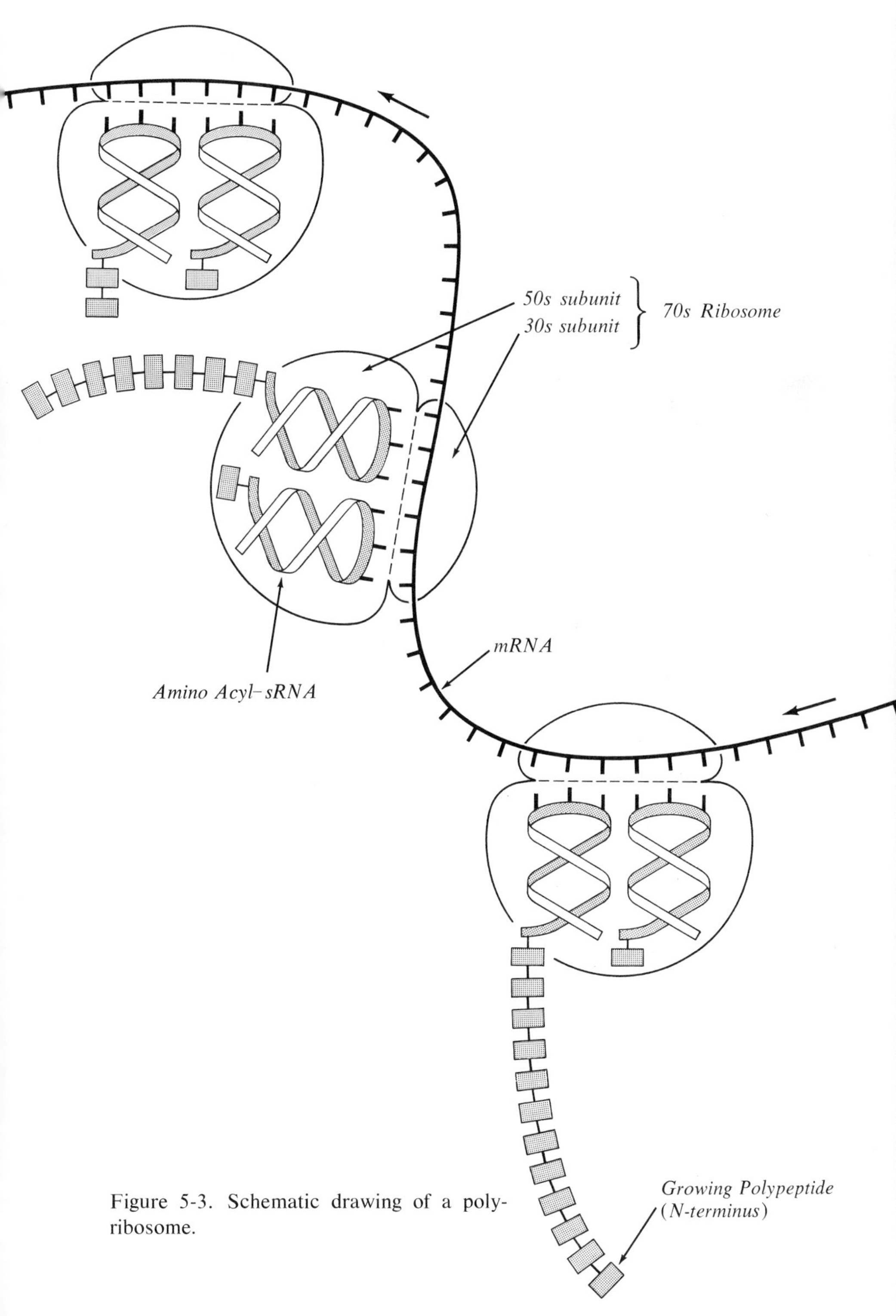

Figure 5-3. Schematic drawing of a polyribosome.

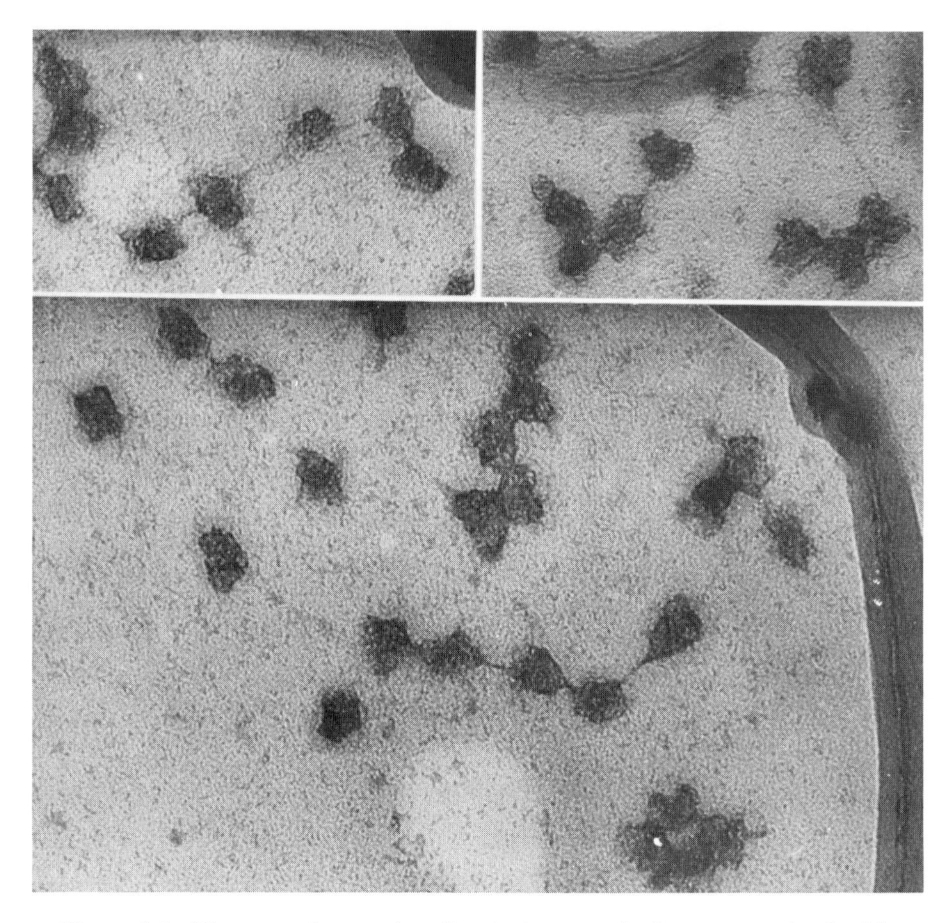

Figure 5-4. Electron micrographs of reticulocyte polyribosomes stained with uranyl acetate. (Courtesy of A. Rich)

size that each chain is the result of transcription and translation of a different chromosomal segment – that is, transcription and translation of a different gene. Supporting this hypothesis are studies of bacteria which lack tryptophan synthetase activity. Some strains are defective in one polypeptide chain, whereas others are defective in the other. All the bacteria with defects in one chain have been found to bear defects in one chromosome segment; likewise, all those with defects in the other chain have defects in a different segment of the chromosome. Similar results have been obtained with multistranded, nonenzymatic proteins including hemoglobin. These results are consistent with the view that all polypeptide synthesis *in vivo* is the result of a translation of nucleic acid information in a ribosome-amino acyl-sRNA system.

Questions and Problems

5·1 Differentiate between transcription and translation of nucleic acids.

5·2 Isolated protein-synthesizing ribosomes sometimes have DNA "attached." Explain the presence of this DNA and its mode of attachment to the ribosome.

5·3 If you added 5-fluoro uracil to the culture medium of a bacterium and all protein synthesis ceased within several minutes, what would you conclude?

5·4 Design an experiment that shows protein is synthesized in the cytoplasm; in the nucleus.

5·5 Since ribosomes are found in the nucleus, it is not surprising that some protein synthesis occurs there. An acidic protein extract of the calf thymus nucleus that incorporates tryptophan into polypeptides is reported to be unaffected by sRNA, rRNA, and RNase. What bearing does this observation have on the summary statement of Section 5·10?

5·6 Knowing that the DNA-containing vaccinia virus replicates in the cytoplasm of human-tissue culture cells, design an experiment to show that mRNA can be made from a cytoplasmic DNA template.

5·7 The DNA of HeLa human-tissue culture cells can be collected, fragmented, and separated into two portions: with and without attached nucleoli. How would you test these portions for the presence of genes for rRNA? What results would you expect?

5·8 Design an experiment to show that synthesis of polypeptide chains begins at the N-terminal end.

5·9 Justify the use of the plural in the title of this chapter.

5·10 Give two pieces of evidence that the genes encoding rRNA of different species differ in the sequence or the number of bases.

5·11 Define the term "messenger nucleic acid."

References

Bremer, H., Konrad, W., Gaines, K., and Stent, G. S. 1965. Direction of chain growth in enzymic RNA synthesis. J. Mol. Biol., 13: 540–553. (One proof that mRNA grows from 5′ toward 3′.)

Brenner, S., Jacob, F., and Meselson, M. 1961. An unstable intermediate carrying information from genes to ribosomes for protein synthesis. Nature, Lond., 190: 576–581. Reprinted in *Papers on Bacterial Viruses, Second Edition.* Stent, G. S. (Editor). Boston: Little, Brown and Co., 1965, pp. 402–409. (A first report of mRNA.)

Brown, D. D., and Gurdon, J. B. 1964. Absence of ribosomal RNA synthesis in the anucleolate mutant of *Xenopus laevis*. Proc. Nat. Acad. Sci., U.S., 51: 139–146.

Dintzis, H. M. 1961. Assembly of the peptide chains of hemoglobin. Proc. Nat. Acad. Sci., U.S., 47: 247–261.

Gross, F., Hunt, H., Gilberg, W., Kurland, C. G., Risebrough, R. W., and Watson, J. D. 1961. Unstable ribonucleic acid revealed by pulse labelling. Nature, Lond., 190: 581–585. (A first report of mRNA.)

Hurwitz, J., and Furth, J. J. 1962. Messenger RNA. Scient. Amer., 206 (No. 2): 41–49.

Lindahl, T., Adams, A., Geroch, M., and Fresco, J. R. 1967. Selective recognition of the native conformation of transfer ribonucleic acids by enzymes. Proc. Nat. Acad. Sci., U.S., 57: 178–185. (Importance of tertiary structure of sRNA.)

Low, R. B., and Wool, I. G. 1967. Mammalian ribosomal protein: analysis by electrophoresis in polyacrylamide gel. Science, 155: 330–332. (Ribosomal proteins differ in mammals and *E. coli.*)

Maxwell, E. S., Barnett, L. M., Howard, F. B., and Miles, H. T. 1966. Helix formation between polyribonucleotides and purine nucleosides. III. J. Mol. Biol., 16: 440–453. (Affects translation of the polymer.)

McCarthy, B. J., and Holland, J. J. 1965. Denatured DNA as a direct template for *in vitro* protein synthesis. Proc. Nat. Acad. Sci., U.S., 54: 880–886.

McConkey, E. H., and Hopkins, J. W. 1965. Subribosomal particles and the transport of messenger RNA in HeLa cells. J. Mol. Biol., 14: 257–270. (Movement from chromosome to cytoplasm of mRNA complexed with a 45s ribosomal subunit or with protein.)

Petermann, M. L. 1965. *The Physical and Chemical Properties of Ribosomes.* New York: American Elsevier Publ. Co., Inc.

Rich, A. 1963. Polyribosomes. Scient. Amer., 209: (No. 6): 44–53, 178.

Scherrer, K., Marcaud, L., Zajdela, F., London, I. M., and Gros, F. 1966. Patterns of RNA metabolism in a differentiated cell: A rapidly labeled, unstable 60s RNA with messenger properties in duck erythroblasts. Proc. Nat. Acad. Sci., U.S., 56: 1571–1578. (Evidence suggesting that giant nascent 60s RNA, containing about 15,000 nucleotides, is converted to 10s functional hemoglobin mRNA.)

Spirin, A. S. 1964. *Macromolecular Structure of Ribonucleic Acids.* New York: Reinhold Publishing Corporation.

Suzuka, I., Kaji, H., and Kaji, A. 1966. Binding of specific sRNA to 30s ribosomal subunits: effect of 50s ribosomal subunits. Proc. Nat. Acad. Sci., U.S., 55: 1483–1490. (Evidence that site 1 is in the 30s subunit and that site 2 is generated with the formation of the 70s ribosome.)

Synthesis and Structure of Macromolecules, Cold Spring Harb. Sympos. Quant. Biol., 28.

Wagner, R. P., and Mitchell, H. K. 1964. *Genetics and Metabolism, Second Edition.* New York: J. Wiley & Sons, Inc.

CHAPTER 6

The Nucleic Acid Code for Translation

At the ribosome a single nucleotide of the mRNA cannot correspond to a single amino acid since translation must account for some twenty amino acids. Nucleotide "letters" of mRNA must be grouped, therefore, into "words" so that translation to the language of proteins may occur. Let us consider now the coding unit, or *codon*, of a messenger nucleic acid – that segment which binds with a single amino acyl-sRNA.

6·1 *Synthetic polyribonucleotides used as mRNA are translated into polypeptides in an* in vitro *ribosome-amino acyl-sRNA system.*

We can study the mechanism of protein synthesis *in vitro* by using the following cell-free system: a suspension of ruptured *E. coli* cells, ribonucleoside 5′-triphosphates of A, G, C, and U, and the 20 amino acids usually found in protein (Figure 6-1). When radioactively-labeled amino acids are added to the system, we can readily detect incorporation into polypeptides. If RNase or DNase is added, the synthesis is stopped. Evidently the RNase stops the synthesis by degrading the mRNA present in the *E. coli* suspension, so that genetic information is no longer available to be read. The DNase acts by degrading DNA so that no new mRNA can be made.

Since the mRNA present in the *in vitro* system is responsible for directing polypeptide synthesis, it is interesting to see the effect of adding synthetic polyribonucleotides of known composition to the system as mRNA. When poly U is added, phenylalanine is incorporated into protein, and a polypeptide consisting only of phenylalanines (polyphenylalanine) is produced. Hence we conclude that a sequence of U's codes for phenylalanine *in vitro*.

When poly U is mixed with poly A so that the strands base-pair with each other, the amount of phenylalanine incorporated is partially or completely reduced. The synthetic messenger thus seems to be most effective *in vitro* when it is single-stranded, as is mRNA *in vivo*. When

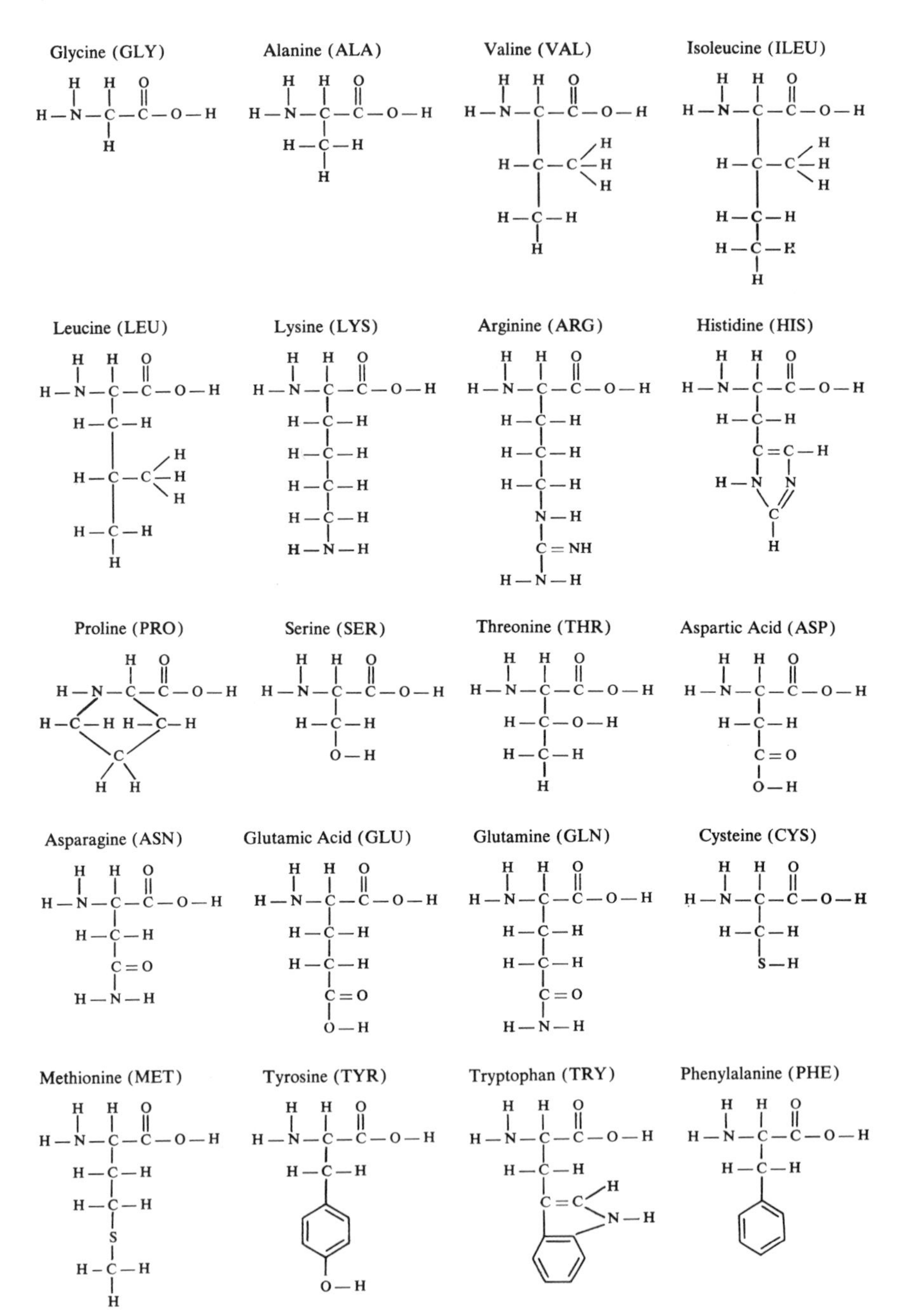

Figure 6-1. Twenty of the most common amino acids.

single-stranded poly A is used in the *in vitro* system, polylysine is produced; when poly C is used, polyproline is made. Poly G, however, does not work well as messenger in this system. Its effectiveness is reduced probably because G-G interactions that occur when the polymer folds back on itself interfere with the ability of guanine to base pair with cytosine in an sRNA.

Polyribonucleotides containing two, three, or four different ribonucleotides can also be synthesized and tested *in vitro* for their effects on amino acid incorporation into protein. We recall from Section 4·11 that the enzyme which catalyzes the synthesis of such mixed polymers, polynucleotide phosphorylase, arranges the bases linearly in a random array. Some amino acids require the presence of two different nucleotides in the synthetic polynucleotide in order to be incorporated. Consequently, the unit of coding, the codon, must contain at least two nucleotides. No amino acid requires the presence of all four types of organic bases in the synthetic polynucleotide for incorporation. Hence we hypothesize that either doublets or triplets of synthetic mRNA nucleotides are translated into amino acids. In other words, the *in vitro* codon is either a doublet or a triplet.

6·2 *The* in vitro *codon is a triplet whose base sequence can be determined by the binding of specific amino acyl-sRNA's to ribosomes carrying specific ribonucleotide triplets.*

The incorporation of amino acids into protein *in vitro* requires that very long polynucleotides (for example, a poly U of 500 to 1000 nucleotides) be used as messenger. It is not surprising, therefore, that a single dinucleotide or trinucleotide cannot stimulate amino acid incorporation. Short polyribonucleotides can be synthesized (or isolated) and tested *in vitro* for their ability to cause the binding of specific amino acyl-sRNA's to ribosomes. (By convention, a tri-ribonucleotide of U with a 3′-terminal phosphate is represented as UpUpUp and one with a 5′-terminal phosphate, pUpUpU.) When pUpUpU, pApApA, and pCpCpC are tested, they are found to direct the binding of phe-, lys-, and pro-sRNA, respectively. Dinucleotides bring about no binding. The simplest explanation for these results is that *in vitro* codons are triplets.

A further finding is that trinucleotides with a 5′-terminal phosphate are more active than those with no 5′-terminal phosphate. Trinucleotides with a 3′- (or 2′-) terminal phosphate are inactive.

Since a polynucleotide containing U and G incorporates valine into protein, the codon for valine includes U and G. The order of the bases in the codon can be investigated by using poly UG, dinucleotides, the trinucleoside diphosphate GpUpU, and its sequence isomers UpGpU and UpUpG. The binding of radioactive C^{14}-val-sRNA to ribosomes is found to be directed both by poly UG and GpUpU but not by UpGpU, UpUpG, or dinucleotides. Moreover, the binding of val-sRNA is specific – GpUpU has no effect on the sRNA's of seventeen other amino acids. From these results, we conclude that a codon for valine is GUU and that val-sRNA carries the complementary *anticodon* CAA (AAC, when read from the 5′- toward the 3′- and of the sRNA). The anticodon is thought to be a triplet of bases in the loop of the sRNA cloverleaf opposite the termini.

6·3 *Many* in vitro *codons for amino acids are known. The code for translation is degenerate. Some triplets are nonsense for amino acid, and some are ambiguous.*

From studies such as those described above, the *in vitro* coding ability of all 64 triplets of the general type BpBpB, where each B can be A, U, C, or G, has been determined (Figure 6-2). We note from the table that the code is *degenerate,* that is, more than one triplet is translated into the same amino acid. The major degeneracy occurs at the third position, the 3′ end of the triplet. For example, when the first two bases are specified, the same amino acid may be coded for whether the third base is (1) U, C, A, or G (GU*U*, GU*C*, GU*A*, and GU*G* all code for valine), (2) either pyrimidine (both AG*U* and AG*C* code for serine), or (3) either purine (both CA*A* and CA*G* code for glutamic acid). Degeneracy also occurs in the first position. Arginine is *A*GA and *C*GA; leucine is *C*UG and *U*UG. Amino acids which have been synthesized from a common precursor *in vivo* and which thus possess structural and metabolic similarities often have similar codons – e.g., phenylalanine (*U*U*U* and *U*U*C*) and tyrosine (*U*A*U* and *U*A*C*).

Some triplets (UAA and UAG) do not code for any amino acid *in vitro,* or do so only under certain conditions. Such "no-amino-acid sense" or *nonsense* codons may have other informational functions, such as to signal the start or end of translation of mRNA. Evidence supporting this possibility is that polypeptide chains are released from the ribosome only if the mRNA contains U and A, which suggests that a chain-terminating codon contains these bases.

The *in vitro* code is sometimes *ambiguous;* that is, a single codon may be translated into different amino acids. Although UUU is translated into phenylalanine under "usual" *in vitro* conditions, it is also translated into isoleucine and to a lesser extent serine and leucine when the ribosome is treated with streptomycin. Low temperature and high Mg^{++} ion concentration also cause ambiguity.

SECOND BASE

FIRST BASE	U	C	A	G	THIRD BASE
U	UUU } phe	UCU } ser	UAU } tyr	UGU } cys	U
	UUC } phe	UCC } ser	UAC } tyr	UGC } cys	C
	UUA } leu	UCA } ser	UAA non	UGA ?	A
	UUG } leu	UCG } ser	UAG non	UGG try	G
C	CUU } leu	CCU } pro	CAU } his	CGU } arg	U
	CUC } leu	CCC } pro	CAC } his	CGC } arg	C
	CUA } leu	CCA } pro	CAA } gln	CGA } arg	A
	CUG } leu	CCG } pro	CAG } gln	CGG } arg	G
A	AUU } ileu	ACU } thr	AAU } asn	AGU } ser	U
	AUC } ileu	ACC } thr	AAC } asn	AGC } ser	C
	AUA } ileu	ACA } thr	AAA } lys	AGA } arg	A
	AUG met	ACG } thr	AAG } lys	AGG } arg	G
G	GUU } val	GCU } ala	GAU } asp	GGU } gly	U
	GUC } val	GCC } ala	GAC } asp	GGC } gly	C
	GUA } val	GCA } ala	GAA } glu	GGA } gly	A
	GUG } val	GCG } ala	GAG } glu	GGG } gly	G

Figure 6-2. The *in vitro* mRNA codons for amino acids.
non = possible nonsense or special function codons
Ambiguities are not indicated.

6·4 *Messenger RNA is translated unidirectionally in successive triplet codons* in vivo.

Phage T4 has been used extensively and productively to study the nature and consequences of the genetic code *in vivo*. One region of T4 DNA is of particular interest to us, because it will be used to demonstrate *in vivo* much of what has already been shown *in vitro*.

The rII region of T4 DNA is composed of two adjacent genes, *A* and *B*. A defect in the *A* gene which results in a defective *A* polypeptide has no effect on the production of the *B* polypeptide, and vice versa. Genetic changes can be induced at different places in the *B* gene by chemical agents which cause the substitution of one base for another. Such a change sometimes causes the loss of all *B* activity. In some instances, however, *B* activity can be restored by a chemical which causes the re-substitution of the original, functional base. A different kind of change is brought about by acridine dyes, which act by causing the addition (+) or loss (−) of one or more whole nucleotides (see Section 7·4, p. 83) rather than the substitution of one nucleotide for another. The sequence of nucleotides is thereby thrown out of phase, and is not likely to be read properly. For example, with a deletion of *b*, the message *abc def g*.. ... becomes *acd efg* ... .

If acridines do induce changes as described above, +− or −+ doubly-defective organisms should have some *B* activity (provided that the two defects in the *B* gene are near each other), since the reading of nucleotides should once more be in phase. Such phages do indeed possess some *B* function (Figure 6-3). Moreover, it should be possible to increase the number of defects of the same type (all − or all +) until the number of nucleotides subtracted from or added to the *B* gene equals the number in a codon. At this point, the nucleotides beyond the last defective codon would again be in phase for correct translation, and some *B* activity would be restored. Accordingly, phages carrying two, three, four, five, and even six different − (or +) defects have been constructed. Some of the three or six − (or +) defectives have *B* activity; the combination of four − and one + also shows *B* activity. No activity is found, however, if the defects fail to add up to three or an integral multiple of three. These results demonstrate that mRNA from gene *B* is translated as consecutive, nonoverlapping codons and that a codon is most probably three successive nucleotides.

One particular strain, carrying deletion number 1589, lacks part of both the *A* and *B* genes. Phages with this deletion show no *A* but partial *B* activity. When single + (or −) acridine-induced defects in the *A* region are introduced into deletion 1589 phages, the *B* gene is always suppressed. In other words, *B* gene activity is stopped by defects in the *A* gene. (When deletion 1589 phage are made doubly-defective in the *A* region, +− double defects can, but −− or ++ combinations cannot, maintain *B* activity.) These findings show that in a deletion 1589 phage, if the reading is out of phase due to a nucleotide addition or subtraction in *A*, all subsequent codons (that is, those in gene *B*) will be misread. These results and others prove that the codons in rII mRNA are always read unidirectionally − from *A* toward *B*.

Other support for the code being triplet *in vivo* comes from the following physical evidence: (1) the α and β chains of hemoglobin, about 150 amino acids long, are each encoded by an mRNA of approximately 450 nucleotides; and (2) the protein coat of the satellite tobacco necrosis virus (STNV), approximately 300 amino acids long, is encoded by a single-stranded genetic RNA of about one thousand nucleotides.

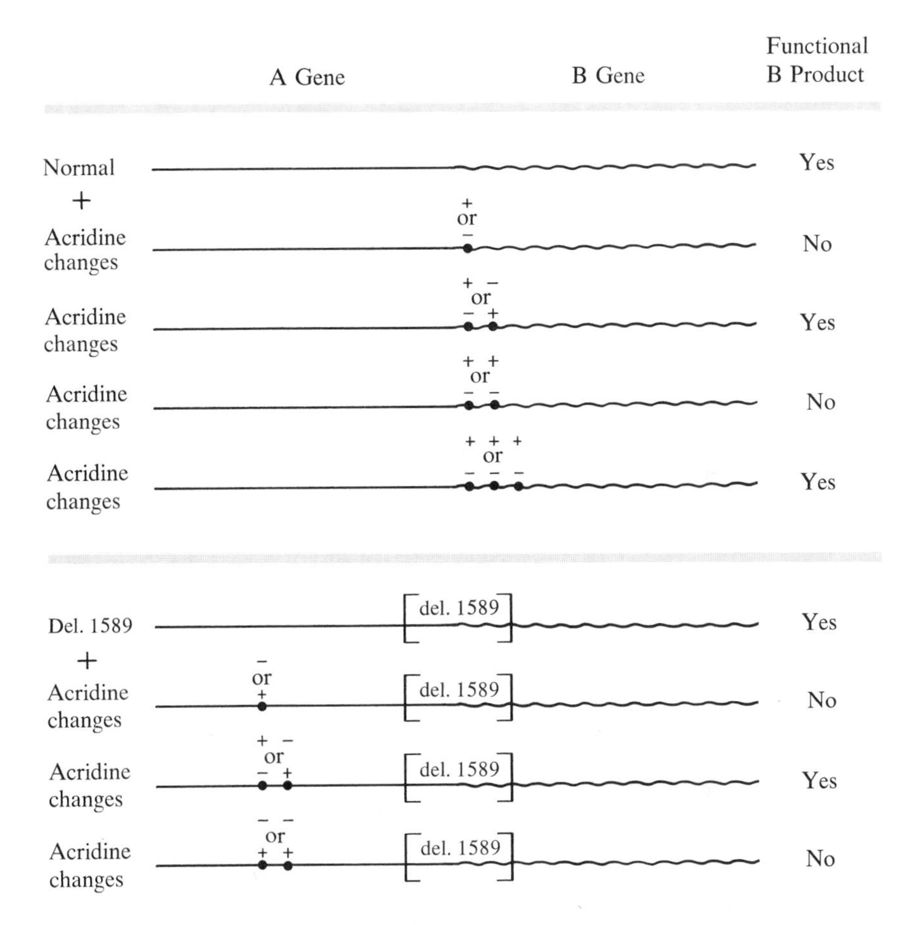

Figure 6-3. Effect of acridine-induced changes in the *A* and *B* genes of the rII region of ϕT4 on functional product of gene *B*. Brackets show portions of *A* and *B* lost in deletion 1589.

6·5 *Genetic changes can produce missense and nonsense codons.*

As noted in the previous section, the addition or subtraction of a single nucleotide to phage DNA causes the triplet codons in that region to be read out of phase. The triplets that the sRNA now reads include nucleotides from triplets which previously had been adjacent. The triplets which result after such a phase shift fall into three categories: (1) *sense codons,* which read or are translated the same as before, (2) *missense codons,* which code for a different amino acid, and (3) *nonsense codons,* which code for no amino acid.

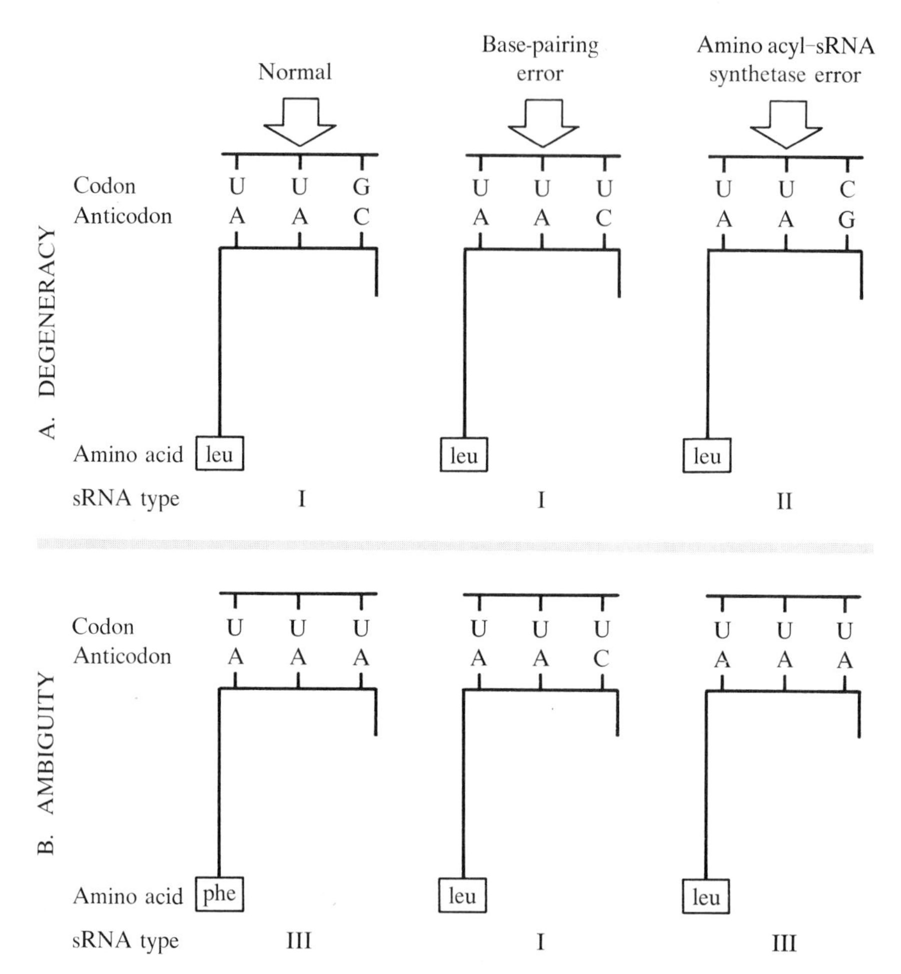

Figure 6-4. Several possible types of degeneracy and ambiguity. The examples of degeneracy are also examples of ambiguity since they involve codons for phenylalanine.

6·6 *Because there is often more than one sRNA for a given amino acid, the* in vivo *code is highly degenerate.*

It has been found that the frequency of some amino acids in the protein of different organisms remains nearly constant even though the $\frac{A+T}{C+G}$ ratio varies greatly. This finding indicates that the *in vivo* code must contain more than one triplet for these amino acids; that is, it must be degenerate. A consequence of this degeneracy is that since the sRNA "adapters" are related to the codon by their anticodon, they must also be degenerate.

Leu-sRNA of *E. coli* can be separated into three types, each with different coding properties *in vitro* and, presumably, *in vivo*. The first type responds preferentially to poly UG, the second type preferentially to poly UC (Figure 6-4A), and the third to poly U and copolymers rich in U (including poly UC). The discovery that leucine is carried by different sRNA's provides an explanation of how six different triplets can code for the same amino acid. Two different leu-sRNA's contribute leucine to separate sites in a chain of hemoglobin synthesized *in vitro*, indicating that each sRNA responds to a distinct codon. Similar results have been obtained with two ser-sRNA's. Since twenty-nine sRNA's specific for sixteen amino acids have been detected in *E. coli* and up to now about sixty different sRNA's have been isolated, it appears that degeneracy of the code is extensive.

6·7 *The* in vivo *code may be ambiguous.*

In certain instances (see Section 6·3), a given codon may be translated into more than one amino acid (Figure 6-4B). This ambiguity can occur when the amino acyl-sRNA synthetase makes an error and links an incorrect amino acid to the sRNA. One such error occurs when a phe-sRNA synthetase of *Neurospora crassa* attaches phenylalanine to the wrong sRNA of *E. coli*. Ambiguity can also result if the wrong sRNA anticodon base-pairs with the mRNA. The UUU codon, for example, is translated *in vitro* both by phe-sRNA and one type of leu-sRNA. Since UUU acts as a codon for leucine here, we should note that the base-pairing error also increases the degeneracy of the code. The factors causing ambiguity *in vitro* presumably also operate *in vivo*. Determinations of amino acid sequence in a polypeptide of hemoglobin in the rabbit and mouse indicate that ambiguity occurs *in vivo;* even when this polypeptide is apparently encoded by a normal gene, an amino acid normally present at a given position is sometimes replaced by another having a similar codon *in vitro*.

6·8 *Some nonsense codons can act as sense codons when a base analog is incorporated in mRNA.*

When 5-fluoro uracil (FU) is added to the culture medium of *E. coli*, it is sometimes incorporated into mRNA being synthesized. Since FU is similar in structure to U, it can substitute for U. When this *base analog* substitution occurs, there is a much greater chance that an sRNA will "mistake" FU for C than if U were present. If, for instance, the original triplet is UAA (a nonsense codon, which prevents translation of the messenger past that point) then a reading of FUAA as CAA, a sense codon, will allow translation to continue.

6·9 *Some nonsense codons can be restored to sense by an external suppressor.*

Several strains of bacteria can produce complete phage protein even when the phage genes involved contain a nonsense triplet. For example, although some ϕf2 have a particular nonsense codon which does not allow the phage to make all of its coat protein in certain strains of *E. coli,* in other strains complete phage coat protein is produced. These latter bacterial strains are able to "suppress" the nonsense triplet of the phage because they make a modified amino acyl-sRNA complex which can sometimes read the nonsense triplet as sense. Such bacteria, we say, contain an *external suppressor* of the nonsense codon.

6·10 *N-formylmethionyl-sRNA is the initiator of polypeptide synthesis in* E. coli.

In an *in vivo* synthesis, the coat protein of normal ϕf2 and the fragment of coat protein produced by ϕf2 with a nonsense codon both start (at the N-terminus) with the amino acid sequence ala-ser-asn-phe-. When the synthesis occurs *in vitro,* however, this sequence is preceded by N-formylmethionine, that is, methionine with a formyl ($-\overset{\overset{\displaystyle O}{\|}}{C}-H$) group attached to the amino group. (Two met-sRNA's are known, only one of which can have its methionine formylated.) This result suggests that, at least in *E. coli,* all polypeptides synthesized start with N-formylmethionine which is subsequently removed enzymatically.

Furthermore, these results indicate that a unique mRNA sequence signals the initiation of all polypeptide chains made in *E. coli.* The start signal may be the codon for N-formylmethionine, perhaps AUG. Since this methionine incorporated at the N-terminus has a blocked amino group, the formation of a peptide bond with the carboxyl group of another amino acid is prevented. *In vitro* a peptidyl-sRNA (for example, diphenylalanyl-sRNA) whose NH_2 group of the amino acid bound to sRNA is also blocked can likewise serve as initiator of polypeptide synthesis.

Among the important consequences of the above findings are (1) that proteins are synthesized in only one direction – from the amino toward the carboxyl end – as noted previously; and (2) that regardless of the codon that terminates the first polypeptide, two polypeptides encoded in the same mRNA cannot become linked linearly because the amino group which begins the second is blocked and cannot form a peptide bond.

6·11 *DNA is colinear with the polypeptide it encodes.*

Although DNA and the polypeptides it specifies are both linear polymers, we would like to know whether the linearity of the polypeptides is dependent upon the linearity of the corresponding DNA, that is, whether *colinearity* exists. We can test for this possibility by using ten different φT4 strains which produce defective head protein of different degrees of completeness. The position of the defect in the phage DNA can be determined for each of these strains and the defective positions arranged in a linear map. When the head protein of each defective strain is analyzed, the length of the polypeptide segment is found to be directly proportional to the distance from one end of this genetic map. The DNA of the phage is, therefore, colinear with the polypeptide it encodes.

6·12 *The genetic code is essentially universal in present-day organisms.*

Despite the degeneracies and ambiguities noted, is the genetic code basically the same for all organisms? In other words, is it universal?

A polypeptide very similar to rabbit hemoglobin can be synthesized in a cell-free system derived partly from rabbit reticulocytes and partly from *E. coli.* φf2 RNA directs the synthesis of phage coat protein not only in extracts of its normal host, *E. coli,* but also in extracts of *Euglena gracilis,* a green unicellular alga. The DNA from the animal viruses polyoma and vaccinia is infective in competent *Bacillus subtilis;* that is, mixing viral DNA with the bacteria gives rise to regular virus particles which can infect the usual animal host. Synthetic polynucleotides have many of the amino acid incorporation properties in certain animal cell-free systems that they have in bacterial cell-free systems. Finally, a marked correlation exists in a variety of organisms between C + G content and the percentages of certain amino acids incorporated into protein. All these results support the hypothesis that, although modifications occur, there is only one basic genetic code for polypeptide synthesis in present-day organisms.

Questions and Problems

6·1 Amino acid incorporation into protein can be studied *in vitro* with synthetic copolymers, polynucleotides in which two different bases alternate, serving as mRNA.

(a) The copolymer of U and C (copoly UC) codes for a polypeptide in which serine and leucine alternate strictly (ser-leu copolypeptide).
(b) Copoly UG encodes cys-val copolypeptide.
(c) Copoly AC encodes thr-his copolypeptide.
(d) Copoly AG encodes arg-glu copolypeptide.
(e) The polymer of ApApGp encodes polylysine, polyarginine, and polyglutamic acid.

How is it possible that a given nucleic acid codes for two or more kinds of polypeptides? Determine from the above results *in vitro* codons for each amino acid incorporated and compare your results with the codons in Figure 6-2.

6·2 In molecular terms, what is the nature of mRNA for the rII region of ϕT4 that (a) has deletion 1589? (b) is wild type, i.e., contains no deletion?

6·3 What can you deduce about the number of nucleotides missing in deletion 1589 phage? What would be the resulting activity of gene *rIIB* if one of a large number of different multi-nucleotide deletions in the *rIIA* gene were present in addition to del 1589?

6·4 Since all the RNA of STNV is used to code for its coat, the virus cannot make an RNA-dependent RNA polymerase. How, then, can this virus replicate?

6·5 Some +− double-defect combinations in the *B* gene of ϕT4 have no *B* activity even though the two defects are close together. How can you explain this finding? How could you test your explanation experimentally?

6·6 Some deletion 1589 phage that are also defective in the *rIIA* gene
(a) show no *B* activity in *E. coli* host strain KB unless FU is added to the culture medium, and
(b) show *B* activity in *E. coli* host strain KB-3 even in the absence of FU.
What is the translational effect (1) of the defect in *rIIA*, (2) of FU, and (3) of changing the host?

6·7 Short synthetic polyribonucleotides of types
1) ApApApApApCpAp...pApApA and
2) ApApApApCpAp...pApApA
direct the synthesis *in vitro* of short lysine polypeptides (1) with asparagine at the N-terminus and (2) with threonine at the N-terminus, respectively. What can you conclude from these results about
(a) codons for specific amino acids?
(b) the direction of translation of mRNA?
(c) the starting position of mRNA translation?

6·8 What might be the translational consequence of base substitution in the codon that specifies N-formylmethionine?

6·9 Are the nucleotides comprising a codon or an anticodon adjacent? Justify your answer.

6·10 Unmethylated RNA can be translated *in vitro*, whereas methylated rRNA cannot. What possible bearing do these observations have on the functioning of rRNA *in vivo?*

6·11 Approximately how many amino acids are in the polypeptide chain being synthesized if the average distance from one ribosome to the next is 280A in a polysome composed of 20 ribosomes?

6·12 TMV RNA is composed of approximately 6400 ribonucleotides. Approximate its molecular weight. How much of this RNA is not used to code for TMV coat protein (a polymer of 2200 identical subunits, each of which consists of 158 amino acids)? What do you suppose is the function of this portion?

6·13 What do you conclude about the functioning of amino acyl-sRNA from the finding that cys-sRNA responds to the same mRNA codon after it is converted to ala-sRNA by treatment with Raney nickel?

6·14 The title of this chapter implies the existence of a nucleic acid code for transcription. What specific functions would such a code perform?

6·15 Give the expected relative frequency of each of the different triplets present in a polynucleotide synthesized by polynucleotide phosphorylase from ribonucleoside diphosphates whose bases are in the ratio
(a) 5U : 1C,
(b) 1A : 1U : 1C : 1G, and
(c) 4U : 1A : 1G.

6·16 Cite evidence that codons have the same translational meaning *in vitro* that they have *in vivo*.

References

Adams, J. M., and Capecchi, M. R. 1966. N-formylmethionyl-sRNA as the initiator of protein syntheses. Proc. Nat. Acad. Sci., U.S., 55: 147–155.

Brenner, S., Stretton, A. O. W., and Kaplan, S. 1965. Genetic code: the "nonsense" triplets for chain termination and their suppression. Nature, Lond., 206: 994–998.

Brimacombe, R., Trupin, J., Nirenberg, M., Leder, P., Bernfield, M., and Jaouni, T. 1965. RNA codewords and protein synthesis, VIII. Nucleotide sequences of synonym codons for arginine, valine, cysteine, and alanine. Proc. Nat. Acad. Sci., U.S., 54: 954–960.

Capecchi, M. R. 1966. Initiation of *E. coli* proteins. Proc. Nat. Acad. Sci., U.S., 55: 1517–1524.

Crick, F. H. C. 1966. The genetic code: III. Scient. Amer., 215: 55–62, 150.

Crick, F. H. C., Barnett, L., Brenner, S., and Watts-Tobin, R. J. 1961. General nature of the genetic code for proteins. Nature, Lond., 192: 1227–1232. Reprinted in *Papers on Bacterial Viruses, Second Edition*. Stent, G. S. (Editor). Boston: Little, Brown and Co., 1965, pp. 388–401.

Engelhardt, D. L., Webster, R. E., Wilhelm, R. C., and Zinder, N. D. 1965. *In vitro* studies on the mechanism of suppression of a nonsense mutation. Proc. Nat. Acad. Sci., U.S., 54: 1791–1797.

Fraenkel-Conrat, H. 1964. The genetic code of a virus. Scient. Amer., 211: 47–54, 142.

Gartland, W. J., and Sueoka, N. 1966. Two interconvertible forms of tryptophanyl sRNA in *E. coli*. Proc. Nat. Acad. Sci., U.S., 55: 948–956. (They respond differently to try-sRNA synthetase and codons.)

Imamoto, F., Yamane, T., and Sueoka, N. 1965. Existence of two phenylalanyl-sRNA synthetases in *Neurospora crassa*. Proc. Nat. Acad. Sci., U.S., 53: 1456–1461.

Jones, D. S., Nishimura, S., and Khorana, H. G. 1966. Studies on polynucleotides, LVI: Further syntheses, *in vitro,* of copolypeptides containing two amino acids in alternating sequence dependent upon DNA-like polymers containing two nucleotides in alternating sequence. J. Mol. Biol., 16: 454–472.

Kolakofsky, D., and Nakamoto, T. 1966. The initiation of viral protein synthesis in *E. coli* extracts. Proc. Nat. Acad. Sci., U.S., 56: 1786–1793.

Leder, P., and Bursztyn, H. 1966. Initiation of protein synthesis, I. Effect of formylation of methionyl-tRNA on codon recognition. Proc. Nat. Acad. Sci., U.S., 56: 1579–1585.

Marshall, R. C., Caskey, C. T., and Nirenberg, M. W. 1967. Fine structure of RNA codewords recognized by bacterial, amphibian, and mammalian transfer RNA. Science, 155: 820–825. (Support for universality of the code.)

Morgan, A. R., Wells, R. D., and Khorana, H. G. 1966. Studies on polynucleotides, LIX. Further codon assignments from amino acid incorporations directed by ribopolynucleotides containing repeating trinucleotide sequences. Proc. Nat. Acad. Sci., U.S., 56: 1899–1906.

Nakamoto, T., and Kolakovsky, D. 1966. A possible mechanism for initiation of protein synthesis. Proc. Nat. Acad. Sci., U.S., 55: 606–613.

Nathans, D., Notani, G., Schwartz, J. H., and Zinder, N. D. 1962. Biosynthesis of the coat protein of coliphage f2 by *E. coli* extracts. Proc. Nat. Acad. Sci., U.S., 48: 1424–1431.

Nirenberg, M. W. 1963. The genetic code: II. Scient. Amer., 208: 80–94, 190.

Nirenberg, M. W., Leder, P., Bernfield, M., Brimacombe, R., Trupin, J., Rottman, F., and O'Neal, C. 1965. RNA codewords and protein synthesis, VII. On the general nature of the RNA code. Proc. Nat. Acad. Sci., U.S., 53: 1161–1168.

Nirenberg, M. W., and Matthaei, J. H. 1961. The dependence of cell-free protein synthesis in *E. coli* upon naturally occurring or synthetic polyribonucleotides. Proc. Nat. Acad. Sci., U.S., 47: 1588–1602. (The first cracking of the code.)

Nishimura, S., Jones, D. S., and Khorana, H. G. 1965. The *in vitro* synthesis of a co-polypeptide containing two amino acids in alternating sequence dependent upon a DNA-like polymer containing two nucleotides in alternating sequence. J. Mol. Biol., 13: 302–324.

Reichmann, M. E. 1964. The satellite tobacco necrosis virus: a single protein and its genetic code. Proc. Nat. Acad. Sci., U.S., 52: 1009–1117.

Shih, A.-Y., Eisenstadt, J., and Lengyel, P. 1966. On the relation between ribonucleic acid synthesis and peptide chain initiation in *E. coli.* Proc. Nat. Acad. Sci., U.S., 56: 1599–1605. (Dependence of RNA and protein synthesis on N-formylmethionyl-sRNA.)

Smith, M. A., Salas, M., Stanley (Jr.), W. M., Wahba, A. J., and Ochoa, S. 1966. Direction of reading of the genetic message, II. Proc. Nat. Acad. Sci., U.S., 55: 141–147.

Söll, D., Ohtsuka, E., Jones, D. S., Lohrmann, R., Hayatsu, H., Nishimura, S., and Khorana, H. G. 1965. Studies on polynucleotides, XLIX. Stimulation of the binding of aminoacyl-sRNA's to ribosomes by ribotrinucleotides and a survey of codon assignments for 20 amino acids. Proc. Nat. Acad. Sci., U.S., 54: 1378–1385.

Takanami, M., and Yan, Y. 1965. The release of polypeptide chains from ribosomes in cell-free amino acid-incorporating systems by specific combinations of bases in synthetic polyribonucleotides. Proc. Nat. Acad. Sci., U.S., 54: 1450–1458.

The Genetic Code, Cold Spring Harb. Sympos. Quant. Biol., 31, 1966.

Webster, R. E., Englehardt, D. L., and Zinder, N. D. 1966. *In vitro* protein synthesis: chain initiation. Proc. Nat. Acad. Sci., U.S., 55: 155–161.

Weigert, M. G., and Garen, A. 1965. Base composition of nonsense codons in *E. coli.* Nature, Lond., 206: 992–994.

Weisblum, B., Gonano, F., von Ehrenstein, G., and Benzer, S. 1965. A demonstration of coding degeneracy for leucine in the synthesis of protein. Proc. Nat. Acad. Sci., U.S., 53: 328–334.

Woese, C. R. 1965. Order in the genetic code. Proc. Nat. Acad. Sci., U.S., 54: 71–74.

Woese, C. R., Hinegardner, R. T., and Engelberg, J. 1964. Universality in the genetic code. Science, 144: 1030–1031.

Yanofsky, C., Carlton, B. C., Guest, J. R., Helinski, D. R., and Henning, U. 1964. On the colinearity of gene structure and protein structure. Proc. Nat. Acad. Sci., U.S., 51: 266–272. Reprinted in *Papers on Bacterial Genetics, Second Edition.* Adelberg, E. A. (Editor). Boston: Little, Brown and Co., 1966, pp. 177–183. (A proof of colinearity.)

Yanofsky, C., Drapeau, G. R., Guest, J. R., and Carlton, B. C. 1967. The complete amino acid sequence of the tryptophan synthetase A protein (α subunit) and its colinear relationship with the genetic map of the A gene. Proc. Nat. Acad. Sci., U.S., 57: 296–298.

Zamir, A., Leder, P., and Elson, D. 1966. A ribosome-catalyzed reaction between N-formylmethionyl-tRNA and puromycin. Proc. Nat. Acad. Sci., U.S., 56: 1794–1801.

CHAPTER 7

Mutation of Nucleic Acids

Genetic material does not exist by itself but in an environment of living and nonliving things. Hence, it and the information which it contains are subject to change. Any unusual, more or less permanent change in the amount of genetic material or in its primary structure we will call a *mutation,* and the product of such a change, a *mutant.* By the phrase "unusual change" we mean a modification that occurs rarely in a given biological system. In this chapter we will consider the molecular basis, production, and repair of mutations as well as their transcriptional and translational consequences.

7·1 *Some mutations involve only the sugar portions of a nucleotide.*

Although deoxyribose is the only sugar detected in the DNA of most organisms, an occasional ribose may be present. Arabinose is thought to be incorporated into the DNA of mammalian cells in culture, and D-mannose has been found in the DNA of a mutant of phage SP8. Some *mutagens,* physical or chemical agents which greatly increase mutation frequency, may add an O at the 2′ position of deoxyribose in a DNA strand or remove the 2′ O of ribose in an RNA strand.

7·2 *Mutations can involve base changes in already-formed nucleic acids.*

Each of the bases of DNA and RNA can assume several different arrangements, or *tautomeric forms.* In previous discussions and diagrams, the most likely tautomer of each base (its keto or amino form) was assumed to occur. The tautomers of uracil and adenine, shown in Figure 7-1, differ in the positions at which one hydrogen atom is attached. In both instances this change is accompanied by a shift of electrons so that some double bonds become single bonds, and vice versa. The less likely tautomers are said to be in enol (=C—OH) or imino (=NH) form. The

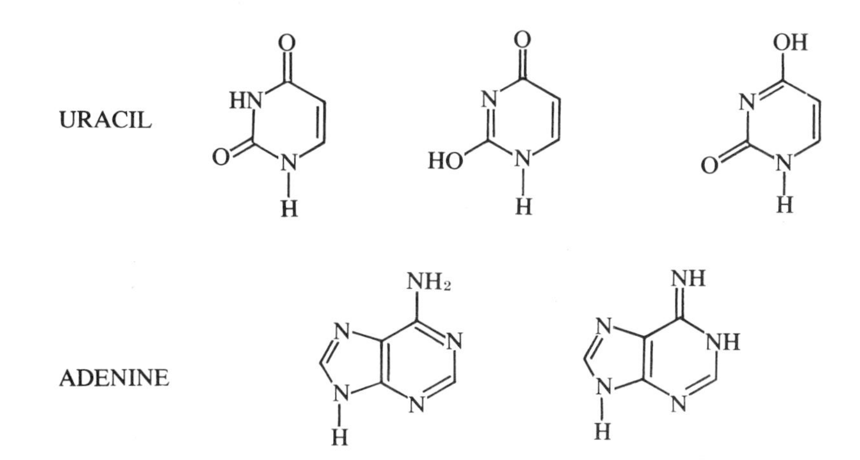

Figure 7-1. Tautomers of uracil and adenine.

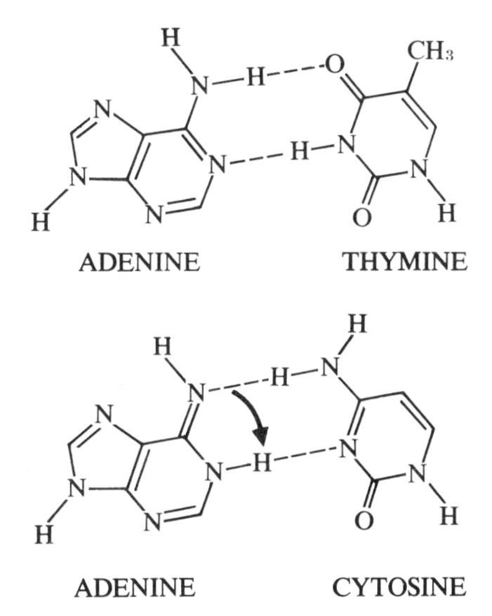

Figure 7-2. Tautomeric shift of adenine which could change its complementary base from thymine to cytosine. Upper diagram shows adenine before, and lower diagram after, undergoing a tautomeric shift of one of its hydrogen atoms. (After J. D. Watson and F. H. C. Crick)

relative frequencies of tautomers depend upon several factors, including the pH.

Although the usual tautomer of A (in amino form) pairs with T, one of the less common imino tautomers of A can base pair with C by forming two hydrogen bonds as shown in Figure 7-2. Reciprocally, a rare imino tautomer of C can pair with A by forming two H bonds. In like manner, T and G can pair by forming three H bonds between G and an enol tautomer of T, or between T and a tautomer of G. A tautomeric shift thus makes a new and "incorrect" purine-pyrimidine base pair possible. It is thought that tautomeric shifts play an important role in spontaneous mutation. High-energy radiation can also produce the unusual A:C and T:G base pairs.

Chemical mutagens can also change individual bases. Nitrous acid (HNO_2), for example, is mutagenic to TMV, T2 and T4 phages, bacteria, yeast, and naked infective genetic DNA. It acts by removing the amino group from purines and pyrimidines of DNA and RNA and substituting a keto group. After *deamination,* (1) A becomes hypoxanthine (see Figure 2-10), which pairs with C instead of T; (2) C becomes U, which pairs with A; and (3) G becomes xanthine, which still pairs with C but with only two H bonds.

Let us now consider a consequence of the adenine-to-hypoxanthine mutation. Cytosine pairs with the hypoxanthine and at the next division base-pairs with G, as it ordinarily does (see Figure 7-3). The outcome of the change from A to hypoxanthine is, therefore, that the original A-containing strand gives rise to a second generation strand with G instead of A at that position. Such a net change from purine to purine (A $\rightleftharpoons$ G) or from pyrimidine to pyrimidine (C $\rightleftharpoons$ T) is called a *transition.* A net change between purine and pyrimidine (A or G $\rightleftharpoons$ C or T) is a *transversion.*

Exposure of ϕT4 to conditions of low pH also induces base changes. *In vitro* it brings about the *depurination* of the phage's nucleic acid — the complete removal of all G and A. When the resulting apurinic acid is returned to higher pH, some purines are thought to rejoin the strand. Mutations thus may involve either the loss of purine bases or their incorrect replacement.

Base changes may also be effected by *rotational substitution,* in which the bonds linking members of a base pair to the sugar are broken (allowing the base pair to rotate 180°) and then reformed. The result of such a substitution, a possible consequence of exposure to high-energy radiation, is a double transversion.

7·3 *Newly-made genes may be mutant because they contain incorrect bases resulting from mistakes in incorporation or replication.*

Base analogs are incorporated into DNA *in vitro* when they are present as deoxyribonucleoside 5′-triphosphates. For example, uracil, 5-bromo uracil (BU), and 5-fluoro uracil (FU) can substitute for T (and for T only); 5-methyl, 5-bromo, and 5-fluoro cytosine can substitute for C only; and hypoxanthine can substitute for G only. *In vivo* 5-bromo, 5-chloro, or 5-iodo uracil can replace some of the thymine in DNA of bacteria, phages, and human cell cultures.

The incorporation of BU into a strand of DNA can be considered a "*mistake of incorporation*" since BU is not an ordinary component. Because the usual tautomer of BU is in the keto state, it is usually incor-

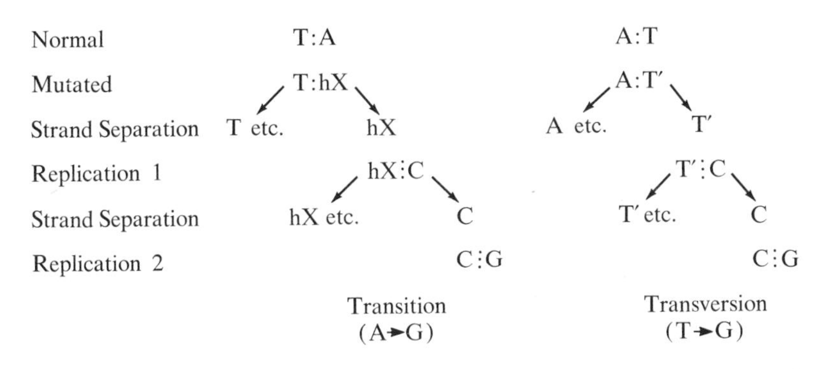

Figure 7-3. A postulated sequence of events leading to transition or transversion. hX = hypoxanthine.

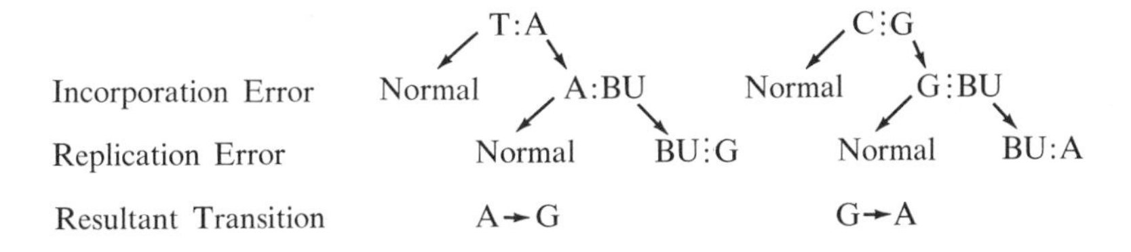

Figure 7-4. Mistakes of incorporation and replication involving 5-bromo uracil (BU). Mistakes of incorporation occur when different tautomers of BU base-pair with A or G in their usual tautomeric forms. A change in the tautomeric form of incorporated BU results in errors of replication that result in A ↔ G transitions.

porated as the complement of A (Figure 7-4). The rare enol tautomer of BU (like the tautomer of T) can pair with G to form G:BU. Overall, therefore, two different kinds of mistakes of incorporation are possible for BU – formation of A:BU pairs and of G:BU pairs. As part of a DNA strand, the BU of an A:BU pair can continue to specify A so that no "*mistake in replication*" follows. If, however, the BU assumes its rare enol form and accepts G as its complement, a mistake in replication will occur – A will be replaced by G, a transition mutation. Since the BU in G:BU is usually in keto form at the time of the next replication, it usually accepts A as its complement, resulting in the G to A transition. In summary, the pyrimidine BU gives rise to purine transitions in both directions (A ⇌ G).

In vitro studies of errors involving BU indicate that it may have some effect on adjacent nucleotides. The DNA copolymer of A and BU, dABU, can serve as primer-template in an extensive synthesis with the deoxyribonucleotides of BU, A, and G. Since the primer-template presumably contains BU and A in strict alternation (Figure 7-5), two nucleotides in a synthesized strand must usually be in the BUA or ABU se-

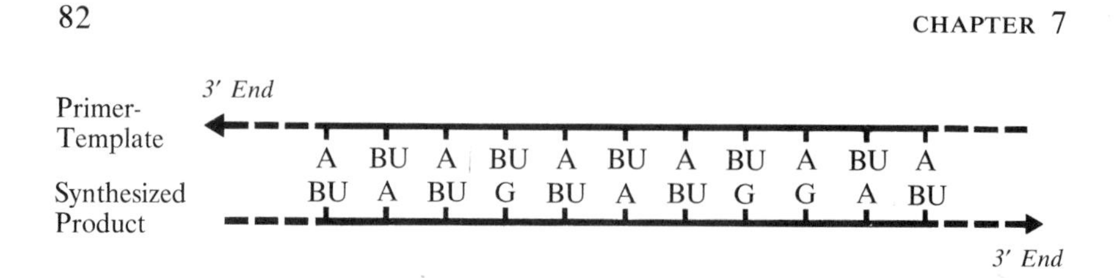

Figure 7-5. Sample base sequences of a primer-template copolymer dABU and of the product synthesized *in vitro* by *E. coli* DNA polymerase using dAPPP, dBUPPP and dGPPP as substrate.

quence. G, however, is also found in the product. If the presence of G in the product is always due to a mistake of incorporation by template BU, G should have BU as its linear neighbor, and should be in either a BUG or GBU dinucleotide sequence. G is in fact incorporated after BU or G with about equal frequency, but is incorporated less often after A. Because G-containing dinucleotide sequences other than BUG and GBU are found, we cannot explain the results only by mistakes in replication made by the BU in the primer-template. Apparently, the presence of BU as a linear neighbor of A causes A to base-pair incorrectly with G. We should keep in mind, however, that the behavior of BU in dABU *in vitro* may not be identical to that of the base analog in native DNA *in vivo.*

2-aminopurine incorporated into DNA also produces base changes. In its normal tautomeric form, it can pair with T by two hydrogen bonds or with C by one. As the less common tautomer, it can bond with C by two H bonds. As a consequence, pyrimidine transitions ($T \rightleftharpoons C$) are possible.

A great deal of work has been carried out to identify the particular base changes occurring in mutations *in vivo.* A useful technique in determining whether the change is a transition or a transversion is to subject the mutant to a mutagen (such as one of those discussed above), which causes specific transitions. If the initial change was a transition, then the frequency of change back to the original condition (the *reversion frequency*) should be higher than if the initial change was a transversion. Most (if not all) the mutations induced by the base analogs mentioned are transitions. About one-third of the mutations induced by ethyl ethane-sulfonate seem to be transversions.

7·4 *Mutation may involve the gain, loss, or rearrangement of one or more whole nucleotides.*

Mutations can involve changes in whole nucleotides. One or more nucleotides can be added, deleted, replaced, inverted, or transposed to a new position (Figure 7-6). All these rearrangements except inversion are possible for single-stranded nucleic acids. Inversion requires a double-stranded nucleic acid, since the same polarity must be maintained along a strand.

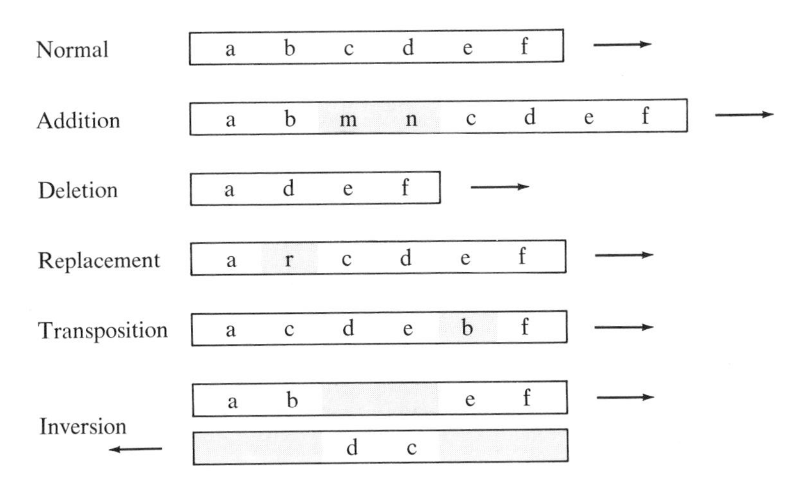

Figure 7-6. Whole nucleotide changes. Arrows show polarity.

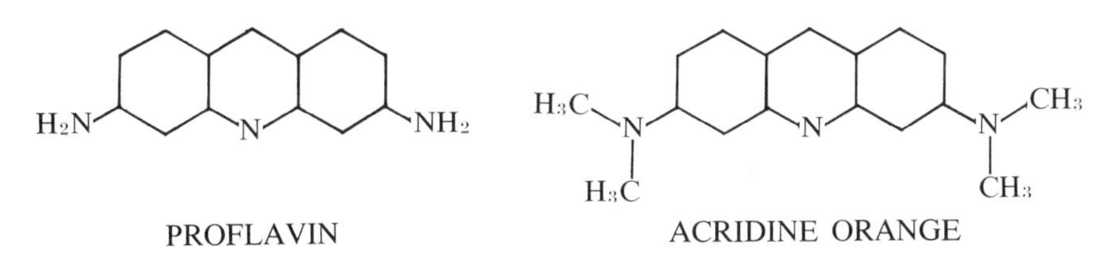

Figure 7-7. Two acridine dyes.

Single whole-nucleotide changes which do not involve breakage of the sugar-phosphate backbone can be brought about by chemical mutagens. An *acridine* (Figure 7-7), for example, is thought to act by binding to the outside of a double-stranded nucleic acid or by becoming inserted between successive nucleotides of a strand in a duplex. Under the latter circumstances the strand seems to be altered lengthwise so that, if used as a template, an unspecified nucleotide may be inserted in the complementary strand at the position corresponding to the acridine molecule. Other molecules, such as free nucleotides or other naturally-occurring substances, may act like the acridines.

As mentioned in Section 4·9, DNA polymerase in the presence of Mn^{++} *in vitro* can use a DNA template to make a complementary strand that contains both deoxyribo- and ribonucleotides, provided of course that the appropriate ribonucleoside 5′-triphosphates are included as substrates. Since the DNA-transcript contains uracil and ribose rather than thymine and deoxyribose, we can consider it a mutant strand. The highly mutagenic character of manganese salts in bacteria implies that such an incorporation may occur *in vivo* as well.

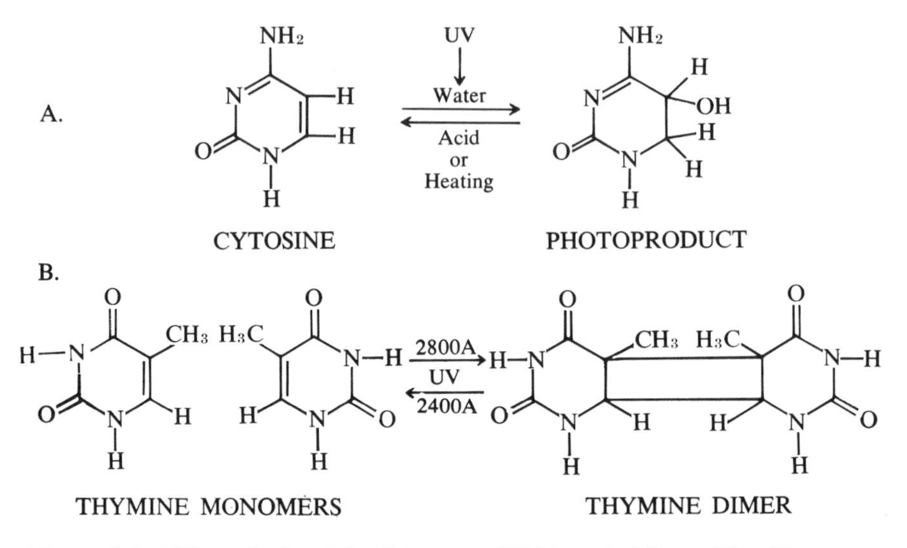

Figure 7-8. Effect of ultraviolet light upon DNA pyrimidines. (The H atoms attached to ring C atoms are shown.)

7·5 *Some mutagens cause pyrimidines to link in pairs. In different enzymatic processes, such dimers can be removed from a double-stranded nucleic acid and the duplex repaired.*

When exposed to *ultraviolet (UV) light,* pyrimidines commonly add a water molecule across the C4-C5 double bond (see Figure 7-8A). Although this photoproduct reverts to its original form upon heating or acidification, it appears to persist frequently enough *in vivo* to weaken the H-bonding with its purine complement and thus cause localized strand separation. Furthermore, two pyrimidines can be induced by UV light to join at their 4 and 5 positions to form pyrimidine dimers (Figure 7-8B). This *dimerization* can result in TT, CC, UU, and mixed pyrimidine dimers (e.g., CT) but rarely (if at all) in the dimer of BU.

Localized strand separation (induced by UV) gives pyrimidines greater freedom of movement and thereby increases the likelihood of dimerization involving bases in different strands, in widely separated regions of one strand, and perhaps in adjacent regions of the same strand. Interstrand dimerization, by producing cross links between nucleic acid chains, inhibits strand separation and distribution. Both hydration and dimerization of double-stranded DNA interfere with transcription; they block DNA synthesis (probably by modifying the major groove) and, it is likely, block RNA synthesis as well (by modifying the minor groove).

Dimer formation may be the reason that UV light destroys the primer-template activity of single-stranded DNA, causes mutations in ϕX174, and destroys naked infective genetic DNA. UV radiation has two opposite effects, however, depending upon the wavelength used. At 2800A UV light promotes the formation of dimers from monomers, whereas at 2400A it promotes the formation of monomers from dimers. In fact, the genetic activity of bacterial DNA inactivated by 2800A UV radiation can be partially restored by light at 2390A.

UV-induced dimers can also be split enzymatically. In the presence of certain blue lights, an enzyme system in *E. coli* can split thymine dimers (including interstrand dimers) into monomers. In this reaction the enzyme attaches to the T dimer, with the blue light providing energy for the breakage. Since this process causes only about 50% recovery from the effects of a single UV treatment, it seems probable that UV radiation produces mutations in ways other than by dimer formation.

Certain strains of *E. coli* are somewhat resistant to UV radiation; that is, they can recover from some of the damage incurred and can resume DNA synthesis. Since this recovery can take place even in the dark, the process cannot involve the splitting of dimers in a photochemical reaction. Instead, the dimers are enzymatically removed from the DNA. After their removal a second enzyme cuts out an adjacent portion of the defective strand (about thirty nucleotides per excised thymine dimer); and a third enzyme fills in the deleted nucleotides as specified by the complementary strand. Overall, this repair enzyme system ensures the preservation of the original information content of the DNA.

Mitomycin C, a mutagenic antibiotic, causes interchain crosslinking of purines in the DNA of some organisms. Since bacteria that can excise pyrimidine dimers are also more resistant to the mutagenic effects of mitomycin C, nitrogen mustard, and nitrous acid, the genes that provide for this excision may also be responsible for the excision of other types of defects in DNA.

7·6 *High-energy radiations often break the nucleic acid backbone.*

When single-stranded DNA viruses such as ϕX174 and ϕS13 incorporate nucleotides with radioactive P^{32} instead of P, a single radioactive decay of P^{32} is sufficient to inactivate them. Phage T2 and others containing double-stranded DNA, on the other hand, require about ten decays for inactivation. One explanation for the results of such *suicide experiments* is that each decay breaks the backbone of the polynucleotide in which it occurs; and in double-stranded nucleic acids a nearby break in the backbone of a complementary strand may lead to the severing of the duplex. Thus, single-stranded nucleic acids will be severed (hence, inactivated) more frequently than double-stranded nucleic acids.

Another important agent which causes breakage of the backbone is X rays, a high-energy electromagnetic radiation. The decrease in sedimentation rate of denatured and native DNA after X-radiation of *E. coli* indicates that the radiation caused single- and double-strand scissions of the DNA backbone. Although double-strand scissions are not repaired when treated cells are reincubated, single-strand scissions are repaired in certain *E. coli* strains. Double-strand scissions in DNA appear to be primarily responsible for the lethality of high-energy radiations in *E. coli.*

7·7 *Mutations have various transcriptional and translational consequences.*

Since mutation involves a change in genetic material, it nearly always brings about a change in information of various types. *Transcriptional information* is encoded in genes (1) that signal the positions for the start and stop of transcription from genetic nucleic acid to genetic or nongenetic nucleic acid, and (2) that encode transcriptional enzymes such as DNA polymerase and DNA-dependent RNA polymerase. *Translational information* is contained in genes that code for (1) ribosomal protein, (2) rRNA, (3) sRNA's, and (4) the enzymes that activate and attach amino acids to sRNA, form peptide bonds, and release the C-terminus of the completed polypeptide from sRNA.

Although we know very little at present about the information of genes coding for transcription, we can expect some mutations in such genes to cause their malfunction. For example, a mutation in the gene that encodes DNA polymerase might give rise to an enzyme that makes a great many errors in replication. Such a mutation would therefore be mutation-inducing.

Mutation of a gene for rRNA or ribosomal protein may result in ribosomes defective in holding or moving mRNA or attached sRNA's. Since the genes which code for rRNA are apparently present in many copies, a mutation that produces a gross defect in only one may not give rise to a readily detectable effect. Some mutations (see Section 5·2) seem able to prevent the functioning of all rRNA genes in the same chromosome. Mutation of a gene encoding an sRNA can affect the RNA molecule's acceptance of an amino acid, its attachment to the ribosome, or its anticodon. Mutations in DNA can change the ability of mRNA to bind to ribosomes and can alter the genetic message – whether it contains information for translation into amino acids or for the ending of polypeptide chains.

Today we can specify the molecular consequences only of genetic changes which affect the amino acid-encoding portions of mRNA and sRNA. With regard to genes transcribed to mRNA, nucleotide additions or deletions that are not a multiple of three result in missense protein, incomplete protein, or a combination of the two. The particular result depends upon the size and position of the change. Single base-substitutions in mRNA may produce a triplet that is sense, nonsense, or missense. A mutation which leads to incorrect chain termination will be detrimental depending upon the point of termination and the particular polypeptide being synthesized. The effect of a single amino acid substitution will also depend upon what polypeptide is involved; for some amino acids are more essential for the proper functioning of a protein than are others.

A mutation that changes an enzyme which links an amino acid with an sRNA can cause numerous proteins to be incomplete or to contain incorrect amino acids. A base-substitution in the anticodon of an sRNA, however, may cause no change in amino acid sequence. On the other hand, it may cause many proteins to carry wrong amino acids, a nonsense triplet in mRNA to make sense, or a sense triplet in mRNA to make nonsense.

Questions and Problems

7·1 Compare the mutagenic efficiency of UV treatment of the same total number of nucleotides in
(a) single- and double-stranded DNA;
(b) single-stranded DNA and single-stranded RNA.

7·2 What evidence can you present for the existence of genes that start or stop transcription? Do you think such information is encoded in triplets?

7·3 What specific consequences would you expect from a mutation which causes a single base-substitution in the sRNA whose anticodon is AAA?

7·4 Name the gene whose mutation is likely to be most detrimental. Justify your choice.

7·5 What will be the effect of a mutation in one gene for rRNA when this rRNA is incorporated in ribosomes that can accept mRNA and sRNA but otherwise function incorrectly?

7·6 Insertion or deletion mutants can be partially suppressed by further mutations which return the reading frame to its normal phase. Explain how a base-substitution mutant can be suppressed by a mutation in
(a) the same polypeptide-encoding gene.
(b) a gene encoding a specific amino acid activating enzyme.
(c) a gene encoding a specific sRNA.
(d) a gene encoding a ribosomal protein.

7·7 Mutation-causing mutations can occur in several different kinds of genes. Explain.

7·8 Under what circumstances can a same-sense base substitution in mRNA affect the encoded polypeptide's (a) quantity? (b) amino acid content?

7·9 How can you explain the finding that a tropical line of a Drosophila species has a lower spontaneous mutation frequency than a temperate line of the same species under identical experimental conditions?

7·10 Under what circumstances would you expect single-strand scissions of the *E. coli* chromosome to be lethal?

7·11 How should a transversion respond to
(a) base analogs or other mutagens that produce only transitions?
(b) acridine dyes?
(c) spontaneous mutation?

7·12 Translation *in vitro* is normal, that is, unambiguous, when ribosomes obtained from a streptomycin-resistant mutant are treated with streptomycin. What does this result indicate about the nature of the streptomycin-resistance locus?

7·13 How can you explain that spontaneous mutations in a polypeptide-encoding gene recur with greater frequency at some sites than they do at other, nearby, sites?

7·14 How can you explain that the "hot-spots" for the spontaneous mutations mentioned in the preceding question and for various chemical mutagens are different?

7·15 The term "incorporation error" is ordinarily used to refer to a rare tautomer of a template base specifying the incorporation of the wrong base during replication. How does the present usage of this term differ? Is present usage justified?

7·16 What would be the transitional consequence of the BU
(a) if a rare tautomer of A caused the incorporation of a rare tautomer of BU?
(b) if a rare tautomer of G caused the incorporation of the normal tautomer of BU?

7·17 What are the transitional consequences when a rare tautomer of guanine
(a) is incorporated?
(b) occurs after incorporation?

References

Benzer, S., and Freese, E. 1958. Introduction of specific mutations with 5-bromouracil. Proc. Nat. Acad. Sci., U.S., 44: 112–119. Reprinted in *Papers on Bacterial Viruses, Second Edition.* Stent, G. S. (Editor), Boston: Little, Brown and Co., 1965, pp. 276–283.

Boyce, R. P., and Howard-Flanders, P. 1964. Release of ultraviolet light-induced thymine dimers from DNA in *E. coli* K12. Proc. Nat. Acad. Sci., U.S., 51: 293–300.

Deering, R. A. 1962. Ultraviolet radiation and nucleic acid. Scient. Amer., 207: 135–144.

de Waard, A., Paul, A. V., and Lehman, I. R. 1965. The structural gene for deoxyribonucleic acid polymerase in bacteriophages T4 and T5. Proc. Nat. Acad. Sci., U.S., 54: 1241–1248.

Drake, J. W. 1966. Spontaneous mutations accumulating in bacteriophage T4 in the complete absence of DNA replication. Proc. Nat. Acad. Sci., U.S., 55: 738–743. (They occur at sites containing GC and not AT base pairs.)

Hanawalt, P. C., and Haynes, R. H. 1967. The repair of DNA. Scient. Amer., 216 (No. 2): 36–43, 146.

Howard-Flanders, P., Boyce, R. P., and Theriot, L. 1966. Three loci in *Escherichia coli* K-12 that control the excision of pyrimidine dimers and certain other mutagenic products from DNA. Genetics, 53: 1119–1136.

Kaplan, H. S. 1966. DNA-strand scission and loss of viability after X irradiation of normal and sensitized bacterial cells. Proc. Nat. Acad. Sci., U.S., 55: 1442–1446.

Lerman, L. S. 1963. The structure of the DNA-acridine complex. Proc. Nat. Acad. Sci., U.S., 49: 94–102.

Orgel, A., and Orgel, L. E. 1965. Induction of mutations in bacteriophage T4 with divalent manganese. J. Mol. Biol., 14: 453–457.

Rosenberg, E. 1965. D-mannose as a constituent of the DNA of a mutant strain of a bacteriophage SP8. Proc. Nat. Acad. Sci., U.S. 53: 836–840.

Setlow, R. B., and Carrier, W. L. 1964. The disappearance of thymine dimers from DNA: An error-correcting mechanism. Proc. Nat. Acad. Sci., 51: 226–231.

Setlow, R. B., and Carrier, W. L. 1966. Pyrimidine dimers in ultraviolet-irradiated DNA's. J. Mol. Biol., 17: 237–254.

Strauss, B., Searashi, T., and Robbins, M. 1966. Repair of DNA studied with a nuclease specific for UV-induced lesions. Proc. Nat. Acad. Sci., U.S., 56: 932–939.

Wang, S. Y., Patrick, M. H., Varghese, A. J., and Rupert, C. S. 1967. Concerning the mechanism of formation of UV-induced thymine photoproducts in DNA. Proc. Nat. Acad. Sci., U.S., 57: 465–472.

CHAPTER 8

Genetic Recombination in Viruses; Genetic Transformation of Bacteria

Any rearrangement of genetic material is a *genetic recombination.* Genetic recombination can involve the primary, secondary, tertiary, and quaternary structures of genetic nucleic acids and thus can be expected to have an effect on the information they contain. It can involve, for example, the fragmentation or rearrangement of segments of a single strand; the separation or pairing of complementary strands; a change in tertiary configuration; or the grouping or separation of duplexes. We will begin our consideration of genetic recombination by looking at certain recombinational events in viruses and bacteria.

GENETIC RECOMBINATION IN VIRUSES

8·1 *Phages inject their genetic material into bacterial hosts, where viral progeny are made.*

Before considering recombination in viruses, we should become familiar with some details of their life cycle. A T-even phage (that is, ϕT2, T4, or T6) attaches itself tail-first to an *E. coli* host and injects all its DNA (MW = 1.2×10^8) plus a small amount of protein into the bacterium (see p. 5). An eclipse period follows (Figure 8-1, B–D) during which the phage DNA replicates to produce a pool of phage DNA. Near the end of the eclipse period (Figure 8-1D), a certain amount of DNA from the pool is surrounded by phage head protein (coded in ϕDNA). The assembly of mature phage is completed with the addition of other protein components (see Figure 1-2). About 20 to 40 minutes after infection, a phage DNA-coded enzyme, lysozyme, ruptures or lyses the bacterial cell wall and liberates infective phage progeny. This *lytic cycle* is the only possible course of existence for *intemperate,* or *virulent,* phages.

We can calculate the number of phage particles in a sample by the following technique. A few phage particles are allowed to infect a much

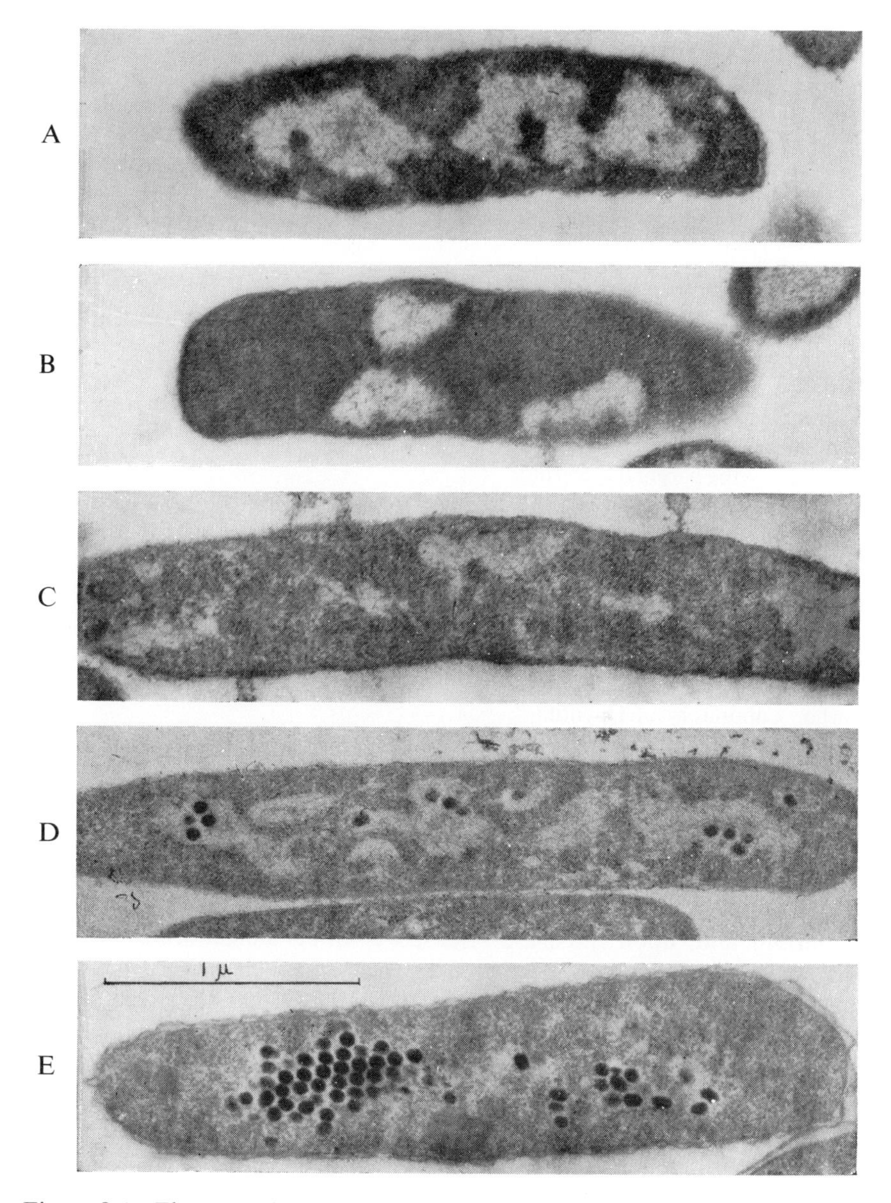

Figure 8-1. Electron micrographs of growth of T2 virus inside the *E. coli* host cell. (A) Bacillus before infection. (B) Four minutes after infection. (C) Ten minutes after infection. The thin section photographed includes the protein coat of T2 which can be seen attached to the bacterial surface. (D) Twelve minutes after infection. New virus particles are starting to condense. (E) Thirty minutes after infection. More than 50 T2 particles are completely formed and the host is about ready to lyse. (Courtesy of E. Kellenberger. Reprinted from Scientific American, 204: 100, 1961.)

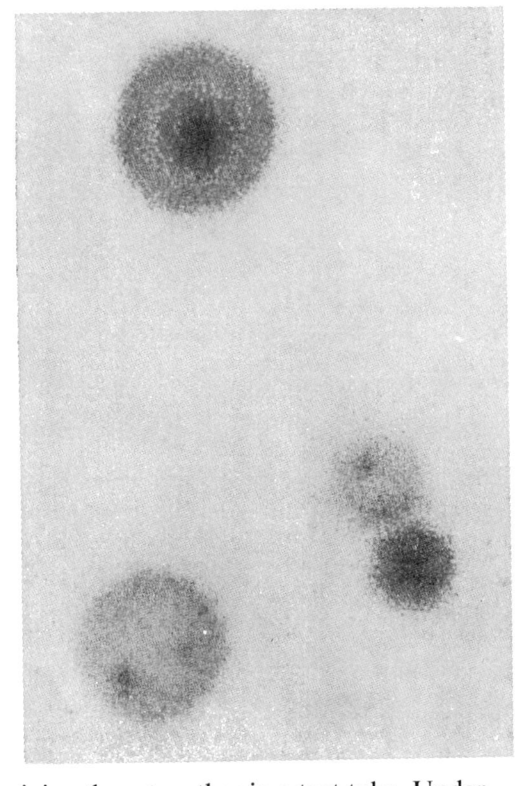

Figure 8-2. Plaques produced by parental and recombinant phage types. Progeny phage of a cross between $h\ r$ and $h^+\ r^+$ were tested on a mixture of suitable indicator bacteria. The large clear and the small turbid plaques are made by the parental types of phage progeny ($h\ r$ and $h^+\ r^+$, respectively). The small clear and the large turbid plaques are produced by the recombinant types of progeny ($h\ r^+$ and $h^+\ r$, respectively). (Courtesy of A. D. Hershey and the Cold Spring Harbor Laboratory of Quantitative Biology)

greater number of bacteria by mixing them together in a test tube. Under these conditions, each phage will infect a different host. The contents of the tube is then poured onto an agar-containing plate, and the plate incubated. Several hundred daughter phage are produced in each infected bacterium and, upon lysis, are released to infect neighboring bacteria. Several such cycles produce a progressively increasing zone of lysis in the continuous, somewhat opaque bacterial lawn that is detected as a clearing, or *plaque*. Since each plaque is derived from a single phage, the number of plaques corresponds to the number of phage in the infecting sample.

Some genetically different strains of a phage produce plaques with a characteristic size or shape. Strains may also vary in host range, that is, the types of bacteria they are able to infect.

8·2 *Phages with new combinations of genetic material occur among the progeny obtained from a multiply-infected host.*

One mutant strain of T phage differs from the more common, wild-type strain with respect to the "markers," *host range* (h) and *plaque type* (r). When sensitive bacteria are multiply infected with double mutant ($h\ r$)

and wild-type ($h^+ r^+$) phages, not only do the *parental types* ($h\,r$ and $h^+ r^+$) occur among the progeny but also the new types $h^+ r$ and $h\,r^+$ (Figure 8-2). Since the frequency of these new types is significantly greater than the spontaneous mutation frequency of $h\,r$ and $h^+ r^+$ to $h^+ r$ or $h\,r^+$, there must have been a rearrangement of genetic material – a genetic recombination. Note that the technique being used to detect genetic recombination requires that a bacterium be infected with two phages having different genetic alternatives, or *alleles,* at two *loci,* or places, in their genetic material.

8·3 *Frequencies of genetic recombination are directly proportional to distances between mutant loci. From such data, a map of phage loci can be constructed.*

Assuming that phage recombination results from a change in the primary structure of its nucleic acid, we expect that the greater the distance between two nucleotides in a given DNA segment, the greater the chance that recombination will occur between them. We can determine the frequencies of recombination by multiply infecting a bacterium with two phage strains that differ genetically at three loci. If a host carries phage of types $\underline{a\,b\,c}$ and $\underline{a^+ b^+ c^+}$, we expect the frequency of recombinant progeny or *recombinant types* with respect to the a and b loci ($a^+ b$ and $a\,b^+$ being *recombinants*) plus the frequency of recombinants with respect to the b and c loci ($b^+ c$ and $b\,c^+$) to equal the frequency of recombinants with respect to the a and c loci ($a^+ c$ and $a\,c^+$).

If we determine the recombination frequencies for all known markers of ϕT4, we find that groups of three loci generally show the additive relationship mentioned above, especially when the loci are close to each other. The *genetic recombination map* is therefore linear, that is, unbranched. It is not possible to construct the map as a straight line, however, since genes at opposite ends of such a line are also found to be close to each other. The loci must therefore be arranged in a circle or ring (Figure 8-3) (although electron micrographs show an open or rod duplex structure in the mature phage). Either way, all ϕT4 genes are on the same chromosome (in this instance, a single molecule of DNA) and thus are said to be *linked.*

8·4 *The genetic material of some phages contains redundant loci.*

The T4 plaque mutant r lyses rapidly to produce a plaque larger than that of the wild-type (r^+). When a bacterium is infected with both r and r^+ phages, the progeny usually produce plaques of either mutant or wild type. About 2% of the observed plaques, however, are *mottled;* that is, they are partly r and partly r^+ in appearance. The phage in a mottled

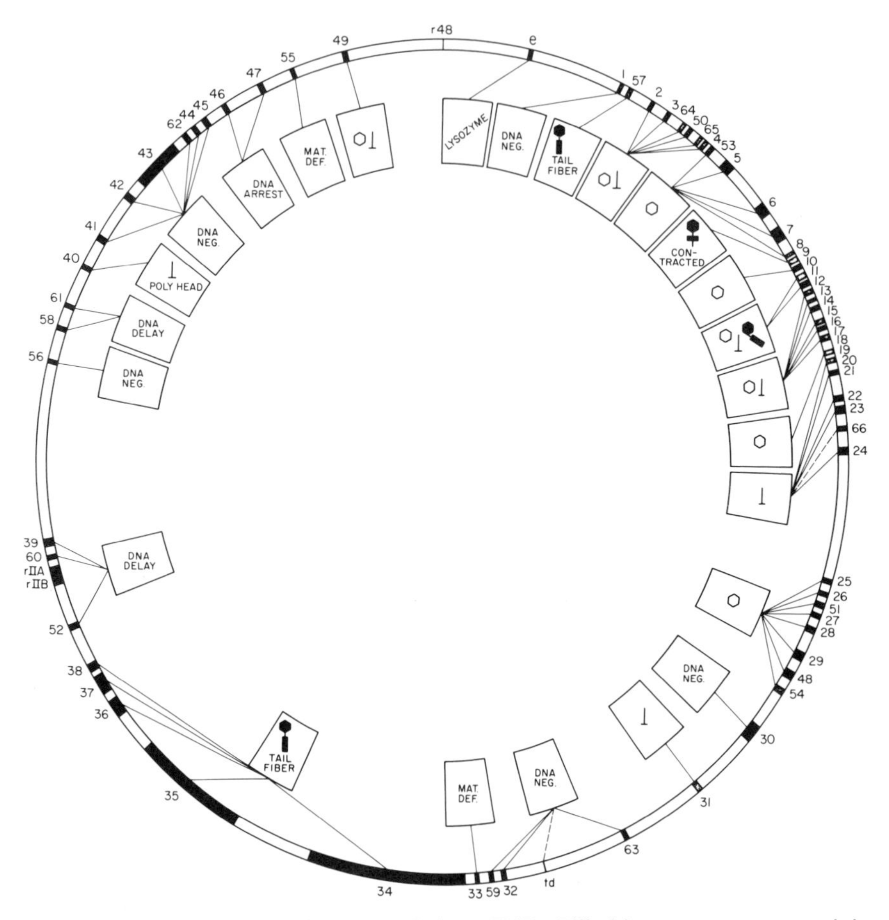

Figure 8-3. A recombination map of phage T4D. Filled-in areas represent minimal lengths for genes. The symbols for phage components represent the typical morphological products present in lysates of mutant-infected *E. coli.* (Courtesy of R. S. Edgar; see Edgar, R. S., and Wood, W. B., Proc. Nat. Acad. Sci., U.S., 55: 498, 1966.)

plaque themselves produce either r or r^+ plaques. Since both parental types are present, the mottled plaque could not have resulted from a *haploid* phage, one with only one r locus. Further studies show that a phage producing mottled plaques is *diploid;* that is, it contains two r loci. A diploid individual which carries two different alleles of a given gene is said to be *hybrid,* or *heterozygous,* for that gene. When the alleles are the same, the individual is *pure,* or *homozygous.* Mottling occurs because a single heterozygous phage, $r^+ r$, produces r^+ and r progeny in the same plaque. Note that these haploid progeny are recombinants since their parent was diploid.

It is unlikely that any T-even phage is completely haploid or completely diploid; but a single phage can be diploid for several loci. *Redundant loci,* those genes present in diploid condition, can occur either in the same double helix or in a separate fragment of DNA. In the following experiment the redundant loci seem to be in the same duplex of T-even DNA. Let us assume that the DNA is terminally redundant and can be represented in its open form as: $\frac{\text{a b .... a b}}{\text{a}'\text{b}' \text{.......... a}'\text{b}'}$, where segment a is complementary to a′, and b complementary to b′. A DNase that can attack only the free 3′ position of open circle DNA will thus produce $\frac{\text{.......... a b}}{\text{a}'\text{b}' \text{..........}}$. Subsequently, the double-stranded circle (a b / a′ b′, dashed circles) can form by base pairing. Such circles have been found with the electron microscope after but not before treatment with DNase. We might hypothesize, therefore, that during phage recombination the chromosome is a double-stranded circle that opens at nearby loci in the two strands. DNA synthesis then follows to make both ends double-stranded and thus produces the terminal redundancy observed in mature phage.

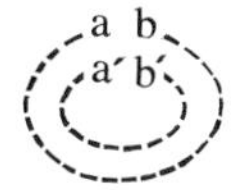

8·5 *Some phage recombination seems to involve the breakage of DNA from both parents and the subsequent union of fragments.*

Temperate phages are those which do not always lyse the hosts they infect. The bacteria that survive infection by temperate phage are subsequently *immune* to lysis after reinfection by identical or similar phage. Occasionally, however, such bacteria – called *lysogens* – or their progeny are lysed by the temperate phage already harbored. We can detect lysogens in the following way: when temperate phages infect nonlysogenic bacteria, the resultant plaques have a turbid center caused by the growth of bacteria which did not lyse but became lysogens.

If we multiply infect *E. coli* with two different mutants of the temperate phage *lambda* (λ), recombinant progeny arise. Determining the frequencies of recombinant phage obtained from such crosses, we can arrange all known loci of lambda in a single linkage map. In contrast to the circular genetic recombination map of ϕT4, the map of ϕλ (as well as ϕT5) is open (Figure 8-4).

To study further the recombination process in lambda, we infect an unlabeled host with two different strains whose DNA has been made heavier with both C^{13} and N^{15}. Progeny phage are ultracentrifuged and the fractions of different density are analyzed for recombinants. Since a peak in the recombinant curve is found at the density of the heavy parental phage, it is clear that all the DNA of these recombinants is original parental DNA. A simple explanation for this result is that the genetic material of these progeny is formed by the breakage of parental DNA and the union of segments from both parents.

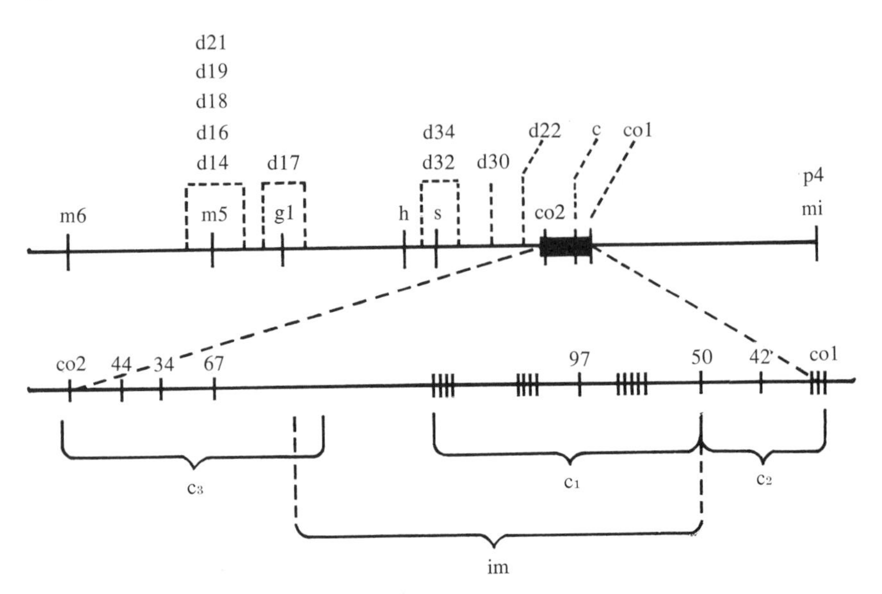

Figure 8-4. Diagrammatic representation of the linkage group of the temperate phage lambda. The upper diagram shows the linear arrangement of various markers for host range or plaque size or type. The *d* symbols refer to specific defective mutants. The *c* region is marked by a thicker line and is shown enlarged in the lower diagram. It is composed of three sub-regions, c_3, c_1, c_2. The *im* refers to the segment controlling immunity. (After F. Jacob and J. Monod)

8·6 *Genetic recombination can occur also between RNA viruses.*

SWE, with markers *a* and *c*, and MEL, with markers *A* and *C*, are two haploid strains of *influenza virus,* a single-stranded RNA virus. Although its usual host is the mammalian cell, it can also infect cells of the chicken egg. When SWE and MEL viruses are allowed to multiply infect a chicken egg, progeny are obtained not only of the parental types (*a c* and *A C*) but also of the recombinant types (*A c* and *a C*). These and other experiments prove that genetic recombination occurs between RNA-containing viruses as well as DNA-containing viruses.

Different strains of *poliomyelitis virus,* another RNA virus, also show genetic recombination. The resultant RNA seems to occur in one piece in these recombinants, whereas the RNA of recombinant influenza particles appears to be in several pieces. Consequently, more than one mechanism may be involved in recombination between RNA viruses that attack animals. We do not yet have any evidence that genetic recombination occurs between the RNA viruses that attack plants. The difficulties of multiply infecting plant cells with TMV or other viruses may account for the lack of definite results in experiments testing for genetic recombination.

GENETIC TRANSFORMATION OF BACTERIA

8·7 *The genetic material of a bacterium can be specifically changed by DNA from a different strain. Such genetic transformation proves that DNA is genetic material in bacteria.*

The bacterium Pneumococcus (*Diplococcus pneumoniae*) occurs in several genetically different forms. One type, S, is surrounded by a polysaccharide capsule, and forms a colony with a smooth surface. Type R lacks this coat, and produces a colony with a rough surface. When heat-killed S cells are added to nutrient broth in which R cells are growing and the mixture is poured onto nutrient agar, numerous colonies of type S appear. No matter what subtype of S is heat-killed, live bacteria of that type are obtained after mixture with R cells. Thus, we see that R cells have undergone a *genetic transformation* to S cells.

To determine the chemical nature of the transforming agent, we test the transforming ability of different fractions of heat-killed S bacteria. Those containing protein, RNA, or capsule polysaccharide are completely inactive. Only the fraction containing DNA is able to transform type R bacteria to type S. The purest DNA extracts (containing no detectable amounts of unbound lipids, polysaccharides, or proteins) retain full transforming ability. As we might expect, RNases have no effect on the transforming ability of a purified DNA fraction. DNases, however, can block transformation entirely. The process therefore requires undegraded DNA.

Note that since pure DNA can transform bacteria, no contact is necessary between donor and recipient cells. Hence, genetic transformation does not require the mediation of a virus. The DNA alone carries the genetic information which transforms a bacterium.

8·8 *Genetic transformation is a type of genetic recombination in which one single-stranded segment of DNA is substituted for another. The process involves the binding, penetration, synapsis, and integration of donor DNA in a recipient cell.*

Studies of genetic transformation in bacteria show that the process occurs in a series of discrete steps. A necessary prerequisite to the first step is that the bacteria be *competent,* for only at certain times in their life cycle can they accept transforming DNA.

Binding: When bacteria are at a competent stage, DNA is at first bound reversibly to the cell surface at several receptor sites. Only DNA of high molecular weight can bind to these sites; but it does not have to be transforming DNA. Nontransforming DNA (for example, from distant genera) can also bind to the cell surface, thereby saturating the receptor sites and preventing transforming DNA from binding.

Penetration: The DNA which becomes permanently bound to such sites penetrates the bacterium. Penetrating DNA must have a minimal molecular weight of 5×10^5.

Synapsis: Once inside the recipient cell, the DNA is thought to pair locus for locus, that is, to *synapse,* with the corresponding segment of the recipient's DNA. Since synapsis can occur between DNA's from the same and, in some instances, from different species, transformation is not only possible within a species, but also between species. We should not be surprised by the latter possibility, because different species produce many of the same polypeptides and consequently possess some similar or identical genetic information. Transformation between species is, however, relatively infrequent. The greater the difference between the species, the less the likelihood that their DNA's will synapse. The transforming ability of DNA which has penetrated a cell seems to depend primarily upon its similarity to the DNA of the recipient cell.

Integration: Certain experimental evidence indicates that the transforming DNA is *integrated,* that is, stably incorporated, into the recipient's DNA and that the corresponding segment of the recipient's DNA is absent. For instance, if we take the DNA from a cell of type A' (which has been transformed from a cell of type A) and use it to transform an A'' cell, we get only A' transformants. The transforming agent is thus the DNA of the *immediate* donor. Consequently, the initial A to A' transformation must have involved the replacement of genetic material of A by that of the donor, A'.

The result of transformation in bacteria is new information for the recipient cell. We should keep in mind, though, that the bacterium does not itself make this new material but merely incorporates it. Thus, transformation is essentially a recombination of genetic material within certain cells.

Details of the incorporation process have been provided by experiments involving double-stranded donor DNA that has been radioactively labeled. Apparently, only single-stranded DNA is incorporated into a bacterium's genetic material, either strand capable of insertion so long as it is at least 900 nucleotides long. No appreciable DNA synthesis seems to be involved in the integration of transforming DNA into recipient DNA.

8·9 *A single-stranded segment of transforming DNA may become integrated during replication of the DNA of the recipient cell.*

In proposing a mechanism for transformation, we must keep in mind the various stages mentioned earlier. Since we know that single-stranded DNA is the transforming agent, we can explain synapsis as base pairing

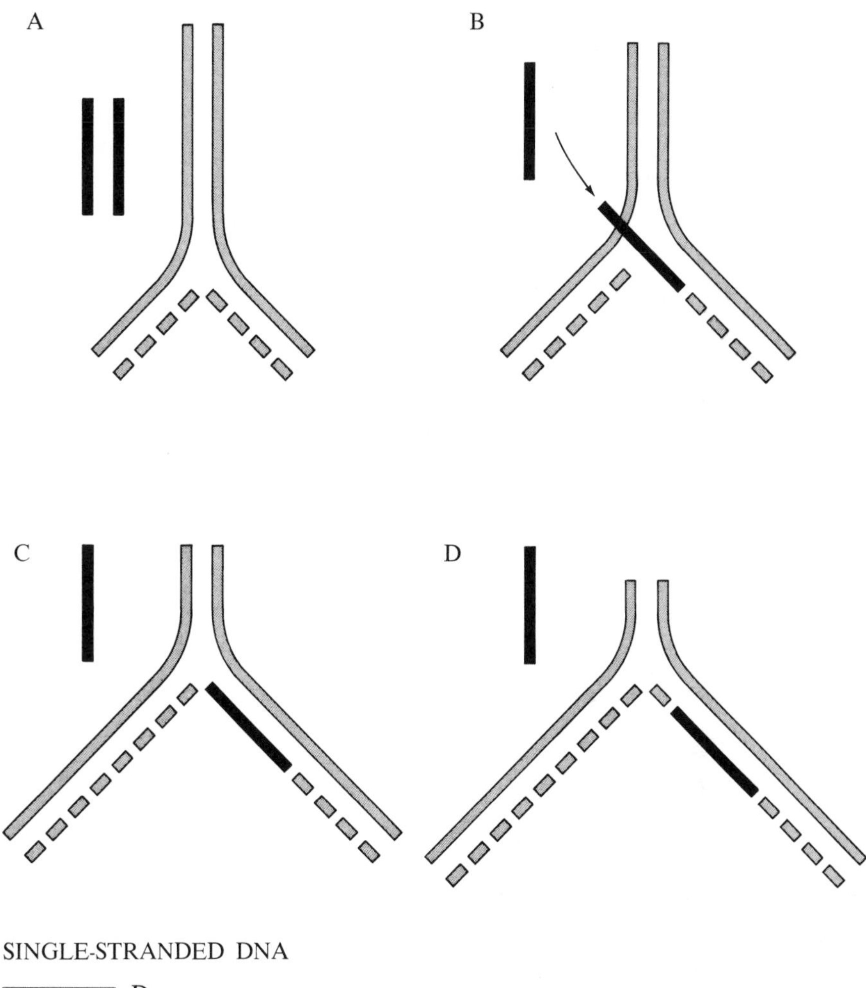

SINGLE-STRANDED DNA

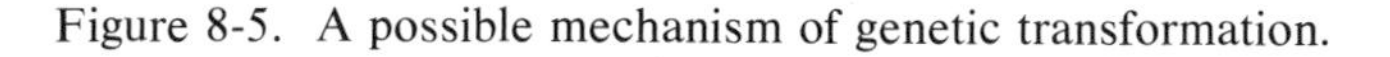

Figure 8-5. A possible mechanism of genetic transformation.

between this DNA segment and a similar, complementary part of the bacterium's DNA, single-stranded at this time because of replication (Figure 8-5). A competent cell would thus be one whose loci to be transformed are in a single-stranded condition. As long as sufficient complementarity exists between single-stranded donor and recipient DNA, we can expect that the transforming material can become part of the strand being synthesized. Since DNA need not be synthesized for the loci of the donor DNA, DNA polymerase may perhaps act before and after the transformed segment.

If, according to this hypothesis, the base sequence of the donor's DNA is not exactly complementary to the host's, the duplex will be hybrid for the transformed region. Consequently, the next DNA replication will produce one duplex with the donated loci and one with the original, parental loci. Such an hypothesis may also account for some genetic recombination between phages.

8·10 *Recombination maps for bacterial genes can be constructed using frequencies of double transformation.*

Within a species, different loci are transformed with characteristic frequencies. Using strains that differ at two loci, we can study the frequency of *double transformations,* that is, the frequency with which recipients are transformed for both loci. When the frequency of double transformation is greater than the product of the frequencies with which the individual genes are transformed, both loci involved in the double transformation are apparently in the same transforming DNA fragment. Using double transformation frequencies we can construct a *linkage map* for genes within segments of the bacterial chromosome. As expected, the maps of the segments are linear.

8·11 *After a cycle of chromosomal replication, the genetic material of bacteria is distributed to progeny in an orderly manner.*

Some bacteria are completely haploid only under special circumstances (for example, when in spore form). They are at various stages of diploidy when their DNA is being replicated; that is, they are diploid for replicated sections and haploid for sections not yet replicated. In some instances a second (and even a third) cycle of replication is in progress before the first cycle is completed; hence, different genes are present in single, double, and quadruple amount. When replication is not underway, some bacterial strains are stabilized as haploids and others as diploids. Regardless of the ploidy, however, when bacterial division takes place, each daughter bacterium normally receives a complete set of genes.

The mechanism for this orderly distribution seems to involve a *mesosome,* a structure formed by invagination of the cell membrane to which each chromosome is attached. After the chromosome divides, so does the cell membrane, daughter chromosomes being attached to daughter cell membranes. Thus, each daughter cell is assured of receiving a copy of each chromosome.

Questions and Problems

8·1 How could you demonstrate that recombination between T phages does not occur from the time the phages are mixed until the time their DNA is injected into a host?

8·2 How do you suppose TMV enters a tobacco cell? Correlate the structure of TMV and T phages with their ability to multiply infect a host cell.

8·3 What specific enzymes are required for transformation as hypothesized in Section 8·9 and Figure 8-5?

8·4 How could you prove that *E. coli* strain K12 (λ) is lysogenic for lambda by making use of a nonlysogenic strain?

8·5 Crosses involving three independently-arisen mutants in the A gene of the rII region of ϕT4 give the following results: no r^+ recombinants obtained from either $r1 \times r2$ or $r2 \times r3$; some obtained from $r1 \times r3$.
(a) What is the relative order of the three mutant sites?
(b) What can you conclude about the nucleotide basis for mutant $r2$?

8·6 Mutant *rIIA 1011* and mutant *rIIB 114* both produce large plaques when they attack *E. coli* strain B; they produce no plaques on strain K12. On the other hand, r^+ phage produce small plaques on both strains. (What is the effect of these *rII* mutants on host range?) A mixed infection of strain K12 by the two mutants produces many small plaques – the two mutants acting cooperatively to produce the same effect as the r^+. Explain such *complementation* in terms of transcription and translation.

8·7 Approximately one-half of the genes in the ϕT4 chromosome have temperature-sensitive alleles which permit phage development at 25°C but not at 40°C. What molecular explanation can you give for such conditional lethal mutants?

8·8 If two phages that are temperature-sensitive mutants for different genes multiply infect a host, both types of mutants can be recovered in the lysate; the mutants thus show complementation (see Question 8·6). Indicate the temperature conditions and methods you would employ to cross two temperature-sensitive mutants and determine the frequency of wild-type recombinants.

8·9 How would you show that the mRNA made from a ϕT2 template in *E. coli* is not as long as the T2 chromosome? (See Asano, K., J. Mol. Biol., 14: 71–84, 1965.)

8·10 If the DNA that penetrates is about 25% of the amount in a bacterial chromosome and the frequency of transformation for a given gene is as high as 25%, what can you say about the chance of integration for a fragment that has penetrated?

8·11 How would you detect and maintain a ϕT4 nonsense mutant that produces an incomplete head protein?

8·12 How could you map the positions of various markers in the *B. subtilis* chromosome assuming that 1) the chromosome always replicates sequentially starting at the same point; 2) stationary phase cultures contain nonreplicating chromosomes; and 3) exponentially growing-cultures contain replicating chromosomes at various stages of completion?

8·13 In Pneumococcus, substances A, B, C, and D are required for growth. Strain 1 can synthesize these substances because it has genes A^+, B^+, C^+, and D^+, respectively; strain 2 cannot because it carries the mutant alleles A^-, B^-, C^- D^-. DNA from strain 1 is used to transform strain 2 and the following results are obtained:

Strain 2 is plated on unsupplemented medium plus	Number colonies formed
ABCD	10,000
nothing	0
BCD	1,080
ACD	1,060
ABD	1,100
ABC	1,098
CD	40
BD	651
BC	973
AD	45
AC	41
AB	801
D	31
C	37
B	650
A	33

(a) Which three of the four loci studied are close together?
(b) Give the sequence of these three loci.

8·14 Defend the statement: "Normally, DNA is sometimes branched *in vivo*."

References

Adelberg, E. A. (Editor) 1966. *Papers on Bacterial Genetics, Second Edition*. Boston: Little, Brown and Co.

Avery, O. T., MacLeod, C. M., and McCarty, M. 1944. Studies on the chemical nature of the substance inducing transformation of pneumococcal types. J. Exp. Med., 79: 137–158. Reprinted *in Papers on Bacterial Genetics,* Adelberg, E. A. (Editor), Boston: Little, Brown and Co., 1960, pp. 147–168.

Benzer, S. 1962. The fine structure of the gene. Scient. Amer., 206 (No. 1): 70–84.

Braun, W. 1965. *Bacterial Genetics, Second Edition.* Philadelphia: W. B. Saunders Co.

Burnet, F. M., and Stanley, W. M. (Editors) 1959. *The Viruses;* Vol. 1, *General Virology;* Vol. 2, *Plant and Animal Viruses;* Vol. 3, *Animal Viruses,* New York: Academic Press.

Fox, M. S. 1966. On the mechanism of integration of transforming deoxyribonucleate. J. Gen. Physiol., 49: 183–196.

Gellert, M. 1967. Formation of covalent circles of lambda DNA by *E. coli* extracts. Proc. Nat. Acad. Sci., U.S., 57: 148–155.

Hayes, W. 1964. *The Genetics of Bacteria and their Viruses.* New York: J. Wiley & Sons, Inc.

Hershey, A. D., and Chase, M. 1951. Genetic recombination and heterozygosis in bacteriophage. Cold Spring Harb. Sympos. Quant. Biol., 16: 471–479. Reprinted in *Papers on Bacterial Viruses, Second Edition,* Stent, G. S. (Editor), Boston: Little, Brown and Co., 1965, pp. 204–217.

Kellenberger, G., Zichichi, M. L., and Weigle, J. J. 1961. Exchange of DNA in the recombination of bacteriophage λ. Proc. Nat. Acad. Sci., U.S., 47: 869–878.

Lacks, S. 1966. Integration efficiency and genetic recombination in pneumococcal transformation. Genetics, 53: 207–235. (Presents a somewhat different molecular explanation of transformation.)

Meselson, M., and Weigle, J. J. 1961. Chromosome breakage accompanying genetic recombination in bacteriophage. Proc. Nat. Acad. Sci., U.S., 47: 857–868. Reprinted in *Papers on Bacterial Viruses, Second Edition,* Stent, G. S. (Editor). Boston: Little, Brown and Co., 1965, pp. 218–229.

Postel, E. H., and Goodgal, S. H. 1966. Uptake of "single-stranded" DNA in *Hemophilus influenzae* and its ability to transform. J. Mol. Biol., 16: 317–327. (Transformation occurs with denatured DNA.)

Stent, G. S. 1963. *Molecular Biology of Bacterial Viruses.* San Francisco: W. H. Freeman & Co.

Stent, G. S. (Editor). 1965. *Papers on Bacterial Viruses, Second Edition.* Boston: Little, Brown and Co.

Streisinger, G., Emrich, J., and Stahl, M. M. 1967. Chromosome structure in phage T4, III. Terminal redundancy and length determination. Proc. Nat. Acad. Sci., U.S., 57: 292–295.

Thomas, C. A., Jr. 1966. The arrangement of information in DNA molecules. J. Gen. Physiol., 49: 143–169. (Terminal redundancy in φT2 revealed by DNase action.)

Wu, R., and Kaiser, A. D. 1967. Mapping the 5′-terminal nucleotides of the DNA of bacteriophage λ and related phages. Proc. Nat. Acad. Sci., U.S., 57: 170–177.

Yoshikawa, H., and Sueoka, N. 1963. Sequential replication of *Bacillus subtilis* chromosome, I. Comparison of marker frequencies in exponential and stationary growth phases. Proc. Nat. Acad. Sci., U.S., 49: 559–566. Reprinted in *Papers on Bacterial Genetics, Second Edition,* Adelberg, E. A. (Editor). Boston: Little, Brown and Co., 1966, pp. 279–286. (Chromosome mapped using transformation frequencies.)

CHAPTER 9

Genetic Recombination in Bacteria – Episomes and Transduction

In the last chapter we saw that genetic recombination occurs when a chromosome fragment is incorporated into a chromosome. The present chapter investigates recombinations in bacteria in which entire chromosomes join to each other and, once joined, can separate.

9·1 *An episome is a piece of genetic material that can exist either by itself as a chromosome or as part of another chromosome. A redundant portion of a chromosome may be a necessary prerequisite for deintegration of an episome.*

Let us consider hypothetically a ring-shaped chromosome which includes two identical regions, as shown in Figure 9-1A. (We might recall that the DNA of ϕT4 – although it is less than one-twentieth the size of bacterial DNA – contains some genetic redundancies.) An appropriate twist will bring these parts together so that single strands of one region will base-pair with their complements in the other (Figure 9-1B). Breakage and reunion of the strands as indicated in Figure 9-1B will then result in the formation of two rings from one – a new combination of the original genetic material.

According to this model, a chromosome might release some genetic material which could exist either by itself as a chromosome or as part of another. Such genetic material, which can exist in either of these two states, is called an *episome*. We can expect that an episome integrated with another chromosome will replicate along with that chromosome. A free, or unintegrated, episome might replicate (1) faster or slower than a chromosome in the same cell, (2) at the same rate, or (3) not at all. Since they are genetic material, episomes might be DNA or RNA.

9·2 *The genetic material of lambda (and probably of all other temperate phages as well) is an episome.*

When lambda, a temperate phage, infects *E. coli*, the chromosome of the phage has two possible fates, as we noted earlier (Section 8·5). It can remain free of the host chromosome and complete the lytic cycle (Figure 9-2B), thus lysing the bacterium. (Such DNA replicates faster than the DNA of its *E. coli* host.) Or it can assume a circular form and become integrated into the host chromosome, where it replicates along with other loci but does not lyse the cell (Figure 9-2C). With the lambda chromosome integrated, the bacterium produces lysogenic progeny which also contain the lambda chromosome. Under certain conditions, however, the integrated genetic material or *prophage* is freed, or deintegrated, and enters a lytic cycle. We see therefore that the DNA of lambda behaves like an episome. In fact, it is likely that the genetic material of all temperate phages is episomal.

9·3 *In genetic transduction a temperate phage mediates genetic recombination between bacteria by carrying genes from one host to another.*

E. coli and the closely-related bacterium *Salmonella typhimurium* usually can synthesize most of the organic molecules they need for growth from the relatively simple nutrients supplied in a minimal medium; hence, they are called *prototrophs*. Many mutant strains, however, cannot grow unless the minimal medium is supplemented by one or more specific nutrients. Such nutritionally-dependent organisms are called *auxotrophs*.

Among the many different auxotrophic strains of Salmonella is one which requires methionine, and another which requires threonine. We can represent these strains as $M^- T^+$ and $M^+ T^-$, respectively. If we centrifuge a liquid culture of the $M^+ T^-$ strain to remove most of the bacteria, heat the supernatant liquid for 20 to 30 minutes to kill any remaining bacteria, and then add this liquid to a culture of the $M^- T^+$ strain, a great many prototrophic colonies appear on the minimal medium. Spontaneous mutation cannot account for all these prototrophs. Moreover, since treatment of the supernatant liquid with DNase does not reduce the number of prototrophs, we can rule out genetic transformation as the mechanism for the genetic change.

Several experiments point to what this M^+ factor is. If we add a filtrate of the $M^- T^+$ strain to $M^+ T^-$ cells (an experiment opposite to that described above), essentially no prototrophs arise. Other results show

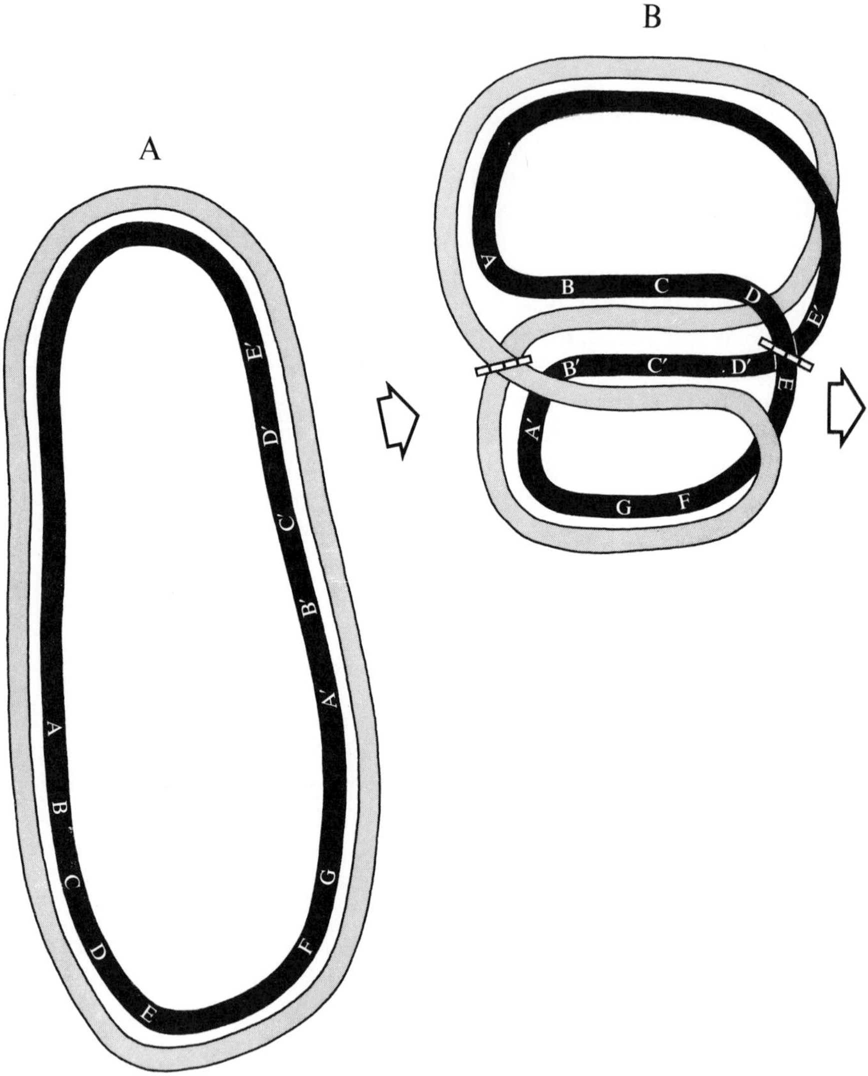

Figure 9-1. Postulated mechanism of genetic recombination in which a small ring chromosome leaves (A-C) or enters (D-E) a large ring chromosome. Interrupted lines represent places of breakage; black lines represent one complement and gray lines the other complement of DNA. Primed letters indicate duplicated loci.

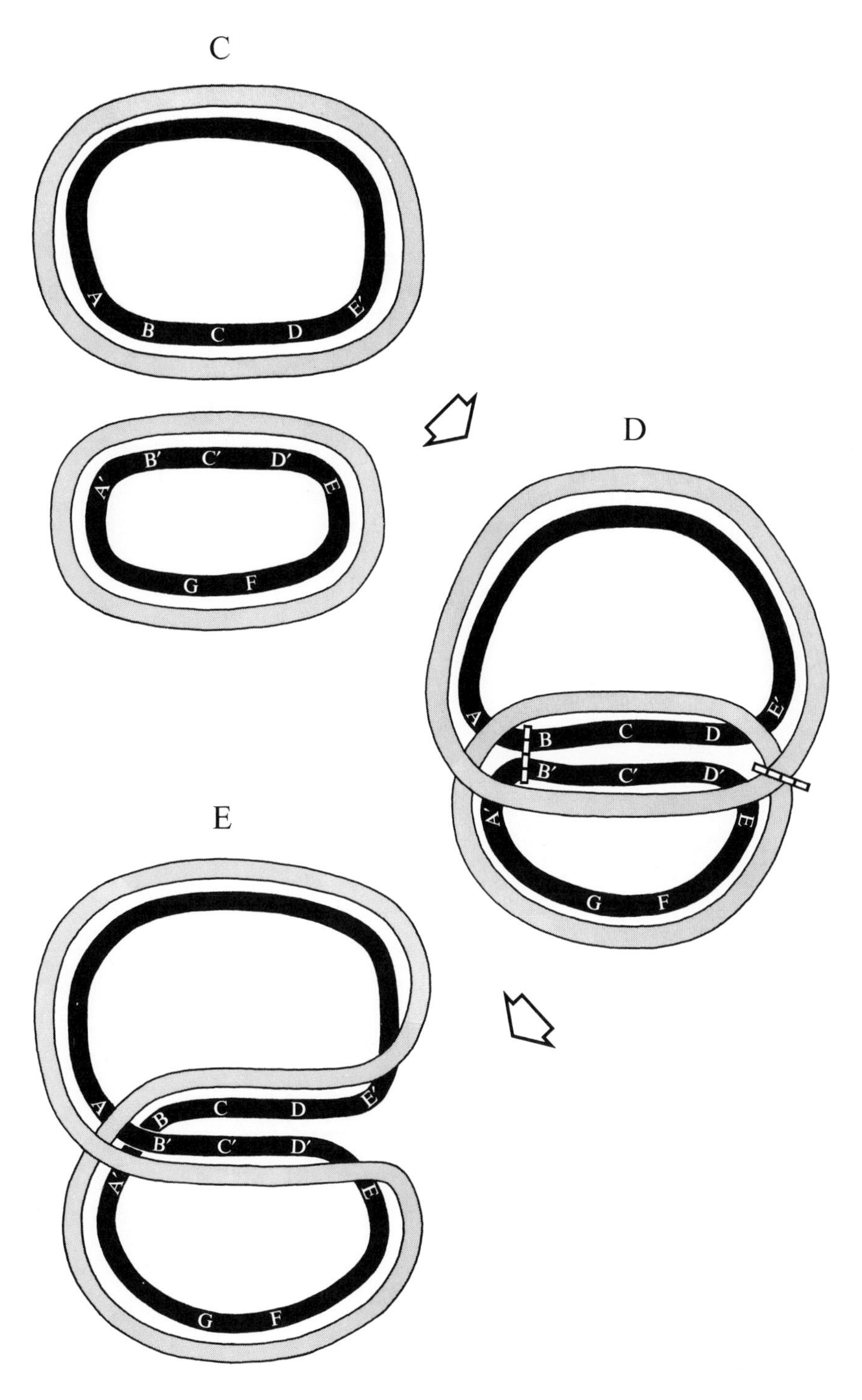
C
A
B
C
D
E′
A′
B′
C′
D′
E
G
F
D
A
B
C
D
E′
B′
C′
D′
A′
E
G
F
E
A
B
C
D
E′
B′
C′
D′
A′
E
G
F

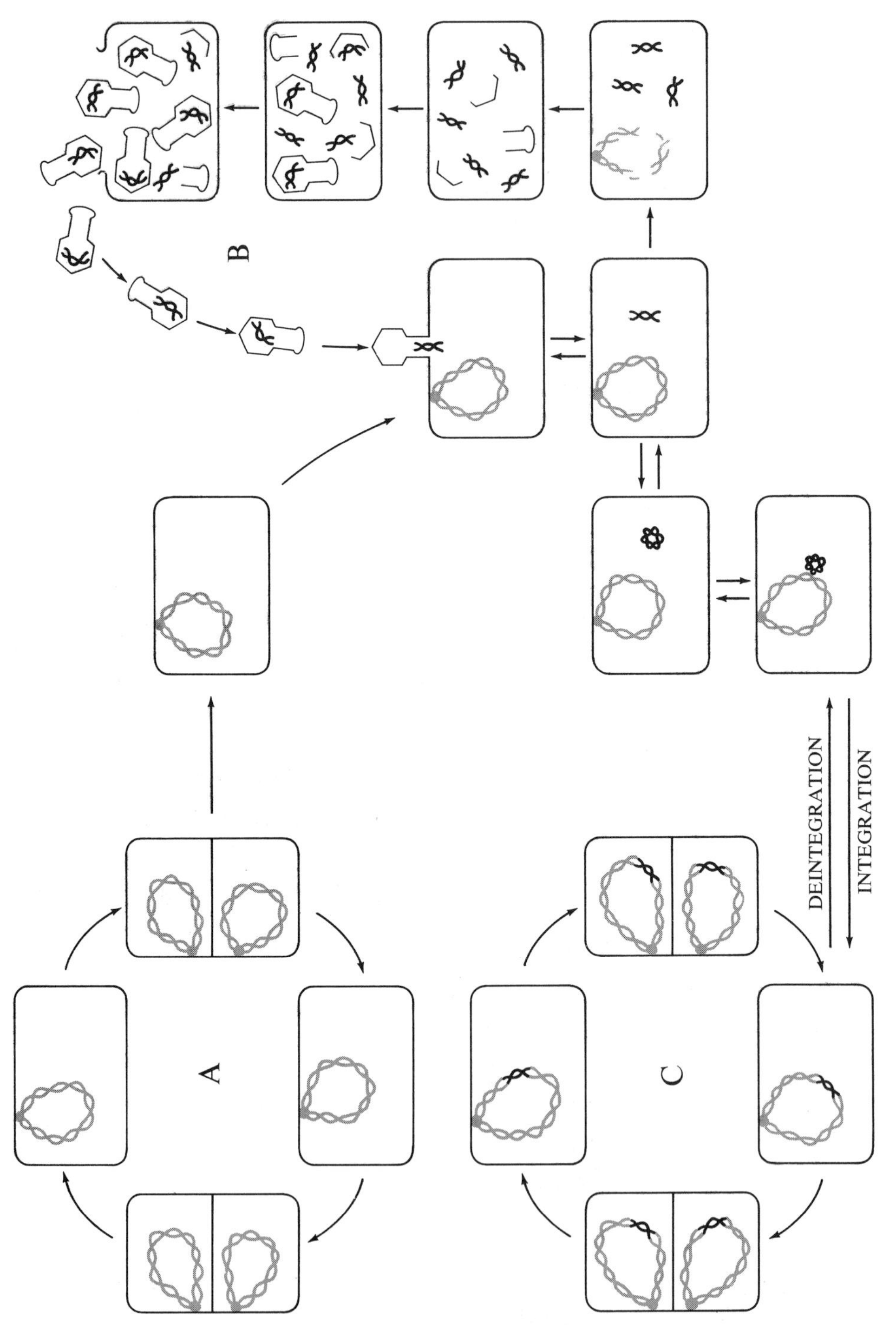

Figure 9-2. Diagrammatic representation of the life cycles of bacteria and temperate phage. A = cycle for nonlysogenic bacteria; B = lytic cycle of temperate phage; C = cycle for lysogenic bacteria. Gray spot represents mesosome; gray duplex material represents bacterial DNA; black portions, phage DNA.

that $M^+ T^-$ bacteria (donors) but not $M^- T^+$ (recipients) are lysogens for the temperate phage P22, and that the M^+ factor can pass through filters that hold back bacteria but not viruses. Since DNA is genetic material in Salmonella, the M^+ factor is likely to be DNA, too. If it were located inside a phage particle this genetic material would be unaffected by DNase – a result mentioned earlier. From these observations, we conclude that ϕP22 can somehow transfer genetic material (in one instance, the DNA which comprises the M^+ locus) from one host to another. Such genetic recombination is called *genetic transduction.*

9·4 *In generalized transduction, a small segment from one of many regions of the bacterial chromosome can be transduced. Because these segments sometimes include several loci, a genetic recombination map for bacteria can be constructed from frequencies of multiple transduction.*

A phage can transduce loci present in its last host only. ϕP22 can transduce many, perhaps all, of the loci in Salmonella and thus is said to be capable of *unrestricted* or *generalized transduction.* In generalized transduction a given locus is transduced in about one of every million singly-infected cells. Since only single loci are usually transduced, apparently only a rather short DNA segment is transduced at one time. In this respect, transduction is similar to transformation.

Sometimes, however, several loci are transduced by a single phage. The relative frequencies of these *multiple transductions* in Salmonella can be used to construct its genetic recombination map – a single circle, as in *E. coli.*

9·5 *The transducing segment of DNA either is integrated into the host's DNA (complete transduction) or fails to be integrated (abortive transduction).*

In most experiments the prototroph obtained by transduction of an auxotroph produces a colony identical to that of any other prototroph. In this process of *complete transduction* (Figure 9-3, column B), the transduced genetic material becomes integrated with the chromosome of the host, and supplies genetic information which had previously been lacking.

Occasionally, though, great numbers of minute colonies occur – about ten times as many as the large, prototrophic colonies (Figure 9-4). We can account for the presence of these minute colonies in the following way. An auxotrophic cell receives by transduction a segment of DNA which contains the information to make the bacterium prototrophic (Figure 9-3, column C). This DNA, however, is not incorporated into the chromosome of the host, nor is it replicated. But it is transcribed to mRNA. Consequently, a polypeptide is produced which makes the bacterium prototrophic, so the cell can grow and divide. Only one of the first two daughter cells, however, receives the transduced chromosomal segment. This cell can grow normally and divide; the other can grow only for the period of time that the necessary polypeptide remains (a small amount was donated to it by the parent cell). A minute colony is formed, therefore, only one of whose cells is genetically a prototroph. This failure of complete transduction to occur is called *abortive transduction.*

9·6 *Some temperate phages transduce host genes located only in one small region of the chromosome. This process is called restricted or specialized transduction.*

Bacteria of *E. coli* strain K12(λ) are lysogens for lambda; that is, the genetic material of lambda has become part of the host DNA. We can induce the prophage to deintegrate by briefly exposing a culture of lysogens to ultraviolet light. Several hours later the bacteria are lysed and great numbers of phage progeny are liberated. If these lambda are tested for their transducing ability, we find that only a few different bacterial markers are transduced. These markers are all located in or adjacent to a chromosome region that controls galactose fermentation, the *Gal* region. Lambda is thus capable only of *restricted* or *specialized transduction.*

Since lambda transduces loci only of the *Gal* region, it appears that the genetic material of the phage is incorporated into the *E. coli* chromosome only in or near the *Gal* region. Because lambda DNA must synapse with the host chromosome before being integrated into it, we hypothesize that the phage and bacterial chromosomes have some nucleotide sequence in common. Studies of lambda show that part of its DNA base sequence is identical to a portion of the *E. coli* chromosome, as indicated by the base-pairing of denatured DNA from the phage and its host. A possible mechanism of incorporation is suggested in Figure 9-1.

When the DNA of a transducing phage enters a bacterium, the host becomes diploid for certain loci. It is often desirable – especially when more than one allele for a given locus is present – to distinguish the genetic constitution of an individual, its *genotype,* from the traits or characters the genotype produces, its *phenotype.* Thus, a Gal^- bacterium that receives Gal^+ from a transducing phage has a $Gal^+\ Gal^-$ genotype and a Gal^+ phenotype. (Phenotypes are not italicized.) Sometimes Gal^+ Gal^- individuals give rise to $Gal^+\ Gal^-$ progeny, demonstrating that, unlike in abortive transduction, transduced bacterial genes can replicate

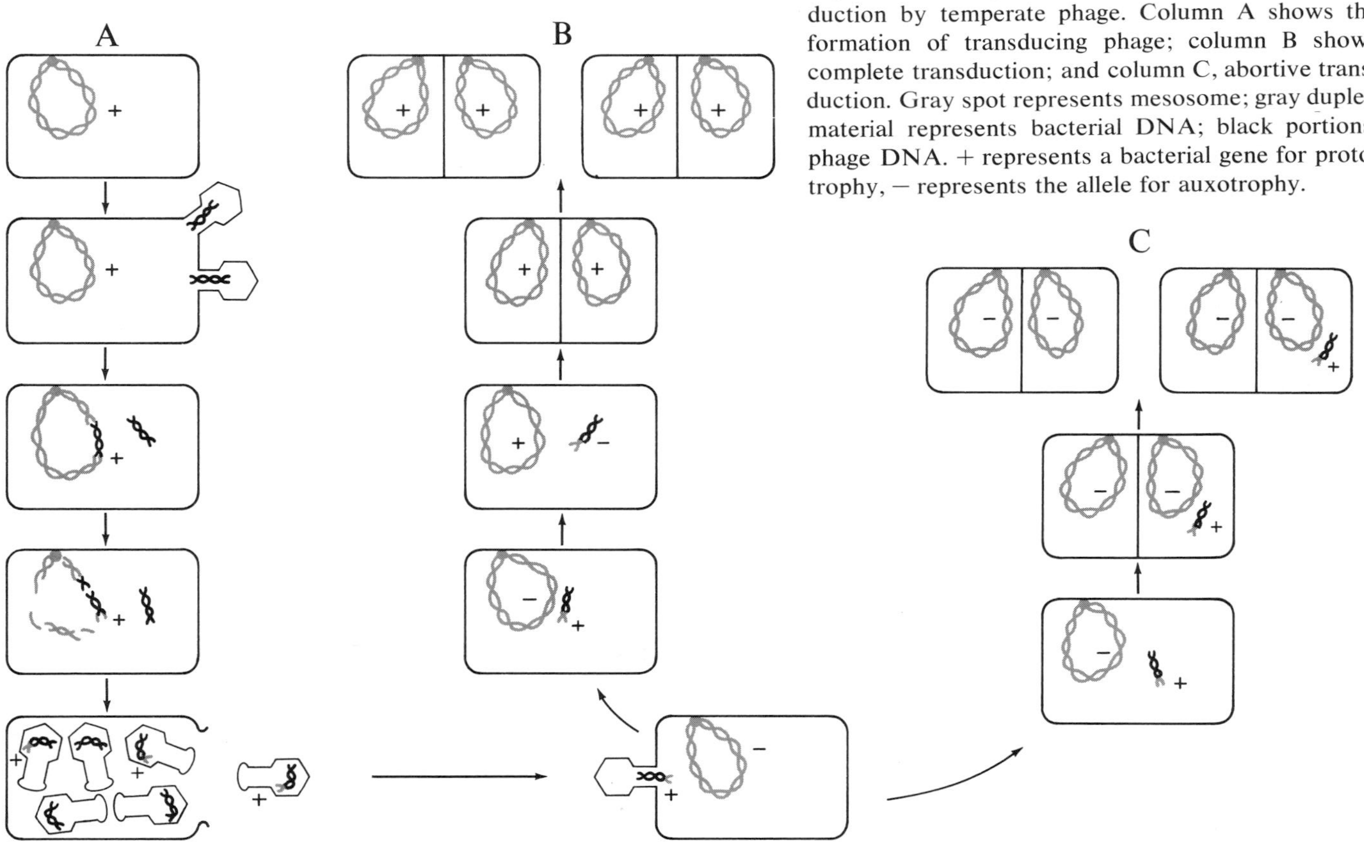

Figure 9-3. Diagrammatic representation of transduction by temperate phage. Column A shows the formation of transducing phage; column B shows complete transduction; and column C, abortive transduction. Gray spot represents mesosome; gray duplex material represents bacterial DNA; black portions, phage DNA. + represents a bacterial gene for prototrophy, − represents the allele for auxotrophy.

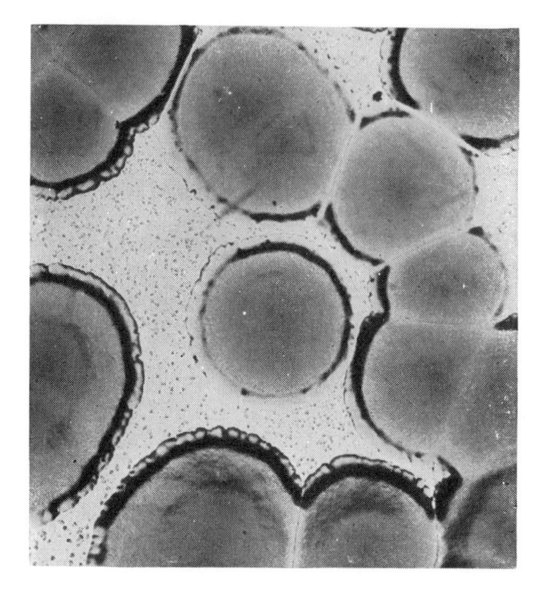

Figure 9-4. Large and minute (period-sized) colonies of Salmonella, representing complete and abortive transductions, respectively. (Courtesy of P. E. Hartman)

even if they are not integrated. At other times, such partial diploids become haploid after the transduced and host alleles exchange positions by a genetic recombination involving synapsis and breakage.

9·7 *The chromosomal loci which are transduced replace a part of the phage chromosome. Transducing phage thus are missing some of their genetic material and produce defective progeny.*

In most transduction studies, each cell is infected with many phage particles; and the cells which have been transduced have become lysogens. If, however, a *single* temperate phage infects a bacterium, the result is usually one of three mutually exclusive events for the host: lysis, lysogeny, or transduction. (Note that in this instance lysogeny does not accompany transduction.) If infected by a single transducing P22 phage, then, Salmonella cannot be made lysogenic, but can be if simultaneously infected with one or more nontransducing ϕP22 particles. A transducing ϕP22 thus must be defective in its genetic material. It is hypothesized, therefore, that transducing phage result from the abnormal deintegration of prophage.

A lambda phage which transduces bacterial loci also lacks a portion of its own genetic material. The *Gal* locus has been found to replace segments of different size in the transducing phage's DNA. One such defective lambda particle, called λdg, retains certain phage properties but is unable to replicate, to give rise to infective progeny, and to lysogenize its host. When a host cell is infected with both a λdg particle and a non-transducing λ, the genetic material of the λ can make the host lysogenic and permits the defective phage DNA to multiply after induction. At the time of lysis of such a doubly-infected cell, infective phages of both non-transducing and transducing types are liberated.

Since transformation does not normally occur in *E. coli* – probably because of difficulties in penetration of DNA – Gal^- individuals exposed to Gal^+ DNA isolated from λdg remain auxotrophs. When, however, Gal^- auxotrophs are simultaneously exposed to Gal^+ DNA of λdg and to nontransducing lambda, the phage serves as a "helper" for λdg DNA penetration; and transformation to Gal^+ occurs.

Questions and Problems

9·1 How would you determine whether a genetic recombination was due to phage-mediated transduction?

9·2 Devise a molecular model of how deintegration of temperate phage DNA could give rise to a transducing phage.

9·3 Under what circumstances is a recipient bacterium haploid with respect to a transduced locus?

9·4 In 1965 Ikeda, H., and Tomizawa, J. (J. Mol. Biol., 14: 85–109) carried out the following experiments. After *E. coli* which are genetically unable to synthesize thymine are fed 5-bromo uracil to make their DNA "heavy," they are infected with the generalized transducing phage P1*kc* and incubated until lysis in a medium containing
(a) thymine,
(b) 5-bromo uracil, or
(c) thymine and phosphate labeled with radioactive phosphorus.
Analysis of phage progeny by density-gradient centrifugation showed that transducing particles from the first two media have similar densities and that those from the third are *not* radioactive.
What do you conclude about the phage genetic material in transducing phage and the origin of transduced segments from these observations?

9·5 Design an experiment showing that a phage is passive with regard to the genes it transduces in the respect that it retains no "transducing memory" of any hosts previous to the last.

9·6 Should the transduced DNA in an abortive transduction be considered genetic material? Explain.

9·7 Where are the genes for immunity to lysis by subsequent phage infection located?

9·8 In what way is TMV a "helper" virus for STNV?

9·9 When a motile Salmonella is placed on the surface of nutrient agar, growth and reproduction can be traced by the branching trail that is produced through the medium. Design an experiment to detect abortive transduction of the gene for motility.

9·10 How can you explain the finding that temperate phage Mu 1 can inactivate any one of many different loci of the *E. coli* chromosome?

9·11 Design an experiment to convert abortive transductions to complete transductions using ultraviolet light. How do you suppose this conversion is accomplished?

References

Adelberg, E. A. (Editor) 1966. *Papers on Bacterial Genetics, Second Edition,* Boston: Little, Brown and Co.

Campbell, A. 1962. Episomes. Advances in Genetics, 11: 101–145.

Campbell, A. 1964. Transduction, pp. 49–89, in *The Bacteria* (Vol. 5), *Heredity,* Gunsalus, I. C., and Stanier, R. Y. (Editors). New York: Academic Press.

Jacob, F., and Wollman, E. L. 1958. Episomes, added genetic elements. (In French) C. R. Acad. Sci., Paris, 247: 154–156. Translated and reprinted in *Papers on Bacterial Genetics,* Adelberg, E. A. (Editor), Boston: Little, Brown and Co., 1960, pp. 398–400.

Jacob, F., and Wollman, E. L. 1961. Viruses and genes. Scient. Amer., 204 (No. 6): 92–107.

Lwoff, A. 1966. Interaction among virus, cell, and organism. Science, 152: 1216–1220. (Nobel Prize Lecture on the history, significance, and molecular biology of lysogeny.)

Signer, E. R., and Beckwith, J. R. 1966. Transposition of the *lac* region of *Escherichia coli.* III. The mechanism of attachment of bacteriophage ϕ80 to the bacterial chromosome. J. Mol. Biol., 22: 33–51.

Zinder, N. D. 1958. 'Transduction' in bacteria. Scient. Amer., 199: 38–43.

Zinder, N. D., and Lederberg, J. 1952. Genetic exchange in Salmonella. J. Bact., 64: 679–699.

CHAPTER 10

Genetic Recombination in Bacteria – Episomes and Conjugation

We have seen that bacterial genes can undergo genetic recombination in a number of ways: by cell division, by genetic transformation, and by genetic transduction mediated by a temperate phage. In this chapter we shall consider another type of episome involved in recombination in bacteria.

10·1 *In certain strains of bacteria a genetic recombination occurs which cannot be satisfactorily explained as transduction or transformation.*

One auxotrophic strain of *E. coli* requires three nutrients in addition to minimal medium for growth. Another strain needs a supplement of three different nutrients. If we mix these strains and then plate them on a minimal medium, which contains none of these six nutrients, we obtain a number of prototrophs – recombinants for three loci. Since it is unusual for three different loci to be transformed or transduced at the same time, we may not be able to explain this recombination as genetic transformation or transduction. Transformation can be ruled out because treatment of the bacteria with DNase does not appreciably change the number of prototrophs.

To see if the recombinants arise as the result of transduction, we can carry out the following experiment. The arms of a U-tube are separated by a sintered glass filter, and one of the two auxotrophic strains in minimal medium is added to each arm. The sintered glass prevents the bacteria but not the culture medium, soluble substances, and small particles (including viruses) from passing back and forth. Yet, essentially no prototrophs are found in platings from either arm. Thus, virus-mediated transduction does not seem to account for the recombination.

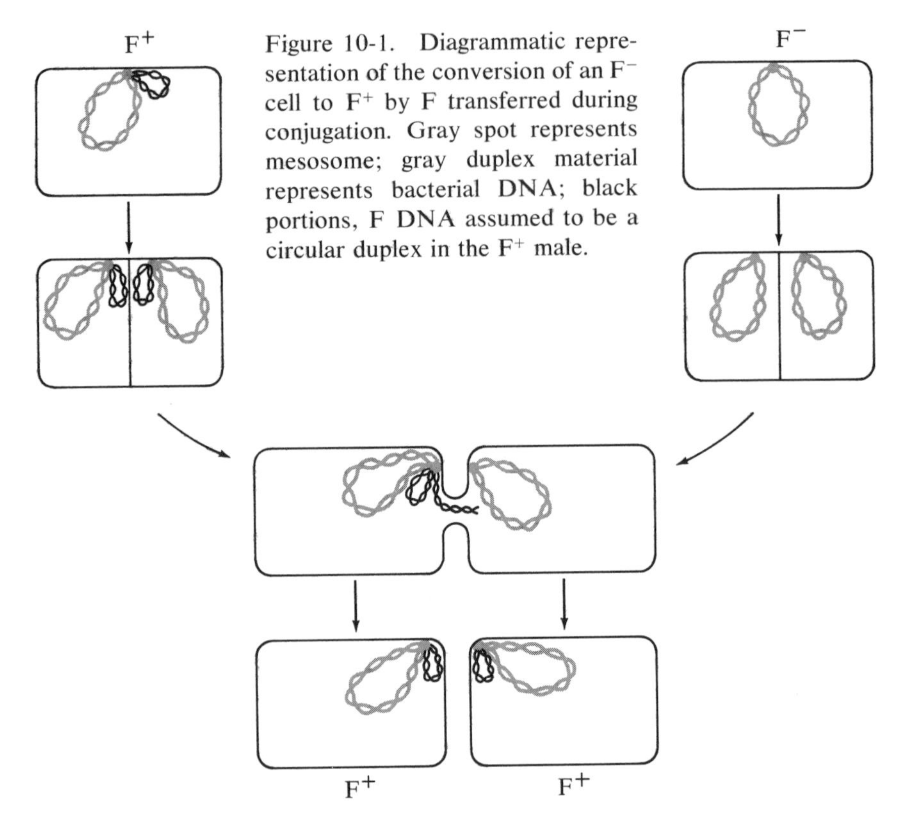

Figure 10-1. Diagrammatic representation of the conversion of an F^- cell to F^+ by F transferred during conjugation. Gray spot represents mesosome; gray duplex material represents bacterial DNA; black portions, F DNA assumed to be a circular duplex in the F^+ male.

10·2 *The recombination is the result of conjugation, which involves the transfer of genetic material from donor cell to recipient, and requires contact between them.*

Further studies show that cell-to-cell contact is necessary for recombinants to be produced. The contact allows the transfer of genetic material from one type of cell, the donor (or male) cell to another, the recipient (or female) cell. This process, called *conjugation,* can thus be considered a sexual process. The donor strain is also called F^+ (F for "fertility") and the recipient, F^-.

10·3 *Maleness is due to the presence of the sex factor, F, a special particle of DNA.*

Male (F^+) sexuality results from the presence of the *sex factor, F,* an infective, self-reproducing particle separate from the bacterial chromosome. F is transferred from male to female only after contact (Figure 10-1). Some properties of F^+ males are: (1) F^+ cells can spontaneously change to F^-; (2) if a single F^+ male is placed in a culture of F^- cells,

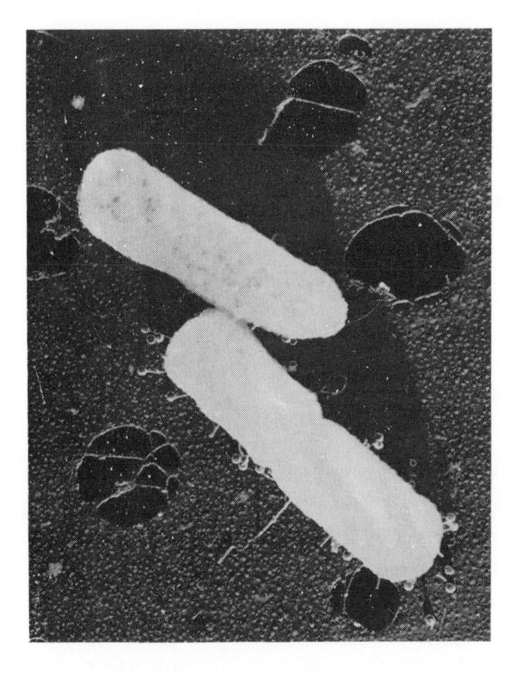

Figure 10-2. An electron micrograph showing conjugation in *E. coli* between an F^- cell and an Hfr cell. The Hfr cell has ultraviolet-killed, tadpole-shaped phage adsorbed on its surface; the F^- cell does not, since it is genetically resistant to this phage. Although not shown in the photograph, thread-like connections, called *pili,* are sometimes seen between conjugants and may also be involved in the transfer of genetic material. When exconjugants of such visibly marked pairs of Hfr and F^- cells are isolated by micromanipulation and are cultured, only the colonies from the F^- partner yield recombinants. (Courtesy of T. F. Anderson)

soon thereafter all cells are F^+; (3) F^- cells converted to F^+ produce F^+ progeny; and (4) F^+ cells have a low frequency of recombination – only about one in 10^4 transfers bacterial chromosomal DNA into an F^- cell.

Since the F factor does not retain its ability to convert F^- to F^+ when removed from the cell, it does not appear to be a typical virus. Some of its chemical and physical characteristics can be determined by density gradient centrifugation. When F is transferred by conjugation to a bacterium of a different genus, Serratia, a DNA band appears in the cesium chloride density gradient that is not found in Serratia alone. This band is due to the DNA of F, which is found to contain nearly 1.0×10^5 base pairs, about 2% of the total number in an *E. coli* chromosome.

10·4 *Since an F particle can exist either by itself as a chromosome or as part of an* E. coli *chromosome, it is an episome.*

In addition to F^- and F^+, another mating type can arise from F^+ cells. This type produces a *high frequency of recombination* in its mates during conjugation, and hence is called *Hfr*. Hfr cells are donors like F^+ (Figure 10-2). In a cross of Hfr with F^-, most of the progeny are F^- with a rare Hfr individual. Hence, Hfr bacteria do not seem to carry the free, infective F particle which would result in F^+ progeny. On rare occasions, however, an Hfr cell can spontaneously revert to F^+ – the strain from which the Hfr originated. These F^+ strains are identical to other F^+ lines and contain infective F particles. Therefore, since Hfr individuals come

Minutes	Recombinants Having Hfr Markers
0	None
8	T
$8\frac{1}{2}$	T, L
9	T, L, Az
11	T, L, Az, T_1
18	T, L, Az, T_1, Lac
25	T, L, Az, T_1, Lac, Gal

Figure 10-3. Recombinants obtained when conjugation is artificially interrupted at various times after mixing F^- and Hfr strains. The Hfr strain has markers for T, L, Az, T_1, Lac, Gal. (After W. Hayes)

only from F^+ and revert only to F^+ even though they do not seem to contain an F particle, they must somehow retain F in a masked or bound form. The following evidence supports the hypothesis that the Hfr bacterium has an F particle integrated into its chromosome.

We can study further the properties of the Hfr factor and its role in conjugation by means of an *interrupted-mating experiment.* If we mix two particular strains of Hfr and F^- bacteria in a 1:20 proportion, we can be assured of rapid contact of all Hfr with F^- cells. At various intervals after mixing, we withdraw samples and subject them to the strong shearing force of a blender. This treatment separates conjugants apparently without affecting their viability, their ability to undergo recombination, or their ability to express the characteristics under test. The bacteria are then plated to determine what marker loci of the donor have been transferred to the recipient.

A most important finding of this experiment is that different loci of the male enter the female cell at different, specific times (Figure 10-3). For example, the *T* and *L* markers of the Hfr do not enter F^- until after about $8\frac{1}{2}$ minutes of conjugation, whereas the *Gal* marker requires about 25 minutes of conjugation before it is transferred. From these observations we conclude that the Hfr chromosome or a copy is transferred in a specific manner: one particular end of the genetic material (called the *origin, O*) enters the F^- cell first, and the loci that follow do so in a regular, linear procession (Figures 10-3 and 10-4).

Under normal conditions only a portion of the Hfr chromosome is transferred, since chromosome breakage during conjugation occurs spontaneously. Consequently, the length of the piece which gets into a recipient cell can vary; and the *zygote* of an Hfr cross, which contains the genetic material of the recipient plus whatever is donated, is (usually) only partially diploid. In the interrupted-mating experiment, a recipient becomes Hfr only in the rare event that the terminal marker (the one furthest from the origin) is transferred. The locus responsible for the Hfr

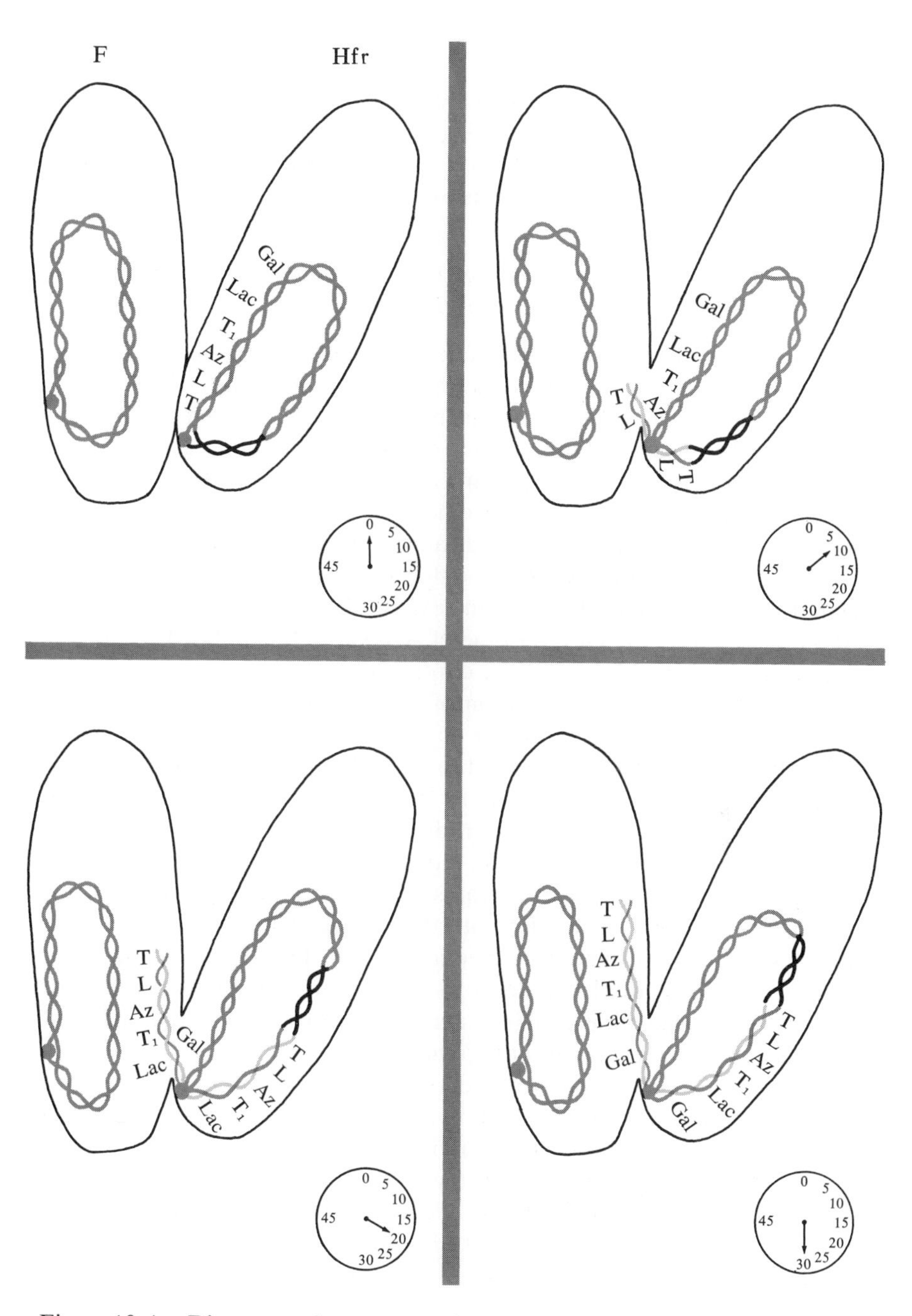

Figure 10-4. Diagrammatic representation of the sequential transfer of an open-ring replica of the Hfr ring chromosome into the F^- cell after conjugation has continued for the number of minutes indicated. See also Figure 10-3. Gray spot represents mesosome; gray duplex material represents bacterial DNA; black portion of duplex represents integrated F; light gray strands represent newly-synthesized complements.

mating type is apparently the locus of an integrated F factor, and seems to be at the end of the chromosome being transferred. Since the sex factor F can exist either autonomously (in F^+ cells) or integrated into the bacterial chromosome (in Hfr cells), it is an episome.

10·5 *The genetic recombination maps for different Hfr strains are different, linear maps of the* E. coli *chromosome.*

We can determine the sequence of certain markers in three different Hfr strains by interrupted-mating experiments. The markers common to all three strains are found to occur in the same order in the recombination map, but the origin is different for each strain and, consequently, so is the position of the Hfr locus (Figure 10-4). These results suggest that (1) at the time of transfer the chromosome or a copy is not a ring but a linear segment of DNA with the Hfr locus at one end, and (2) the reverse directions of entry by chromosomes of different strains may be due to their F particles having been integrated in reverse directions. (Note in Figures 10-5 and 10-6 that the chromosome of AB-312 enters in the direction opposite that of AB-311 or AB-313 chromosomes.)

As we noted earlier, replication of bacterial DNA begins at a single locus. Although this starting point may be random in F^- strains, replication apparently starts at or adjacent to the F-containing end of Hfr strains. After coming into contact with an F^- cell, the Hfr cell synthesizes a new chromosome, and an open-circle (rod) duplex composed of one parental strand and a newly-synthesized complement is transferred to the recipient. Considerable evidence indicates that the cell membrane is the site of DNA synthesis in bacteria; both daughter chromosomes seem to be attached to a mesosome (see Section 8·11). The chromosome to be transferred is apparently attached to the cell membrane near the future conjugation bridge. One daughter chromosome remains in the male; the other is somehow driven into the female.

Since the *E. coli* chromosome consists of about 10^7 nucleotide pairs and is transferred entirely in about two hours, nearly 10^5 nucleotide pairs (a DNA segment of close to 34μ) are transferred in a minute at 37°C. Taking into account variations in the rate of transfer and the efficiency with which a transferred marker is integrated, we can construct a general genetic recombination map for all Hfr donors. This circular map, with relative distances expressed in minutes, is given in Figure 10-7.

10·6 *In deintegrating from the* E. coli *chromosome, an F particle can take with it genes of its host. The process of bringing these bacterial genes into an F^- cell is called F-mediated transduction.*

An Hfr strain reverts to F^+ when the F particle deintegrates from the Hfr chromosome. The particle is then able to replicate autonomously and

SELECTED MARKER	STRAIN AB-311	AB-312	AB-313
his +	42	2.5	–
gal +	12	4	–
pro +	–	8	–
met +	4	22	–
mtl +	3.7	25	49
xyl +	2.8	26	43
mal +	1.5	40	32
ade +	–	–	15
try +	–	–	6
arg +	–	–	0.3

Figure 10-5. Recombination percentages for certain Hfr strains. O = point of origin; – = untested. (After A. L. Taylor and E. A. Adelberg, 1960. See References.)

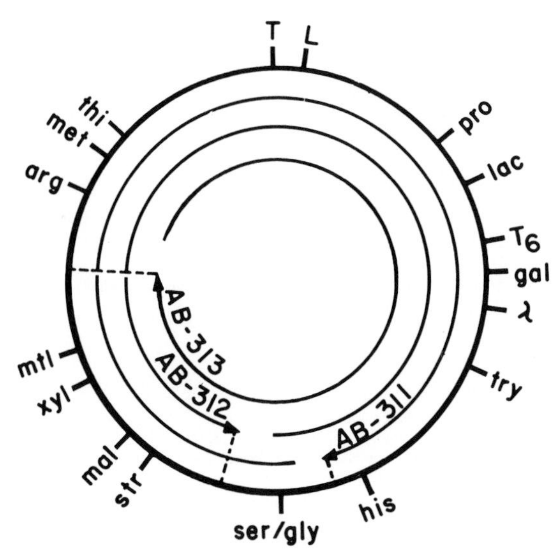

Figure 10-6. Linear chromosomes of three Hfr strains. Arrows show direction of chromosome penetration during conjugation. (After A. L. Taylor and E. A. Adelberg, 1960. See References.)

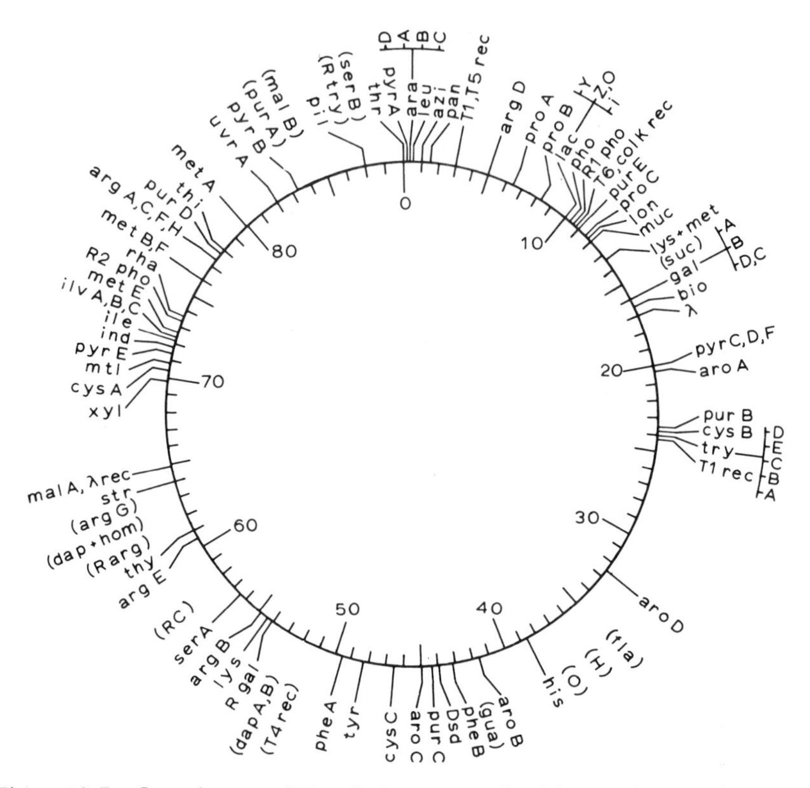

Figure 10-7. Genetic map of *E. coli,* drawn to scale. A key to the genetic symbols appears in the accompanying chart. The map is graduated in one-minute intervals (89 minutes total). Markers enclosed in parentheses are only approximately mapped; the exact sequence of markers in crowded regions is not always known. (Courtesy of A. L. Taylor and M. S. Thoman, 1964. See References.)

LIST OF CHROMOSOMAL MARKERS OF *E. coli*

*Key to genetic symbols **		*Activity affected*
araD	arabinose	L-ribulose 5-phosphate 4-epimerase
araA	arabinose	L-arabinose isomerase
araB	arabinose	L-ribulokinase
araC	arabinose	unknown
argB	arginine	N-acetylglutamate synthetase
argC	arginine	N-acetyl-γ-glutamokinase
argH	arginine	N-acetylglutamic-γ-semialdehyde dehydrogenase
argG	arginine	acetylornithine-δ-transaminase
argA	arginine	acetylornithinase
argD	arginine	ornithine transcarbamylase
argE	arginine	argininosuccinic acid synthetase
argF	arginine	argininosuccinase
aroA,B,C	aromatic amino acids and vitamins	shikimic acid to 3-enolpyruvylshikimate-5-phosphate
aroD	aromatic amino acids and vitamins	biosynthesis of shikimic acid
azi	azide	resistance or sensitivity to sodium azide
bio	biotin	
cysA	cysteine	unknown
cysB	cysteine	3′-phosphoadenosine 5′-phosphosulfate to sulfide †
cysC	cysteine	sulfate to sulfide; four known enzymes †
dapA	diaminopimelic acid	dihydrodipicolinic acid synthetase
dapB	diaminopimelic acid	N-succinyl-diaminopimelic acid deacylase
dap + hom	diaminopimelic acid + homoserine	aspartic semialdehyde dehydrogenase
Dsd	D-serine	D-serine deaminase
fla	flagella	
galA	galactose	galactokinase
galB	galactose	galactose 1-phosphate uridyl transferase

LIST OF CHROMOSOMAL MARKERS OF *E. coli*—CONTINUED

Key to genetic symbols *		Activity affected
galD	galactose	uridinediphosphogalactose 4-epimerase
galC	galactose	operator mutants
gua	guanine	
H	H antigen	flagellar antigen
his	histidine	ten known enzymes and an operator †
ile	isoleucine	threonine deaminase
ilvA	isoleucine + valine	α-hydroxy β-keto acid reductoisomerase †
ilvB	isoleucine + valine	α,β-dihydroxyisovaleric dehydrase †
ilvC	isoleucine + valine	transaminase B
ind	indole	tryptophanase
λ	prophage λ	
lac Y	lactose	galactoside permease
lac Z	lactose	β-galactosidase
lac O	lactose	operator mutants
leu	leucine	three known enzymes and an operator †
lon	long form	filament formation and radiation sensitivity
lys	lysine	diaminopimelic acid decarboxylase
lys + met	lysine + methionine	unknown
λrec,malA	λreceptor and maltose	maltose permease and resistance to phage λ
malB	maltose	probably amylomaltase
metA	methionine	synthesis of the succinic ester of homoserine †
metB	methionine	succinic ester of homoserine + cysteine to cystathionine †
metF	methionine	probably 5,10-methylene tetrahydrofolate reductase
metE	methionine or cobalamin	unknown
mtl	mannitol	probably mannitol dehydrogenase
muc	mucoid	regulation of capsular polysaccharide synthesis
O	O antigen	somatic antigen
pan	pantothenic acid	
pheA,B	phenylalanine	
pho	phosphatase	alkaline phosphatase
pil	pili (fimbriae)	
proA	proline	
proB	proline	supports syntrophic growth of *proA* mutants
proC	proline	supports syntrophic growth of *proA* mutants
purA	purine	adenylosuccinic synthetase
purB	purine	adenylosuccinase
purC,E	purine	5-aminoimidazole ribotide(AIR) to 5-aminoimidazole 4-(N-succinocarboxamide) ribotide
purD	purine	biosynthesis of AIR
pyrA	uracil + arginine	carbamate kinase
pyrB	uracil	aspartate transcarbamylase
pyrC	uracil	dihydroorotase
pyrD	uracil	dihydroorotic acid dehydrogenase
pyrE	uracil	orotidylic acid pyrophosphorylase
pyrF	uracil	orotidylic acid decarboxylase
R arg	repressor	arginine repressor
R gal	repressor	galactose repressor
R1 pho,R2 pho	repressor	alkaline phosphatase repressor
R try	repressor	tryptophan repressor
RC	RNA control	regulation of RNA synthesis
rha	rhamnose	utilization of D-rhamnose
serA	serine	3-phosphoglycerate dehydrogenase
serB	serine	phosphoserine phosphatase
str	streptomycin	resistance, sensitivity, or dependence on streptomycin
suc	succinic acid	
T1,T5 rec	phage receptor site	resistance to phages T1 and T5
T1 rec	phage receptor site	resistance to phage T1
T6, colK rec	phage and colicine receptor site	resistance to phage T6 and colicine K
T4 rec	phage receptor site	resistance to phage T4
thi	thiamine	
thr	threonine	
thy	thymine	thymidylate synthetase
tryA	tryptophan	tryptophan synthetase, A protein
tryB	tryptophan	tryptophan synthetase, B protein
tryC	tryptophan	indole 3-glycerolphosphate synthetase
tryE	tryptophan	anthranilic acid to anthranilic deoxyribulotide
tryD	tryptophan	3-enolpyruvylshikimate 5-phosphate to anthranilic acid
tyr	tyrosine	
uvrA	ultraviolet radiation	reactivation of UV-induced lesions in DNA
xyl	xylose	utilization of D-xylose

* Established systems of genetic nomenclature are retained wherever possible, except that capital letters beginning with the letter A are arbitrarily assigned to functionally related gene loci which do not conform to the system of bacterial genetic nomenclature proposed by M. DEMEREC (1963).

† Denotes enzymes controlled by the homologous gene loci of *Salmonella typhimurium*.

infect other cells. An experiment involving deintegrated F factors gives a somewhat surprising result. Using *Lac*$^-$ F$^-$ cells and a strain of Hfr with F integrated very close to the *Lac*$^+$ locus, we obtain a small number of recombinants which receive *Lac*$^+$ much earlier than in other interrupted-mating experiments. These recombinants have the following properties:

(1) They receive only F and *Lac*$^+$.

(2) They are unstable and occasionally give rise to *Lac*$^-$ F$^-$ individuals. (Hence, the original recombinant must carry both *Lac*$^+$ and *Lac*$^-$ alleles.)

(3) When mated with *Lac*$^-$ F$^-$ cells, they transfer both F and *Lac*$^+$ with a frequency of 50% or higher. (This transfer starts soon after conjugation begins, just like transfer of free F.)

(4) The F-Lac$^+$ element can be transmitted in a series of successive conjugations, each recipient possessing the properties of the original recombinant.

(5) The F-*Lac*$^+$ element causes the transfer of the host chromosome in the same sequence as the original Hfr line but with one-tenth the frequency.

We can explain these results most simply by saying that an F particle can take with it a neighboring piece of the bacterial chromosome, *Lac*$^+$, when it deintegrates (Figure 10-8). Usually, only the F-*Lac*$^+$ particle, a *substituted sex factor,* is transferred in conjugation. This process in which substituted sex factors bring bacterial genes from one cell to another is called *F-mediated transduction, sex-duction,* or *F-duction.* (Note the parallel between substituted sex factors and F on the one hand, and λdg and λ, on the other.)

F-*Lac*$^-$ particles, which consist of F and a mutant *Lac* locus, can also be selected. Since F can become integrated at a variety of loci, different loci can become part of a deintegrated F particle. These F-linked loci make a recipient cell partially diploid. In such cells, recombination can occur between *homologous,* that is, corresponding, loci of the bacterial chromosome and the episome.

When the F-*Lac*$^+$ particle integrates near *Lac,* the entire bacterial chromosome can be transferred during conjugation. If we have an Hfr bacterium with two integrated F factors, the chromosome transferred during conjugation will be in two pieces, each with an F at the end; both segments are transferred to the F$^-$ cell. We see, therefore, that host genes attached to F are mobilized whether they are in an entire chromosome or a small segment.

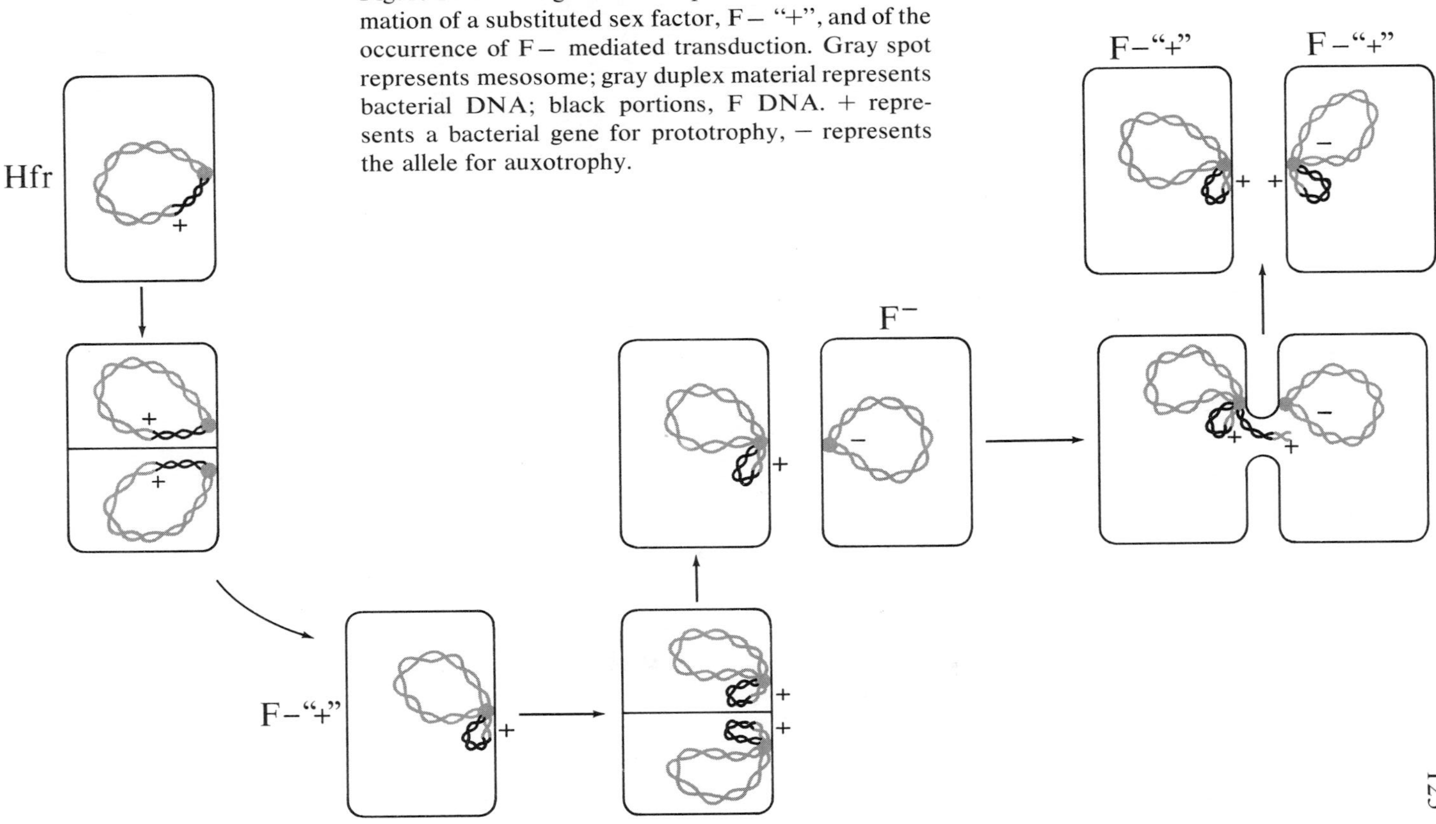

Figure 10-8. Diagrammatic representation of the formation of a substituted sex factor, F– "+", and of the occurrence of F– mediated transduction. Gray spot represents mesosome; gray duplex material represents bacterial DNA; black portions, F DNA. + represents a bacterial gene for prototrophy, – represents the allele for auxotrophy.

10·7 *Genetic recombination can take place between free and integrated episomes. The process seems to occur reciprocally and to involve a four-strand condition.*

When an F^- bacterium lysogenic for lambda is infected with an F-*lambda* particle, the recipient becomes diploid for lambda. Let us consider genetic recombination between the lambda in the bacterial chromosome and the lambda associated with F when they differ at three loci; one contains loci *A B C*, the other, *a b c*. Each of these partially-diploid cells is allowed to multiply to a large colony, and one cell from each is selected. The lambda of these bacteria are induced to form mature phage which are scored with respect to the three marker loci.

Among the recombinant progeny, reciprocal classes are found to be approximately equal in frequency; for example, the number of *A b c* recombinants equals the number of *a B C* recombinants. No more than two kinds of phage are recovered from any cell. Since one parental and one recombinant type are found in some cells, recombination must involve more than two "strands" (if we consider the DNA of each lambda to act as a single strand). We reach this conclusion since if one strand is recombinant, then the other must be also; and we could not obtain both parental and recombinant type phages from the same individual. These and other results suggest that each recombination involves two of four lambda strands. Although it is tempting to suppose that these strands are the four DNA strands of the two lambda duplexes, we have no evidence yet to support this hypothesis. Nevertheless, we can expect the same principle of strandedness to apply whenever recombination occurs between diploid loci of different bacterial chromosomes.

10·8 *Recombination between chromosomes may involve strand breakage, digestion, and repair.*

Some bacteria cannot integrate into their genetic material segments of chromosomes transduced by episomes. These bacteria also appear unable to repair the damage caused by pyrimidine dimerization (see Sections 7·5 and 7·6). Perhaps genetic recombination between chromosomes involves many of the same steps as occur after excision of dimers. Based on this assumption we can propose that such recombinations involve the following: (1) the breakage of a single DNA strand of a duplex, (2) the digestion of a sequence of nucleotides on one side of the breakage point, and (3) a DNA synthesis in which a genetically different complement is used as template to repair the deficiency, thereby producing a genetically hybrid, double-stranded DNA. The next replication of each duplex of this type would produce a "pure" recombinant and a "pure" nonrecombinant duplex.

Questions and Problems

10·1 *E. coli* tryptophan synthetase consists of two polypeptide chains. One chain, composed of 280 amino acids, normally has glycine at a particular position. In one mutant this glycine is replaced by glutamic acid; in another mutant, by arginine.

(a) Assuming that both changes from glycine are single transitions, determine from the *in vitro* codons the *in vivo* codons for all three amino acids.

(b) Rare recombinants obtained from crossing the two mutant strains are normal; that is, they carry the normal amino acid sequence. Using your answer to (a), state the position of exchange in the DNA.

10·2 Design an experiment to identify streptomycin-sensitive *E. coli* strains as Hfr or F^-, making use of the finding that exposure to streptomycin will prevent cell division but not chromosome transfer.

10·3 The chromosome of lambda is an open ring with a gene sequence *susA-susB-susJ-i-susQ-susR*, whereas lambda prophage has the open ring sequence *susJ-susB-susA-susR-susQ-i*. How can you correlate these two gene sequences? (See reference to Kaiser and Inman.)

10·4 Replication of unintegrated F, but not integrated F, is inhibited by exposing *E. coli* to acridine orange. Make use of this finding

(a) to obtain F^- from F^+ cells.

(b) to identify colonies as F^+, Hfr, or F^-.

10·5 How would you show that the rare F^+ males that transfer bacterial loci have first become Hfr males?

10·6 Compare the points of origin expected for Hfr lines derived from F, F-Lac^+, F-Lac^-, and F-Pro^+.

10·7 Why was it necessary that F be in a host other than *E. coli* to determine its chemical and physical characteristics by means of density gradient centrifugation?

10·8 How would you obtain haploid F^- Pro^+ from haploid F^- Pro^- *E. coli* by recombination without subjecting other loci in the F^- cell to recombination?

10·9 When Hfr males conjugate with F^- cells lysogenic for lambda, zygotes normally survive. When, however, Hfr males lysogenic for lambda conjugate with F^- nonlysogens, zygotes produced from matings that have lasted for almost two hours lyse due to the *zygotic induction* of lambda.

(a) How can you explain zygotic induction?

(b) How can you determine the locus of integrated lambda prophage?

10·10 Discuss the relative orientation of two F particles integrated into the same chromosome when all of the chromosome is transferred to an F^- cell.

10·11 In Section 10·7 we assume that the two strands that contain *A* in a recombinant bacterium do not remain in the same cell after its division. Is this assumption justified? Explain.

10·12 Does the molecular mechanism of genetic recombination postulated in Section 10·8 apply to genetic transformation? Explain.

10·13 Discuss the base sequences common both to F and the *E. coli* chromosome. Note that F contains one region (making up 10% of the particle) with a 44% GC content and another region (making up the bulk of the particle) with a 50% GC content.

10·14 In what way should Figure 10-8 be modified in the light of evidence that the deintegration which produces a substituted sex factor in an Hfr male parallels one which produces λdg in a lysogen?

References

Adelberg, E. A., and Pittard, J. 1965. Chromosome transfer in bacterial conjugation. Bacterial. Rev., 29: 161–172.

Gross, J. D., and Caro, L. G. 1966. DNA transfer in bacterial conjugation. J. Mol. Biol., 16: 269–284. (A semiconservative replica of the Hfr chromosome is sent into the F^- cell.)

Guest, J. R., and Yanofsky, C. 1966. Relative orientation of gene, messenger and polypeptide chain. Nature, Lond., 210: 799–802. (As revealed by intra-triplet and other recombinations).

Jacob, F., and Wollman, E. L. 1961. *Sexuality and the Genetics of Bacteria.* New York: Academic Press.

Jacob, F., and Wollman, E. L. 1961. Viruses and genes. Scient. Amer., 204 (No. 6): 92–107. Reprinted in *The Living Cell,* Kennedy, D. (Editor), San Francisco: W. H. Freeman, 1965. pp. 17–30.

Kaiser, A. D., and Inman, R. B. 1965. Cohesion and the biological activity of bacteriophage lambda DNA. J. Mol. Biol., 13: 78–91.

Lederberg, J., and Tatum, E. L. 1946. Gene recombination in *Escherichia coli.* Nature, Lond., 158: 558. Reprinted in *Classic Papers in Genetics,* Peters, J. A. (Editor), Englewood Cliffs, N.J.: Prentice-Hall, Inc., 1959, pp. 192–194.

Pauling, C., and Hanawalt, P. 1965. Nonconservative DNA replication in bacteria after thymine starvation. Proc. Nat. Acad. Sci., U.S., 54: 1728–1735.

Taylor, A. L., and Adelberg, E. A. 1960. Linkage analysis with very high frequency males of *Escherichia coli.* Genetics, 45: 1233–1243.

Taylor, A. L., and Thoman, M. S. 1964. The genetic map of *Escherichia coli* K-12. Genetics, 50: 659–677. Reprinted in *Papers on Bacterial Genetics, Second Edition,* Adelberg, E. A. (Editor), Boston: Little, Brown and Co., 1966, pp. 378–396.

CHAPTER 11

Recombination of Nuclear Chromosomes – Mitosis and Meiosis

We have noted that chromosomal replication is followed by an orderly distribution of genetic material to progeny in bacteria (and blue-green algae). In nucleated cells also special mechanisms of chromosome distribution have evolved: mitosis and meiosis. In this chapter we will study in some detail these two recombinational mechanisms for distributing chromosomes of a parent nucleus to its progeny.

11·1 *The DNA content of a nucleus doubles before nuclear division.*

Unlike the bacterial cell, a cell of a higher organism has its chromosomes bounded by a double-layered *nuclear membrane* during most of its life cycle. During this time, called *interphase* (Figure 11-1A), the cell passes through three successive stages: a period of growth, a period in which the DNA content of the nucleus doubles, and a period of more growth. After interphase the nucleus is ready for division to produce two daughter nuclei, each containing one half the presently-doubled amount of DNA.

Nuclear division is usually followed by cytoplasmic division in the formation of two complete daughter cells. The cytoplasmic components of a parent cell are often distributed unequally between daughter cells, but only rarely are the nuclear contents so distributed. For the nucleus does not simply separate into two parts; it undergoes a highly-ordered series of activities in order to divide – the process of *mitosis*.

11·2 *Mitosis is a spindle-using process in which both of the two daughter nuclei receive a copy of their parent's genetic information.*

During interphase the chromosomes are mostly unwound and, hence, are not seen as discrete bodies under the ordinary microscope. Among the first indications that the nucleus is preparing to divide is the appearance of a mass of thin, separate chromosomes (Figure 11-1B), some of which

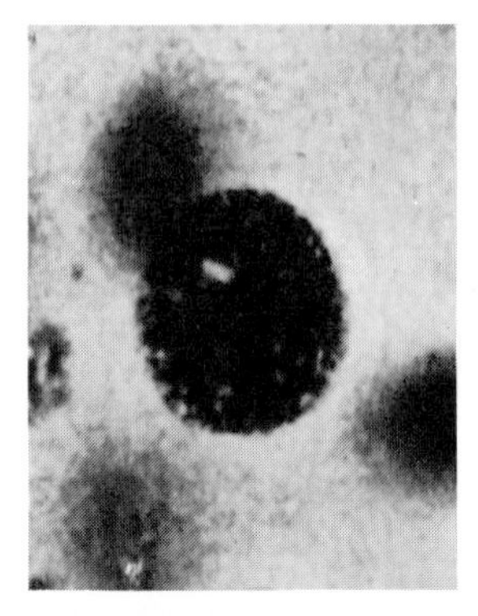

A. INTERPHASE

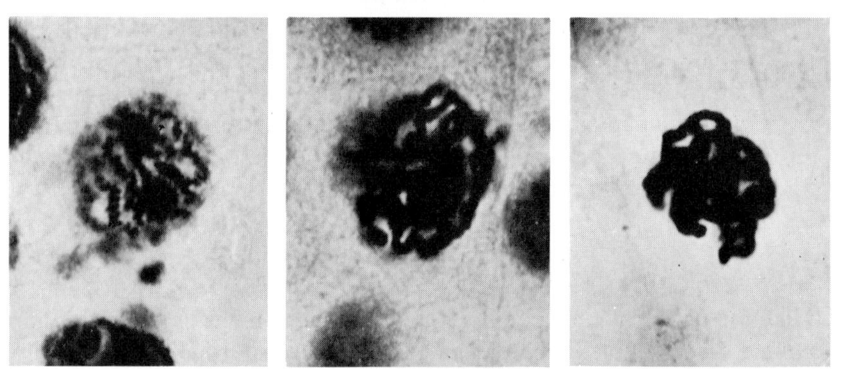

B. Early C. Middle D. Late

PROPHASE

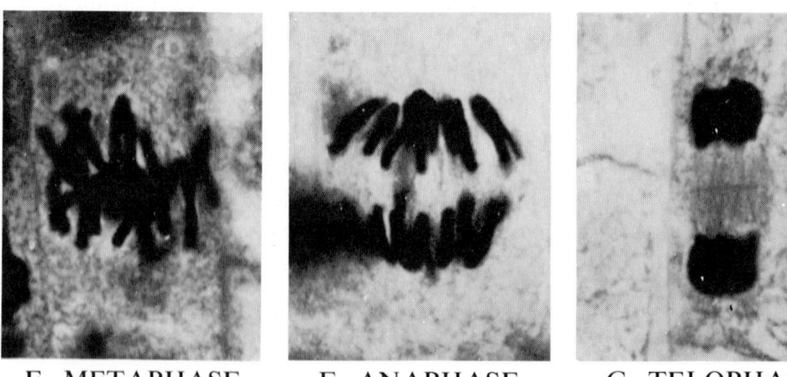

E. METAPHASE (Side View) F. ANAPHASE G. TELOPHASE

Figure 11-1. Mitosis in the onion root tip. (Courtesy of R. E. Cleland) (By permission of McGraw-Hill Book Co., Inc., from *Study Guide and Workbook for Genetics,* by I. H. Herskowitz, copyright 1960.)

are associated with nucleoli. In higher organisms each chromosome is visible as two threads, or *chromatids*. Each chromatid contains besides basic protein and RNA at least one duplex of DNA. The appearance of these chromosomes marks the start of *prophase,* the first stage of mitosis. As prophase continues, the chromatids of each chromosome become shorter and thicker and untwist from one another (Figure 11-1C); the nucleoli become smaller. By the end of prophase (Figure 11-1D) the nucleoli and nuclear membrane have disappeared, and the chromatids are seen as thick rods which move actively for the first time. Motility is not the property of the entire chromosome, however, but is restricted to a particular region called the *centromere.*

The centromeres become joined to fibers of the *spindle,* which has been forming throughout prophase. The completed spindle has a shape similar to that formed when corresponding fingertips are touched together and the hands are separated slightly. The wrists represent the poles of the spindle, and the fingers represent spindle fibers. Chromosomes migrate from whatever their position in the spindle region until each centromere comes to lie in a single plane perpendicular to the midpoint of the axis between the poles (corresponding to the plane determined by the points at which fingertips touch). This is the *equatorial plane* or *equator* of the spindle. The rest of each chromosome can assume essentially any position when all the centromeres have arrived at the equatorial plane. At this point mitosis has reached its middle phase, or *metaphase* (Figure 11-1E).

At metaphase and earlier stages, chromatids of a chromosome are attached to each other at or near the centromere, although elsewhere they are largely free. After metaphase they separate at the centromere, and the two daughter centromeres suddenly move apart, one going toward one pole of the spindle, the other toward the other pole. Once separated, the chromatids are called chromosomes. This stage in which the chromatids separate and move to opposite poles as chromosomes is called *anaphase* (Figure 11-1F).

When the chromosomes reach the poles, the last stage, *telophase,* begins (Figure 11-1G). The subsequent events appear to be the reverse of those during prophase: the spindle disintegrates, a new nuclear membrane is formed around the chromosomes, and nucleoli reappear. The chromosomes once more become thinner and longer and can be seen to consist of two slender threads wound about each other. Finally, as the chromosomes again become invisible, the nucleus enters *interphase* (Figure 11-1A).

From this description we see that mitosis is a mechanism for the exact distribution of previously replicated genetic material, a means of rearranging genetic information so that daughter cells have the same chromosomal constitution as their parents at an identical stage (Figure 11-2).

11·3 *For the chromosome number of a sexually-reproducing species to be maintained, a diploid chromosome number must first be made haploid. Fertilization can then restore the diploid chromosome number.*

The cells of different species frequently differ in the number of chromosomes per nucleus and in chromosome morphology. Chromosomes vary in size, stainability with various dyes, and position of the centromere. Most have a single centromere which is located subterminally, that is, not at an end, and which therefore separates the chromosome into two *arms*.

In sexually-reproducing higher organisms, chromosomes occur in pairs. (The members of a pair are called *homologous chromosomes* or *homologs,* and they assume their positions at mitotic metaphase independently of one another.) The number of chromosomes in a typical mitotic cell of the garden pea is seven pairs. Corn has ten pairs, the domesticated silkworm twenty-eight, and human beings twenty-three. Each species apparently has a characteristic number of chromosomes. But regardless of the number of chromosomes present in the fertilized egg, or zygote, the same number is usually found in every cell of a multicellular organism which has developed from the zygote by mitotic cell divisions.

If all nuclei divided by mitosis, a sex cell or *gamete* would contain the same number of chromosomes as every other cell, all of them derived from the same zygote. Consequently, the number of chromosomes per zygote would increase in successive generations, since the zygote is a combination of two gametes. An increase in genetic material does not occur from one generation to the next, however; all individuals of a species have a characteristic quantity of genetic material. Human gametes do not contain the paired, or diploid, chromosome number – 23 pairs – but (usually) 23 chromosomes in an unpaired, or haploid, condition. Fertilization consequently restores the diploid chromosome constitution, since each gamete (sperm from the father and egg from the mother) provides a haploid set of chromosomes. Clearly, then, all cell divisions cannot be mitotic; the cell must have a way of reducing the number of chromosomes from diploid to haploid. This reduction process is *meiosis.*

11·4 *In meiosis a nucleus begins with a doubled DNA content and by means of two successive spindle-using divisions gives rise to four meiotic products, each containing one-quarter of the initial DNA.*

In *prophase of the first meiotic division* (or *prophase I*), as in mitotic prophase, each chromosome contains the doubled amount of DNA (Figure 11-2). Near the beginning of prophase I, the members of each pair of homologous chromosomes synapse, that is, pair point for corresponding point, to form a bundle of four chromatids. The chromosomes proceed as

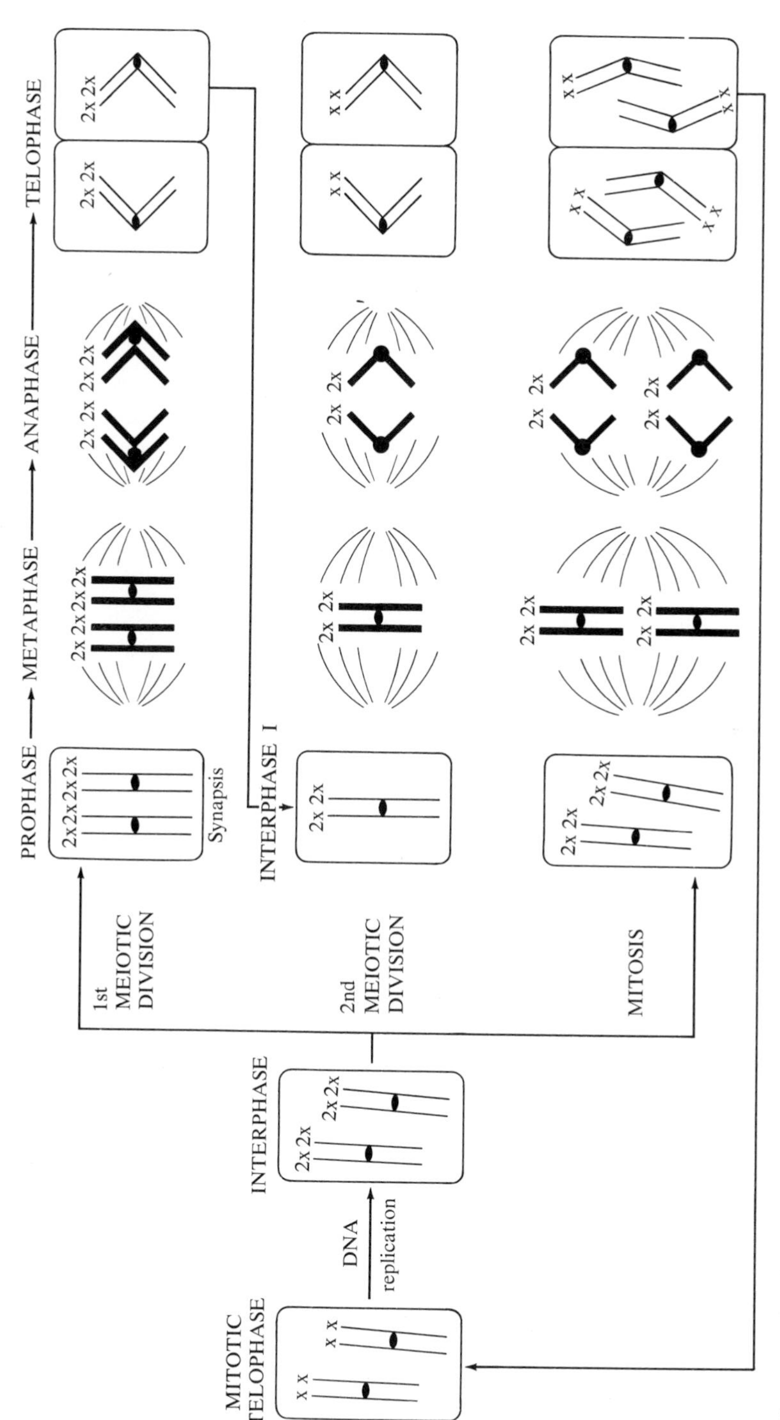

Figure 11-2. Diagrammatic representation of mitosis and meiosis showing the chromatids (cytologically visible threads within a chromosome) ordinarily detectable. The fate of one pair of chromosomes and its DNA content are traced. Each mitotic telophase chromatid contains one or more duplexes whose combined DNA content is represented as x. Mitosis and the second meiotic division produce daughter nuclei with the same number of chromosomes as their parent nucleus, each chromatid containing the normal (x) amount of DNA. The first meiotic division produces telophase I nuclei with the haploid (single, or unpaired) number of chromosomes, each chromatid still containing the doubled (2x) amount of DNA. No DNA replication occurs in interphase I.

pairs to the equator of the spindle for *metaphase I*. At *anaphase I* the members of a pair separate and go to opposite poles, each chromosome still containing its doubled amount of DNA. In *interphase I* after the first telophase, no DNA synthesis takes place.

The *second meiotic division* begins at various times for different organisms and is essentially an ordinary mitotic division. In *prophase II* each chromosome proceeds independently to the equator for *metaphase II*. At *anaphase II* the two chromatids separate and go to opposite poles of the spindle as chromosomes, each containing half as much DNA as earlier. In *telophase II* each chromosome unwinds and can be seen to consist of two chromatids.

Although mitosis involves an alternation of chromosome duplication and separation, meiosis involves one duplication followed by two separations. As a result, the diploid chromosome condition is reduced to haploid in meiosis; the diploid number is maintained in mitosis. Let us now consider meiosis in greater detail (Figure 11-3).

Prophase I is of long duration as compared to mitotic prophase, and can be divided into several stages.

(1) *Leptonema* (thin thread). Soon after interphase, the chromosomes appear long and thin, more so than in the earliest prophase of mitosis.

(2) *Zygonema* (joined thread). Pairs of thin threads synapse with each other. This pairing is very exact, not merely between homologous chromosomes, but between exactly corresponding points as well. Synapsis proceeds zipperwise until the two chromosomes are completely apposed.

(3) *Pachynema* (thick thread). The apposition of homologs becomes so tight that it is difficult to identify two separate chromosomes.

(4) *Diplonema* (double thread). The tight pairing of pachynema is relaxed, so each pair of synapsed chromosomes can be seen to contain four threads, two chromatids per chromosome. A pair of synapsed chromosomes is called a *bivalent* (composed of two *univalents*) if we are referring to chromosomes. But it is called a *tetrad* (composed of two *dyads* or four *monads*) if we refer to chromatids.

Although the chromatids in a tetrad separate from each other in pairs in some places, they are all still in close contact with each other in other places. Each place where the four chromatids are still held together is called a *chiasma* (plural, *chiasmata*) (Figure 11-4A). In a chiasma the two chromatids that synapse to make a pair on one side of the point of contact separate at that point and synapse with different partners on the other side of the contact point (Figure 11-4B). The occurrence of a chiasma assures that the univalents are held together. (Chiasma-like configurations are relatively rare during mitosis.)

As diplonema continues, the chromosomes become shorter and thicker, more compact than at any time in mitosis.

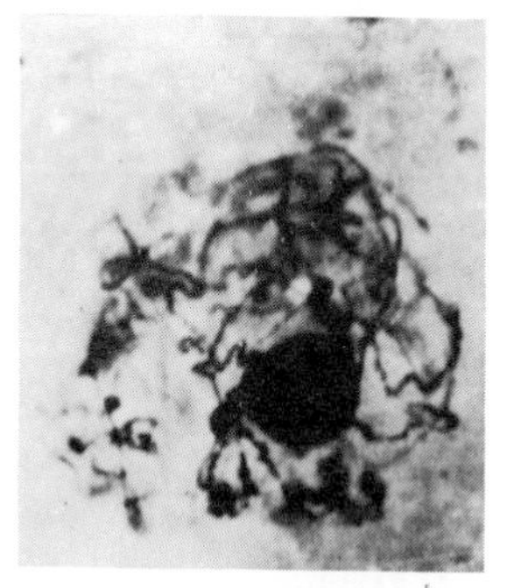

LEPTONEMA

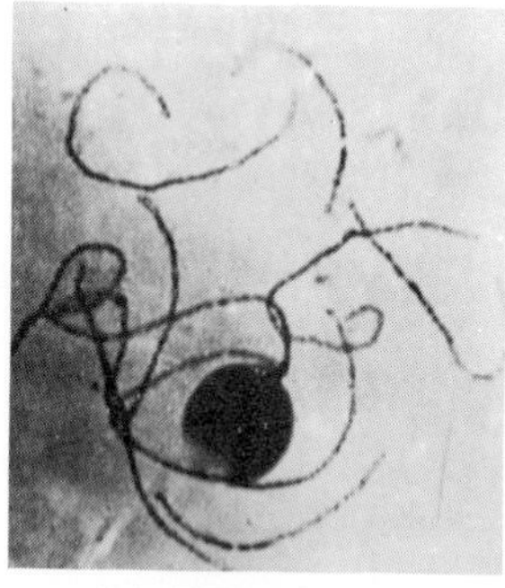

PACHYNEMA

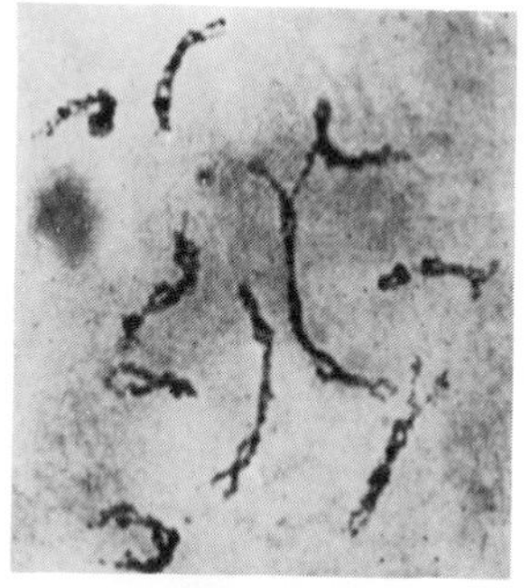

DIPLONEMA

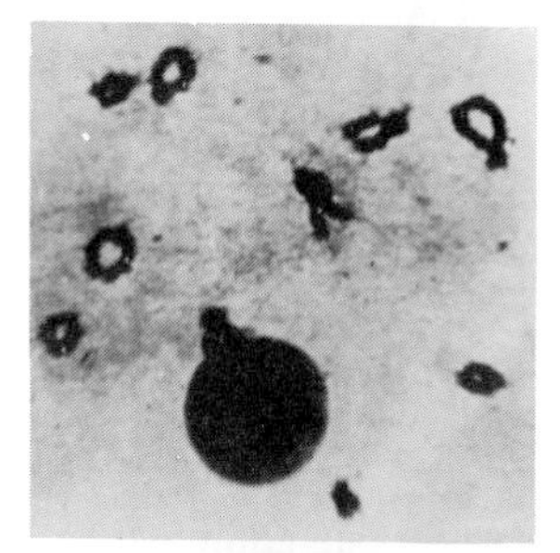

DIAKINESIS

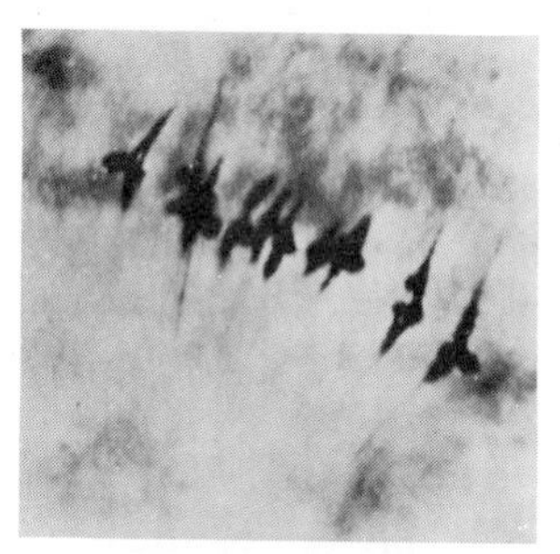

METAPHASE I

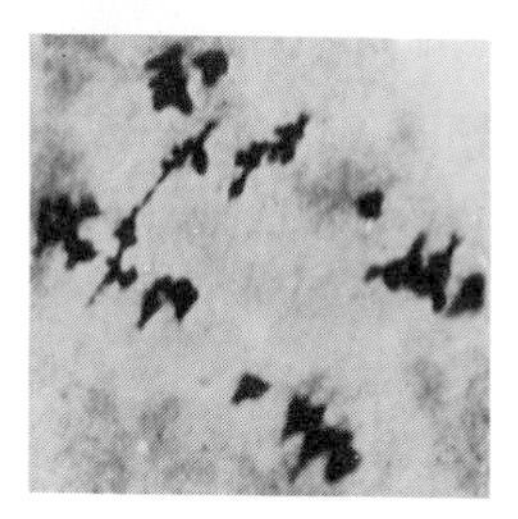

ANAPHASE I (Middle)

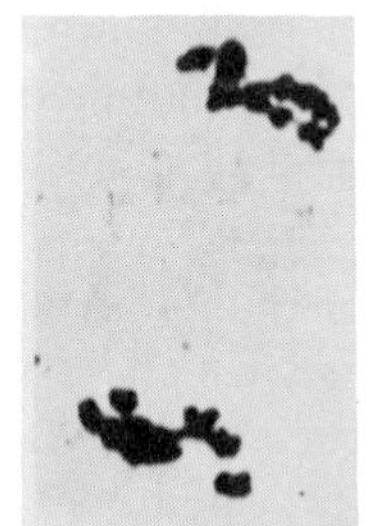

ANAPHASE I (Late)

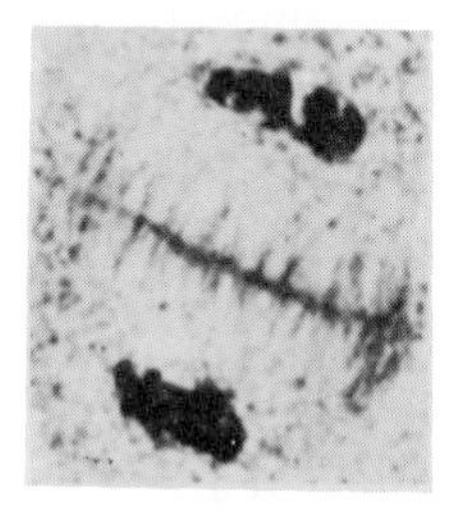

TELOPHASE I

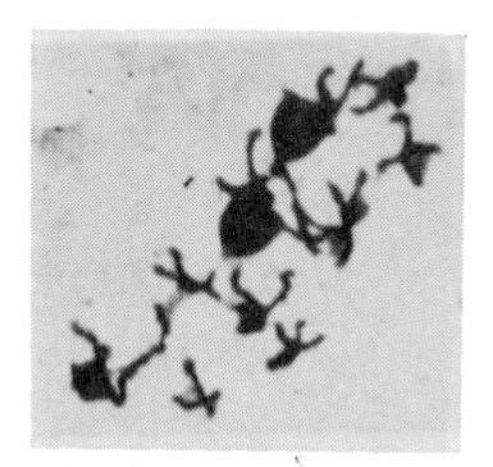

PROPHASE II (Early)

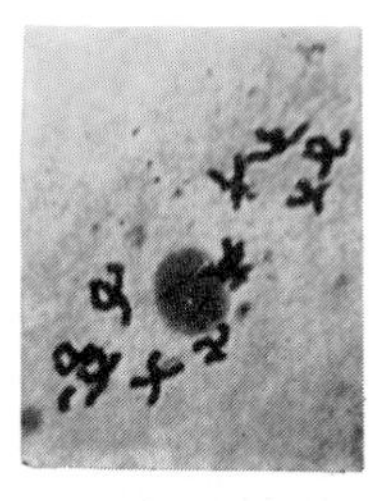

PROPHASE II (Late)

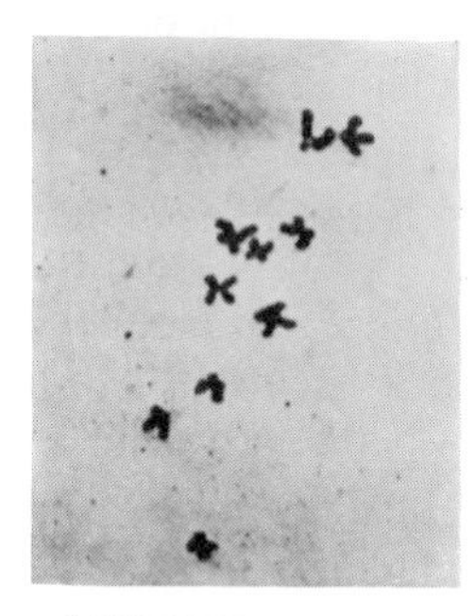

METAPHASE II

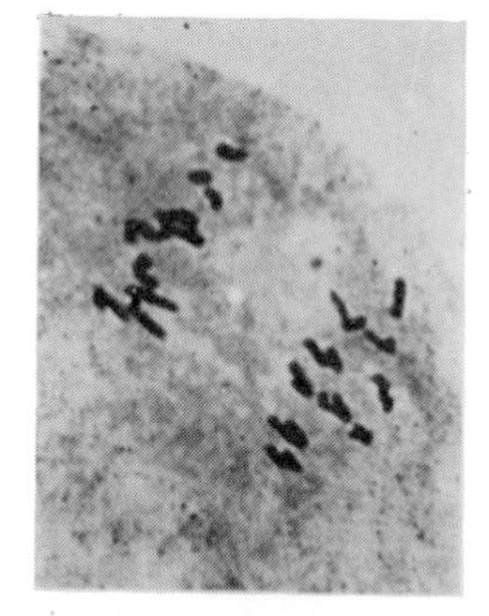

ANAPHASE II

Figure 11-3. Meiosis in corn. Anaphase I (Middle) shows one bivalent whose univalents are delayed in separation because they are still held together by a chiasma. Prophase II and later stages show the events taking place in one of the two nuclei produced by the first meiotic division. (Courtesy of M. M. Rhoades)

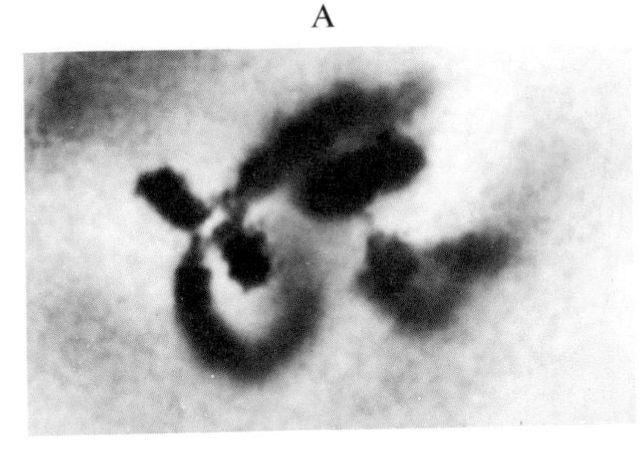

Figure 11-4. Lily diplonema showing chromatids (1–4) with different synaptic partners on different sides of a chiasma. (Courtesy of R. E. Cleland)

(5) In some animals, especially during the formation of female gametes, diplonema is followed by a *diffuse* (or *growth*) stage, in which the nucleus and chromosomes revert to their appearance in a nondividing cell. During this stage a great amount of cytoplasmic growth takes place. In human beings this stage may last for decades, after which the rest of meiosis occurs and mature eggs ready for ovulation are produced.

(6) *Diakinesis* is characterized by the maximal contraction of diplonema chromosomes, or by maximal recontraction of chromosomes which have just been in the diffuse stage. By the end of diakinesis, nucleoli and the nuclear membrane have disappeared and the spindle has formed. Thus ends prophase I.

Metaphase I results from movement of the chromosomes to the equatorial plane as in mitosis, except that they move as bivalents whose tetrad of chromatids is held together by chiasmata. Between diplonema and metaphase I the chiasmata move toward and sometimes off the end of the chromosome arms, that is, away from the centromere, especially if the bivalent is short. As a consequence of this *chiasma terminalization*, fewer chiasmata are ordinarily seen at metaphase I than at diplonema.

During anaphase I the univalents of each bivalent separate from each other at the region of the centromere and proceed to opposite poles of the spindle. This movement completely terminalizes all remaining chiasmata. In telophase I the two daughter nuclei are formed; and interphase I follows. This interphase is of various lengths in different organisms.

Each daughter nucleus then undergoes the second meiotic division, which is very much like mitosis. In prophase II each univalent, a chromo-

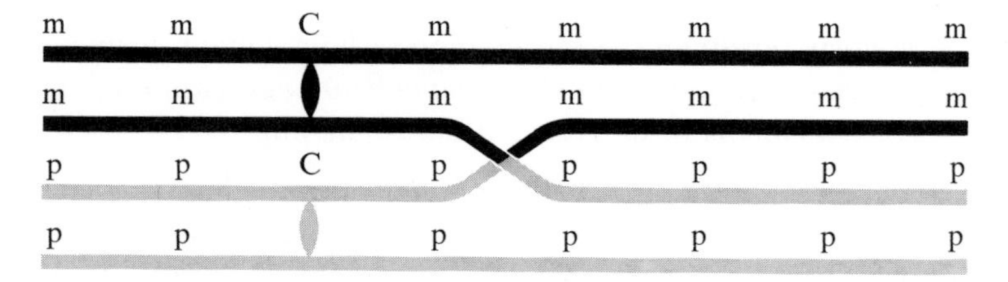

Figure 11-5. Chiasma showing paternal (p) and maternal (m) composition of strands. Compare with Figure 11-4B. C represents a centromere.

some with two chromatids, contracts; at metaphase II each lines up at the equator of the spindle independently. In anaphase II the members of a dyad separate and go to opposite poles as monads, each now a single chromosome which after unwinding is seen to consist of two chromatids. Because two nuclei undergo this second division, four nuclei are formed by the end of telophase II.

11·5 *During meiosis, recombination can occur between maternal and paternal chromatids in a tetrad.*

At some time between the beginning of meiosis and diplonema, an exchange of genetic material can occur between maternal and paternal homologs at the tetrad stage. As a result, two of the four chromatids become "hybrid," that is, they now contain DNA segments from different parents: one recombinant chromatid, for example, is paternal-maternal in composition, whereas the other is maternal-paternal. We should note in Figure 11-4B that when such an exchange has occurred, a chiasma will be seen at diplonema if corresponding paternally-derived (as well as maternally-derived) sections of chromatids remain synapsed. Although some of these exchanges may fail to produce a visible chiasma later, we can in general take every chiasma to be cytological evidence of a prior exchange within a tetrad. We should keep in mind, however, that because of chiasma terminalization the position of a chiasma may be distal to the point of exchange. Henceforth we will assume that chiasma terminalization does not occur during diplonema, so the position of a chiasma may be equated with a point of exchange. Consequently, a tetrad with one chiasma would contain chromatids with the constitutions shown in Figure 11-5. We see that after a single exchange, one chromatid remains entirely maternal and one entirely paternal; but the other two are recombinant strands. Although only two of the four chromatids are involved in a given chiasma, a tetrad usually contains several chiasmata. Thus, it is likely that each of the four chromatids of a tetrad undergoes exchange, and is therefore a recombinant strand.

11·6 *Meiosis results in the segregation of homologous segments of a chromosome pair, and the independent segregation of homologous segments of different chromosome pairs.*

Since a postmeiotic nucleus usually contains only one homolog of a given pair of chromosomes in the premeiotic nucleus, we can see that chromosome segregation has occurred and reduced the chromosome number from diploid to haploid. Homologous segments in a chromosome pair, therefore, must have also segregated.

The particular poles to which homologous segments of a single chromosome pair migrate are determined by the orientation of the centromere of the bivalent at metaphase I and of the centromeres of the univalents at metaphase II. Since each bivalent or univalent is equally likely to become oriented (relative to the poles) in one of two possible ways, the segregation of homologous segments of one chromosome pair will take place independently of the segregation of homologous segments of another chromosome pair. For example, if a corresponding maternal and paternal segment of one bivalent is labeled 1m 1p and that of another bivalent 2m 2p, at the completion of meiosis the four different haploid combinations of these segments – 1m 2m, 1m 2p, 1p 2m, 1p 2p – will be equally frequent. We should note that 50% of these combinations of unpaired segments are parental combinations (1m 2m, 1p 2p) and 50% are nonparental combinations, or recombinations (1m 2p, 1p 2m). We should also note that since the orientation of centromeres is uninfluenced by the number and location of chiasmata in a bivalent, the above principles of segregation apply whether or not homologous segments have been switched in position by prior intratetrad exchange.

11·7 *In sexually-reproducing organisms, the life cycle involves a diploid-haploid-diploid chromosome cycle.*

Since the diploid number of chromosomes is maintained generation after generation in sexually-reproducing organisms, we expect meiosis to occur at some time in the life cycle of such individuals. In most animals meiosis comprises the last two nuclear divisions before the mature sperm or egg is produced. In plants, meiosis usually occurs earlier. But the process itself is essentially the same for both plants and animals. Let us now consider the life cycles of three multicellular organisms which have been especially useful in genetic investigations.

1. *Drosophila melanogaster*

The adult stage of *D. melanogaster,* commonly called the fruit fly, is shown in Figure 11-6. Although its size depends upon nutritional and other environmental factors, an adult is usually 2 to 3 mm long, with females slightly larger than males. The wild-type fly has a gray body color

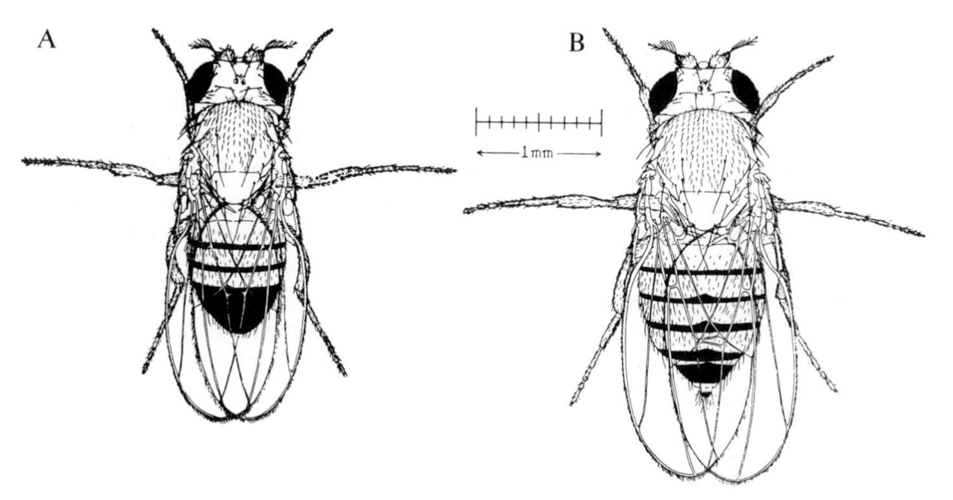

Figure 11-6. Normal (wild-type) *Drosophila melanogaster* male (A) and female (B). (Drawn by E. M. Wallace)

and dull red compound eyes. Males are readily distinguished from females by dark sex combs on their anterior pair of legs, by an abdomen which terminates dorsally in a single broad black band instead of a series of bands, and by a penis and claspers instead of an ovipositor at the ventral end of the abdomen.

The adult male is diploid and has a pair of testes in which *spermatogonia* are produced by mitosis. A spermatogonial cell which enters meiosis is called a *primary spermatocyte*. The first meiotic division produces two *secondary spermatocytes;* the second meiotic division, four haploid *spermatids*. Each spermatid differentiates without further division into a *spermatozoon,* or sperm cell. Thus, for each (diploid) primary spermatocyte entering meiosis, four haploid sperm are produced at the completion of *spermatogenesis*. Sperm are stored in the Drosophila male until they are ejaculated into the vagina of the female, from which they swim into the female's sperm storage organs, a pair of spermathecae and a coiled ventral receptacle.

The adult female (also diploid) has a pair of ovaries, each composed of a series of egg tubes, or ovarioles. At one end of the ovariole are diploid *oogonia*. By four successive mitotic divisions each oogonium produces a cluster of 16 cells, one of which enters meiosis as a *primary oocyte* while the others serve as *nurse cells* for the maturing oocyte. As the oocyte grows it passes down the ovariole, into the oviduct and then the uterus. When it reaches the uterus, the egg is usually no further advanced than metaphase of the first meiotic division. At this time, sperm stored in the female are released to fertilize the egg, after which the first meiotic division continues. The two *secondary oocyte* nuclei produce four haploid nuclei. Three of these become *polar nuclei* and degenerate; the remaining one becomes the haploid *egg* nucleus, completing the process of *oogenesis.* Since the female fruit fly stores hundreds of sperm and uses them a few at a time, a single mating can yield hundreds of progeny.

After fertilization (which restores diplody), embryonic development proceeds for about a day (at 25°C), until the larva hatches from the egg. Four more days and two moults later, the mature larva becomes a pupa; and about four days later the young adult, or imago, ecloses (hatches) from the pupa case. Although mating usually occurs during the first 24 hours of adult life, the female begins to lay eggs at some time in the second day. Overall, the generation time is about ten days. Adults can live up to ten weeks, during which a female can lay several thousand eggs.

2. *Zea mays*

Corn, like the bean and the garden pea, usually has both male and female sex organs on the same plant. Since the diploid corn plant produces male and female spores, *microspores* and *megaspores,* respectively, it constitutes the *sporophyte* stage of the life cycle (Figure 11-7). Microspores are produced in tassels at the end of the stem. Here diploid microspore mother cells, or *microsporocytes,* undergo meiosis to produce four haploid microspores (A), each of which develops into a *pollen grain* (B).

Since a haploid microspore gives rise to haploid gametes, their appearance marks the beginning and end of the male *gametophyte* stage. The haploid microspore nucleus divides mitotically to produce two haploid nuclei. One of these does not divide again and becomes the *pollen tube,* or *vegetative nucleus.* The other nucleus divides mitotically once more, so that the gametophyte contains three haploid nuclei (C). The two nuclei that are formed last function as *sperm nuclei* (D, K).

Near the base of the upper branches of the corn plant are clusters of pistils, each containing one diploid megaspore mother cell, or *megasporocyte.* (The styles of the pistils later become the silks.) The megasporocyte undergoes meiosis to produce four haploid nuclei (E), three of which degenerate (F). The remaining megaspore nucleus divides mitotically (G) as do its daughter and granddaughter nuclei, so that eight haploid nuclei result (I). In the *embryo sac* (J) three of the eight nuclei aggregate at the apex and divide to form *antipodal nuclei.* Two of the eight move to the center to become *polar nuclei,* and three move to the base of the embryo sac to form two *synergid nuclei* and one *egg nucleus.* The pollen tube grows down the style to the embryo sac, where one sperm nucleus fertilizes the egg nucleus (K, L) to produce a diploid (2N) nucleus; the other sperm nucleus fuses with the two polar nuclei to produce a triploid (3N) nucleus. With the occurrence of this *double fertilization* the sporophyte generation is initiated. Mitotic division of the diploid nucleus (L) produces

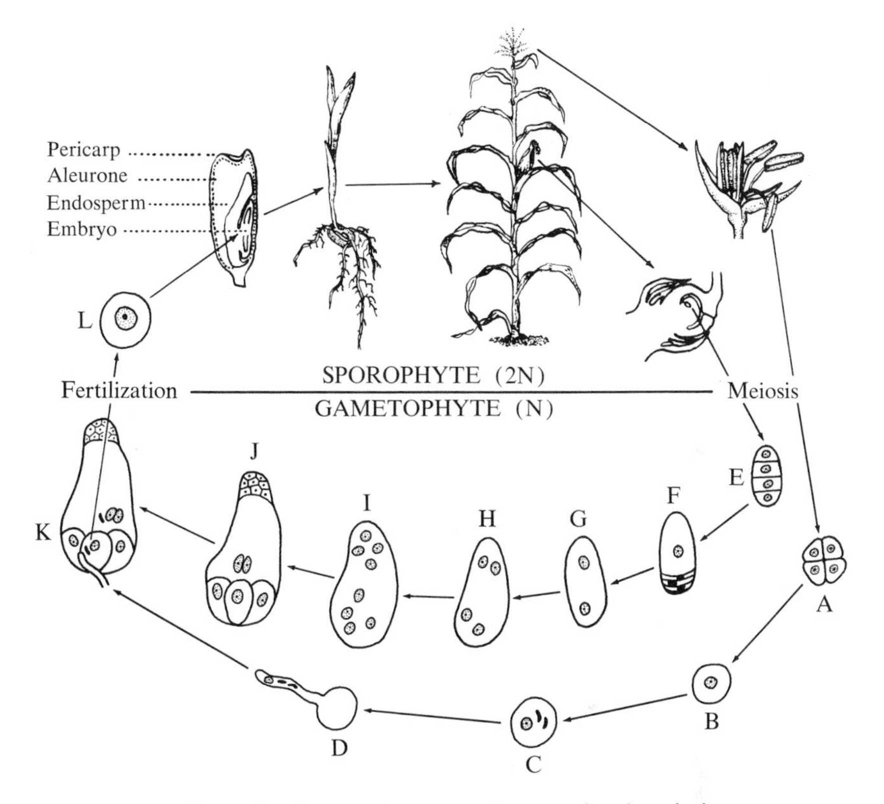

Figure 11-7. Life cycle of corn, *Zea mays*. See text for description.

the embryo, while the triploid nucleus develops into the *endosperm*. The endosperm is later used to nourish the embryo and seedling. The outer surface of the kernel is the *pericarp*, diploid tissue derived from the maternal sporophyte. In other words, the pericarp of a corn kernel is produced by the sporophyte of one generation and the remaining tissue by the sporophyte of the next generation. Development from embryo sac to mature kernel takes about eight weeks, whereas development from kernel to mature sporophyte requires nearly four months.

3. *Neurospora crassa*

Neurospora ("nerve spore") is a bread mold which, in its haploid vegetative stage, is composed of threads, or *hyphae*, which intertwine to form a mat, the *mycelium*. The hyphae branch and fuse with one another at various points. Since the cell walls which partition a hypha into cells are incomplete, the cytoplasm of the filament is continuous, and each hyphal cell is multinucleate.

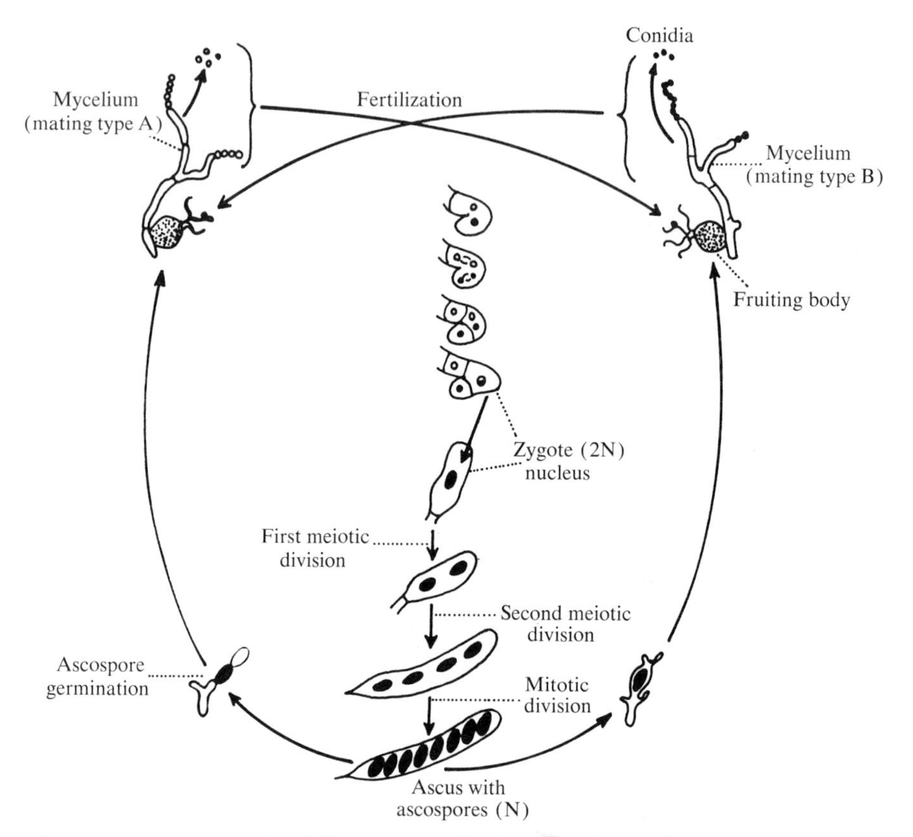

Figure 11-8. Life cycle of Neurospora. See text for description.

Cultures can be propagated asexually either by spores (*conidia*) which contain one or several haploid nuclei, or by transplantation of pieces of mycelium. Sexual reproduction (Figure 11-8) requires the participation of molds of different mating type which produce *fruiting bodies*. A haploid nucleus of one mating type divides mitotically a number of times in a fruiting body of the opposite mating type. Haploid nuclei of both mating types fuse to produce diploid zygotic nuclei. Each of these nuclei then undergoes two meiotic divisions, which result in four haploid nuclei; each haploid nucleus divides once mitotically to form a total of eight haploid nuclei. Next, the cytoplasm and nuclei are partitioned into eight haploid, ovoid bodies, *ascospores*, which are contained in a thin-walled sac, the *ascus*. The mature fruiting body may contain 300 asci, from which ascospores are released and carried in the air. Upon germination the haploid ascospore divides mitotically, and grows, producing the mycelium. Sometimes the hyphae of two different strains (of the same or of different mating type) will fuse to form a *heterocaryon*, in which hyphal cells contain nuclei of both strains.

Questions and Problems

11·1 List the similarities and differences between mitosis and meiosis.

11·2 Draw a single chiasma between two homologs, if they are
(a) both rods;
(b) one rod and one ring;
(c) both rings.
Indicate the four meiotic products for each case.

11·3 In light of your answer to the previous question, what can you conclude about the size and shape of a chromosome and its survival in organisms that undergo meiosis?

11·4 How many bivalents are present at metaphase I in man? Corn? The silkworm? The garden pea?

11·5 The *Drosophila melanogaster* female has a diploid chromosome number of eight. What proportion of its gametes receive centromeres that are all paternally-derived? All maternally-derived? Are all the gametes chromosomal recombinants? Explain.

11·6 By using a microscope, how can you distinguish mitotic prophase from mitotic telophase?

11·7 What recombinational consequences would you expect if a chromosome
(a) lost its centromere?
(b) had two centromeres?
(c) had one extremely long arm?

11·8 Design an experiment that shows chromosomal DNA replicates in interphase, not in prophase.

11·9 Chromosomes have been reported to be attached to the nuclear membrane (see Sved, J. A., Genetics, 53: 747–756, 1966). Assuming that this observation is valid, in what way are the chromosomes of nucleated and nonnucleated cells similar?

11·10 Since the mechanism of chromosome distribution to progeny works efficiently in the absence of a spindle in bacteria, of what advantage is a spindle to other organisms?

11·11 What evidence can you cite that the chromosomes are not digested during interphase?

11·12 Name three mechanisms of chromosomal recombination involving nucleated cells. State what the genetic recombination is in each case.

11·13 Give examples of chromosomal recombination in nucleated cells involving the
(a) primary,
(b) secondary,
(c) tertiary, and
(d) quaternary
structures of DNA.

References

Brachet, J., and Mirsky, A. E. (Editors) 1961. (Vol. 3) *The Cell, Meiosis and Mitosis.* New York: Academic Press.

De Robertis, E. D. P., Nowinski, W. W., and Saez, F. A. 1965. *Cell Biology.* Philadelphia: W. B. Saunders Co.

Grell, R. F. 1962. A new hypothesis on the nature and sequence of meiotic events in the female of *Drosophila melanogaster.* Proc. Nat. Acad. Sci., U.S., 48: 165–172. (Exchange pairing – leading to exchange between chromatids of homologs – precedes distributive pairing – leading to movement as tetrads.)

Schrader, F. 1953. *Mitosis: the Movement of Chromosomes in Cell Division.* New York: Columbia University Press.

Salzman, N. P., Moore, D. E., and Mendelsohn, J. 1966. Isolation and characterization of human metaphase chromosomes. Proc. Nat. Acad. Sci., U.S., 56: 1449–1456.

Sparvoli, E., Gay, H., and Kaufmann, B. P. 1964. Chromosome organization in staminate-hair cells of *Tradescantia paludosa.* Genetics, 50: 288.

Swanson, C. P. 1964. *The Cell, Second Edition,* Englewood Cliffs, N.J.: Prentice-Hall, Inc.

CHAPTER 12

Recombination of Nuclear Genes – Segregation and Sex-Linkage

In the last chapter we considered the recombination of chromosomes and chromosome segments resulting from mitosis, meiosis, and fertilization. We shall now study the consequences of these and other chromosomal recombinations with regard to the genes which the chromosomes contain.

12·1 *The members of a gene pair segregate during meiosis.*

Because homologous segments of a pair of chromosomes segregate during meiosis, so do the genes they contain. Thus, if the members of a chromosome pair carry different alleles at a particular locus, a single haploid meiotic product ordinarily will carry either one allele or the other.

For example, when a diploid parent of *A a* genotype undergoes meiosis, the chance is 50% that a gamete will contain *A* and 50% that it will contain *a*. Consequently, we will obtain equal numbers of both gametes if the sample of gametes is sufficiently large. If the heterozygous parent, *A a*, is mated with a homozygous parent, *a a*, then half the resulting zygotes will be *A a* and half will be *a a*, since the homozygous parent produces only *a* gametes. If, however, the other parent is also heterozygous, random fertilizations between the *A* and *a* gametes of each parent will result in zygotes of three different genotypes: *A A*, *A a*, and *a a*, in the relative proportion of 1:2:1 (see Figure 12-1).

12·2 *The members of gene pairs located in different chromosome pairs segregate independently of each other during meiosis.*

If a second pair of chromosomes contains the alleles *B* and *b* (Figure 12-2), the parent is a *dihybrid,* that is, a heterozygote for two gene pairs. As we noted previously, different pairs of chromosomes arrive at metaphase I independently of each other, and their constituent parts can as-

PARENTS	Aa × Aa
GAMETES	$\frac{1}{2}$A, $\frac{1}{2}$a $\frac{1}{2}$A, $\frac{1}{2}$a
ZYGOTES	$\frac{1}{4}$AA, $\frac{1}{2}$Aa, $\frac{1}{4}$aa

Figure 12-1. Zygotes produced from a monohybrid cross.

sume several different arrangements relative to each other at metaphase. If, as in Case A, no chiasma (hence, no exchange) occurs between the centromere and gene pair *A a* and between the centromere and gene pair *B b*, four genetically different meiotic products will occur with equal frequency, since alignments I and II are equally likely. Identical results are obtained either when a chiasma occurs in one tetrad but not the other (Case B), or when a chiasma occurs in both tetrads (Case C). Both in Cases C1 and C2 the dyads can become oriented with respect to the poles in four equally likely arrangements at metaphase II with the same net result: four equally frequent types of gametes. Regardless of chiasma formation, therefore, the independent segregation of homologous segments of different chromosome pairs guarantees the independent segregation of the different gene pairs they contain.

According to the preceding discussion, the *A a B b* (diploid) parent produces (haploid) gametes of four types with the following frequencies: $\frac{1}{4}$ *A B*:$\frac{1}{4}$ *A b*:$\frac{1}{4}$ *a B*:$\frac{1}{4}$ *a b*. If the other parent is an identical dihybrid, random fertilization will produce diploid zygotes with nine possible genotypes. These genotypes and their relative frequencies are given in Figure 12-3.

Let us look at one particular zygote, *A a B b*, which arose, say, from *A B* and *a b* gametes. It, too, will produce gametes eventually – some of which will contain parental combinations (*A B* and *a b*), while others contain new combinations (*A b* and *a B*). When gene pairs segregate independently, parental and nonparental gametic combinations occur with equal frequency.

12·3 *In many higher organisms the two sexes differ in the morphology of one pair of chromosomes. The morphologically distinct X and Y chromosomes are called sex chromosomes.*

In *Drosophila melanogaster* three of the four chromosome pairs seen at mitotic metaphase (Figure 12-4) appear very similar in the male and female. The fourth pair of a male is, however, quite different from the female's fourth pair, whose members are essentially identical. One member of the male pair looks like the female's type and is called an *X chromosome;* but the other has a distinctive appearance and is called the *Y chromosome.* The Y is present, therefore, once in a male and not at all in a female. Not only in Drosophila but in human beings and all other mammals as well, the male has XY *sex chromosomes* and the female, XX.

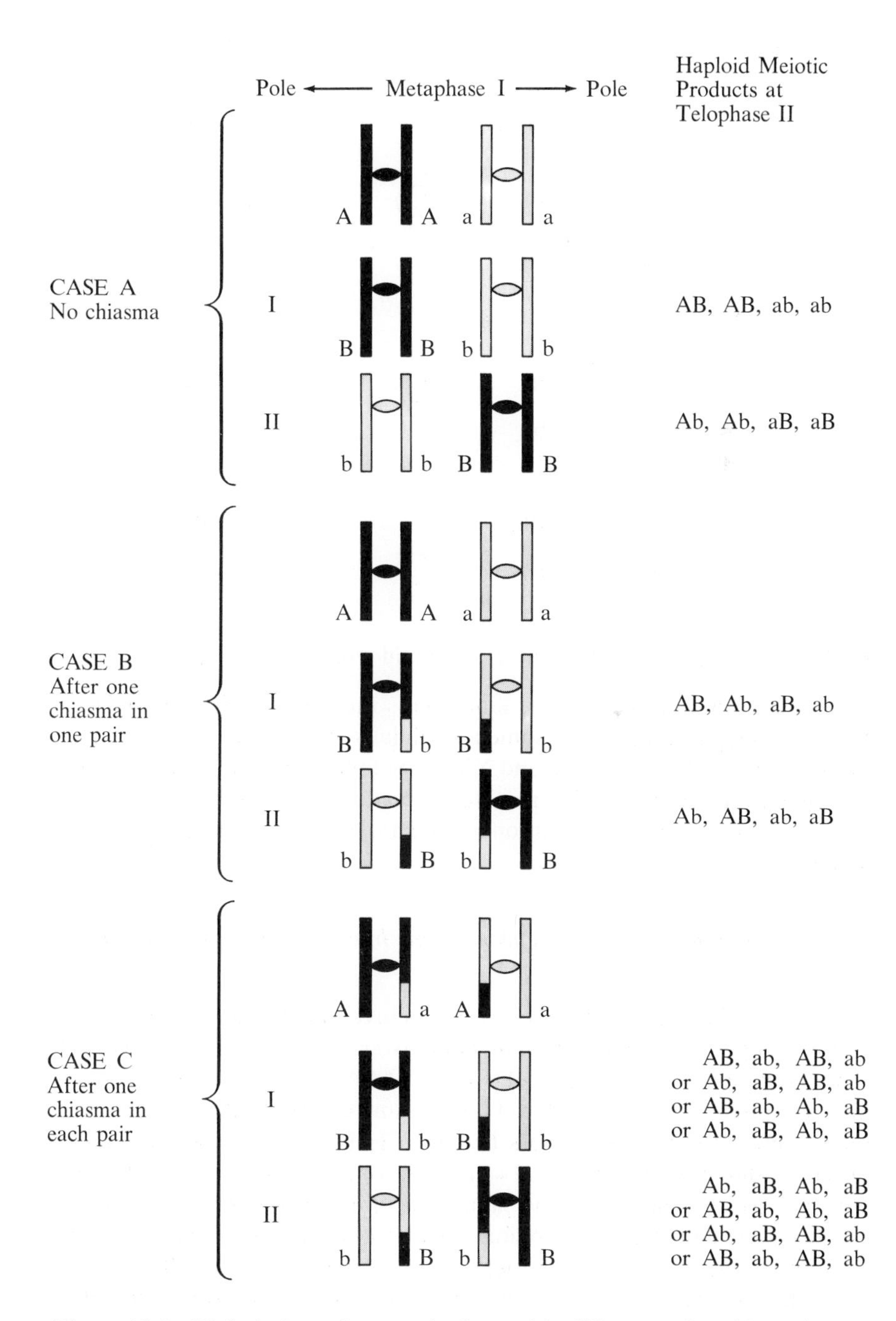

Figure 12-2. Meiotic fate of gene pairs located in different pairs of homologous chromosomes. Note that when all alternatives in Case CI (or CII) are considered, $AB = ab = Ab = aB$ with respect to frequency.

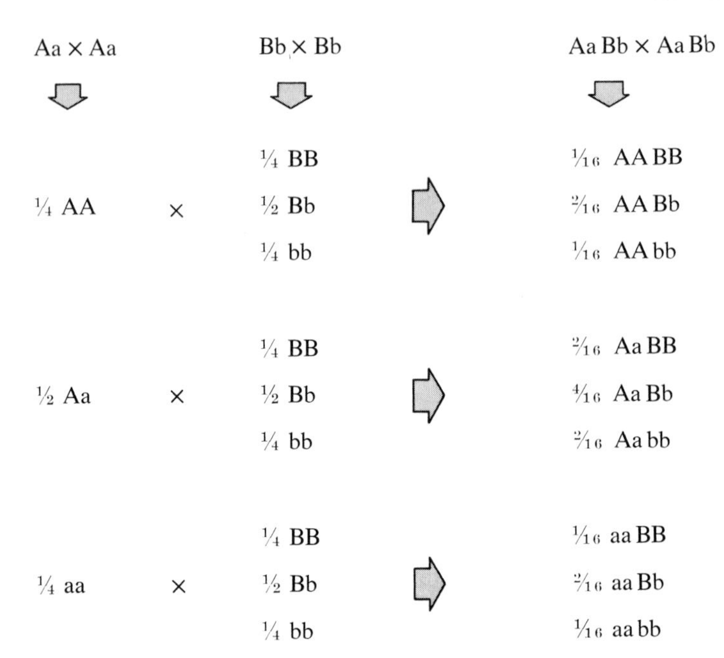

Figure 12-3. Zygotes produced from a dihybrid cross.

In some other organisms, the situation is the reverse. For example, in birds, moths, butterflies, and some amphibians and reptiles, the sex chromosomes are XX in the male and XY in the female. For both kinds of sex determination, however, different sexes make gametes which contain X or Y sex chromosomes in addition to the *autosomes,* the non-sex chromosomes.

12·4 *Some genes in the X chromosome have no loci in the Y chromosome.*

Let us consider the results of two crosses involving the dull red (w^+) and white (w) eye color alleles in *D. melanogaster.* If we cross pure lines, dull red ♀ (female) by white ♂ (male) (Figure 12-5A) gives rise to *first generation* (F_1) progeny that are dull red females and dull red males only. On the other hand, the reciprocal cross (Figure 12-5B) white ♀ by dull red ♂, produces dull red daughters and *white* sons only. Although the first cross gave rise to sons that are of the same eye color as daughters, the reciprocal cross yielded different-looking sons and daughters. If the locus for white eye color were in an autosome, we would expect no difference in eye color among the F_1 progeny of the reciprocal cross, since the autosomal loci would have segregated independently of the sex chromosomes, and sons and daughters would have had the same eye color. Because autosomal genes always give the same results for sons as for daughters, the w

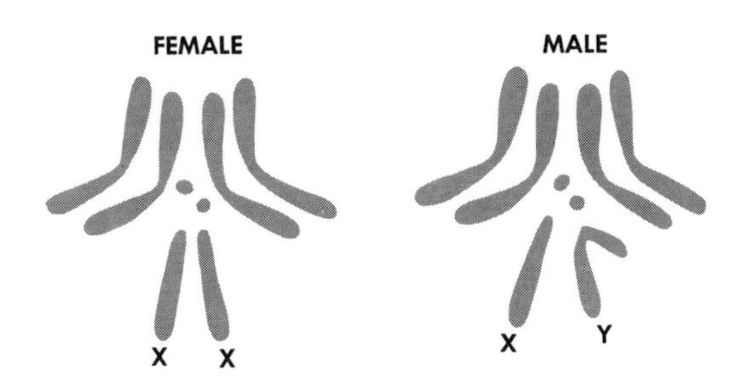

Figure 12-4. Silhouettes of chromosomes of *Drosophila melanogaster* as seen at mitotic metaphase.

	A		B
P_1	dull red ♀ × white ♂	P_1	white ♀ × dull red ♂
F_1	dull red ♂♂	F_1	white ♂♂
	dull red ♀♀		dull red ♀♀

Figure 12-5. Phenotypic results of reciprocal matings involving eye color. ♂♂ = males, ♀♀ = females.

locus cannot be in an autosome. Hence, the locus for white eye color is very likely to be in the sex chromosomes; that is, it seems to be *sex-linked.*

Since females are XX and males XY, we can represent the first cross above as $X^{w^+}X^{w^+}$ ♀ × X^wY^w ♂ with F_1 progeny expected to be $X^{w^+}X^w$ (dull red daughters) and $X^{w^+}Y^w$ (dull red sons) (Figure 12-6, A-1). Reciprocally, X^wX^w ♀ × $X^{w^+}Y^{w^+}$ ♂ should produce $X^{w^+}X^w$ (dull red daughters) and $X^wY^{w^+}$ (dull red sons) (Figure 12-6, B-1). But under experimental conditions the reciprocal cross yields sons with white eyes, not dull red.

We can explain these results by assuming that the Y chromosome carries no locus for *w*. Therefore, the first cross – $X^{w^+}X^{w^+}$ ♀ × X^wY♂ – should give $X^{w^+}X^w$ (dull red daughters) and $X^{w^+}Y$ (dull red sons) (Figure 12-6, A-2); and the reciprocal cross – X^wX^w ♀ × $X^{w^+}Y$♂ – should give $X^{w^+}X^w$ (dull red daughters) and X^wY (white sons) (Figure 12-6, B-2), as is found experimentally.

Recombination studies indicate that other traits, too, are based upon genes that have loci in the X but not the Y chromosome. Such X-linked loci are said to be *X-limited.* In man one type of red-green color blindness is due to an X-limited gene. Color blind women (X^cX^c) who marry normal men (X^CY) usually have normal daughters (X^CX^c) and color blind sons (X^cY). Another X-limited gene is responsible for bleeder's disease, hemophilia (type A).

	A-1		B-1
P_1	$X^{w^+}X^{w^+}$ ♀ × $X^{w}Y^{w}$ ♂	P_1	$X^{w}X^{w}$ ♀ × $X^{w^+}Y^{w^+}$ ♂
F_1	$X^{w^+}X^{w}$ ♀♀	F_1	$X^{w^+}X^{w}$ ♀♀
	$X^{w^+}Y^{w}$ ♂♂		$X^{w}Y^{w^+}$ ♂♂

	A-2		B-2
P_1	$X^{w^+}X^{w^+}$ ♀ × $X^{w}Y$ ♂	P_1	$X^{w}X^{w}$ ♀ × $X^{w^+}Y$ ♂
F_1	$X^{w^+}X^{w}$ ♀♀	F_1	$X^{w^+}X^{w}$ ♀♀
	$X^{w^+}Y$ ♂♂		$X^{w}Y$ ♂♂

Figure 12-6. Two ways (A-1 and B-1, A-2 and B-2) to represent matings A and B in Figure 12-5 genotypically. Shaded genotype must be incorrect.

12·5 *On rare occasions, homologous chromosomes and, hence, the genes they carry fail to segregate during meiosis.*

Other experiments with the X-limited white eye locus in Drosophila have given surprising results. When white females (X^wX^w) are crossed with dull red males ($X^{w^+}Y$), nearly all F_1 progeny are dull red daughters ($X^{w^+}X^w$) or white sons (X^wY). One or two flies per thousand progeny, however, are white daughters or dull red sons (Figure 12-7). Neither contamination nor errors in tallying the phenotypes can account for these exceptional flies. Nor can mutation, since the frequency of mutation from w^+ to w (or the reverse) is several orders of magnitude less than the observed frequency of exceptional flies.

Since the exceptional F_1 females are white-eyed, each must carry X^wX^w (Figure 12-7B). The only source of X^w is the mother, which carries two such chromosomes. Each dull red son must carry X^{w^+}, which could be contributed only by the father. Let us consider how these genotypes might arise.

In a normal meiosis of the Drosophila female, the two X's synapse to form a tetrad. After segregation four nuclei are produced by the end of meiosis, each of which contains one X (Figure 12-8A). One of these nuclei will become the egg nucleus. Sometimes, however, the segregation of the strands of the X chromosome tetrad is aberrant.

(1) At anaphase I both dyads may go to the same pole (Figure 12-8B); hence, none go to the other pole. The latter nucleus, containing no sex chromosomes, then undergoes the second meiotic division to produce two nuclei, neither one having an X. The other nucleus, with two dyads, un-

	A. PHENOTYPES		B. GENOTYPES
P_1	White ♀ × Dull Red ♂		$X^w X^w \times X^{w^+} Y$
F_1 TYPICAL	white	♂♂	$X^w Y$
	dull red	♀♀	$X^{w^+} X^w$
EXCEPTIONAL (Nonmutants)	dull red	♂	? $[X^{w^+}]$
	white	♀	? $[X^w X^w]$

Figure 12-7. Progeny obtained in crosses involving eye color genes in Drosophila.

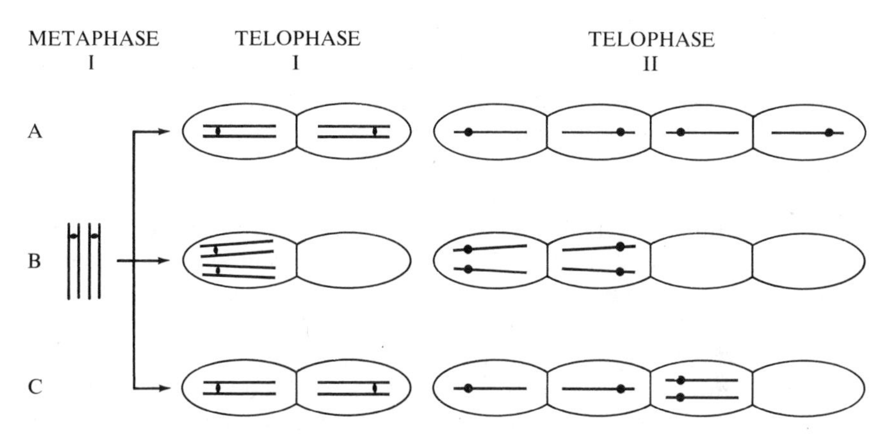

Figure 12-8. Consequences of normal segregation of X chromosomes (A) and of its failure to occur (B and C).

dergoes the second division to produce a pair of daughter nuclei that contain two X's apiece, one from each dyad. The failure of dyads to disjoin at anaphase I thus results in a gamete having a 50% chance of carrying two X chromosomes and a 50% chance of carrying none.

(2) The first meiotic division may be normal, producing two daughter nuclei with one X dyad each. The second meiotic division may proceed abnormally in one of these nuclei (Figure 12-8C), so that the strands of one X dyad fail to separate at anaphase II, both going to the same pole. Consequently, one daughter nucleus will contain two X's and the other will have none. Overall, meiosis in which the monads of one dyad fail to disjoin at anaphase II will result in a gamete having a 25% chance of carrying two X's, a 25% chance it will carry none, and a 50% chance it will carry one.

EGGS	SPERM	OFFSPRING
X^wX^w	X^{w^+}	(1) $X^{w^+}X^wX^w$
X^wX^w	Y	(2) X^wX^wY
0	X^{w^+}	(3) $X^{w^+}0$
0	Y	(4) Y 0

Figure 12-9. Possible genotypes resulting from fertilization by normal sperm of eggs produced after nondisjunction of sex chromosomes.

By either mechanism, *nondisjunction* of chromosomes results in some gametes having two X's and some having none. Since the X chromosome carries a locus for *w*, chromosomal nondisjunction can account for the failure of *w* genes to segregate.

If nondisjunction occurs during meiosis in a white female (X^wX^w), a gamete will be either X^wX^w or 0, where zero indicates the absence of a sex chromosome. Normal sperm produced by a dull red male ($X^{w^+}Y$) will carry either X^{w^+} or Y. Figure 12-9 shows the different zygotes which can result from random fertilization involving these four gametes. Type 1 will likely be dull red; type 2, white; type 3, dull red; and type 4, of undetermined eye color. If types 1 and 4 are lethal (actually, individuals of type 1 do survive rarely), white females (type 2) and dull red males (type 3) survive, as we find experimentally. Cytological evidence that the exceptional white females each contain two X's and one Y and that the exceptional dull red males each contain one X but no Y confirms the occurrence of nondisjunction. Autosomes can also undergo nondisjunction during meiosis.

12·6 *Some Y-linked genes have no loci in the X chromosome.*

Although XY Drosophila are fertile males, X0 individuals are sterile males. The Y chromosome thus seems to be necessary for male fertility, and is found to contain several genes that have no loci in the X. Consequently, a number of male-fertility genes are said to be *Y-limited.*

12·7 *Some sex-linked loci occur both in X and Y chromosomes.*

Since X and Y chromosomes synapse during meiosis and are thus (by definition) homologs, we expect them to have one or more loci in common. One such locus is probably the region of the centromere. In Drosophila chromosomes, *collochores,* regions near the centromere, are involved in the synapsis of all homologous pairs. Also in Drosophila, X and Y chromosomes each carry the locus of the gene for bobbed bristles, apparently one of the loci which are read to form ribosomal RNA and the nucleolus organizer.

Questions and Problems

12·1 Distinguish between segregation and independent segregation.

12·2 In Andalusian fowl, black feathers × white feathers produces blue feathers only in F_1. $F_1 \times F_1$ produces in F_2 $\frac{1}{4}$ black, $\frac{1}{2}$ blue, and $\frac{1}{4}$ white. Define gene symbols and give the genotypes of parents and offspring.

12·3 In chickens, non-barred feather ♀ × barred feather ♂ produces only barred F_1. Barred ♀ × non-barred ♂ produces in F_1 all sons barred, all daughters non-barred. Define gene symbols and give the genotypes of parents and offspring.

12·4 What portion of a Drosophila female's genotype can you determine from the phenotypes of the F_1 when she is mated to a wild-type male?

12·5 Why is hemophilia, rare in human males, still rarer in females?

12·6 Nondisjunction also occurs in Drosophila males during meiosis. Why was this fact ignored in the discussion of the phenotypic consequences of nondisjunction?

12·7 Assume you have radioactive rRNA and Drosophila of the following sex chromosome compositions: X0, XY, XYY, XXY, XXYY. How would you show that rRNA is transcribed both from X and Y templates?

12·8 What types of gametes are formed by the following genotypes if all gene pairs segregate independently? Give gametic frequencies.
(a) $A\,a\;B\,B\;C\,c$ (c) $M\,m\;N\,n\;O\,o$
(b) $D\,d\;E\,E\;f\!f\;G\,g$ (d) $A\,a\;B\,b\;C\,c\;D\,d$

12·9 What proportion of the offspring of the following crosses will be completely heterozygous if all gene pairs segregate independently?
(a) $A\,a\;B\,b \times A\,a\;B\,B$ (c) $A\,a\;B\,b\;c\,c \times A\,A\;B\,b\;c\,c$
(b) $A\,A\;B\,B\;c\,c \times A\,a\;B\,b\;C\,c$ (d) $A\,A' \times A''\,A'''$

12·10 A cross of two green corn plants produces kernels that develop into seedlings of which approximately $\frac{9}{16}$ are green and $\frac{7}{16}$ white. Explain this result in genetic terms. Which genotypes, if any, are lethal?
Note: The six questions that follow involve eye color in *Drosophila melanogaster*. Let
bw = gene producing brown eyes (bw^+ = normal allele),
st = gene producing scarlet eyes (st^+ = normal allele), and
v = gene producing vermilion eyes (v^+ = normal allele).

12·11 If pure stocks are used, reciprocal matings of brown-eyed by dull-red eyed flies produce only dull-red eyed F_1 progeny. What can you decide about the genetic basis for brown eye color from this result?
Crossing F_1 individuals produces dull red and brown flies in the proportion of 3:1 in the F_2. What is your answer now to the preceding question?

12·12 With reference to Question 12·11, what phenotypic results would you expect from mating a pure stock brown female with
(a) an F_1 dull red male?
(b) an F_2 brown male?

12·13 A single mating produced 68 dull red and 21 scarlet Drosophila; the reciprocal mating produced 73 dull red and 23 scarlet. Give the genotypes of parents and offspring. Are the genes involved X-limited? Explain.

12·14 A mating of a brown eyed fly and a scarlet (or red) eyed fly produces only dull red F_1 progeny. $F_1 \times F_1$ gives the following phenotypic results:

375 dull red,
117 brown,
115 scarlet,
33 white.

(a) With respect to the eye pigment, in what way are brown flies and scarlet flies defective?
(b) How many gene pairs are involved?
(c) Where are these genes located?
(d) Give the genotypes of F_1 and F_2 individuals.

12·15 Vermilion (also red) eyed ♂ × dull red eyed ♀ produces only dull red F_1 progeny. The reciprocal cross, dull red ♂ × vermilion ♀ produces dull red daughters and vermilion sons in the F_1.
(a) Where is the locus for the gene for vermilion?
(b) Give the genotypes of all parents and offspring mentioned.
(c) What phenotypic and genotypic results do you expect from a mating of an F_1 dull red daughter and a vermilion male?

12·16 Females homozygous for the genes producing brown and vermilion eye color are white eyed.
(a) What can you conclude about the polypeptide products of the genes for scarlet and vermilion?
(b) A female homozygous for *v* mated to a male homozygous for *st* produces red sons and dull red daughters in the F_1. Give the genotypes of parents and offspring.

12·17 In Drosophila, mutations in X-limited genes that are lethal in males but are viable when heterozygous in females can be induced, detected, and maintained in cultures grown at room temperature. Suppose it is found that 100% of such mutations induced by mutagen Y are still lethal to males grown at a certain lower temperature, but that only 80% of those induced by mutagen Z are still lethal at the lower temperature.
(a) Discuss the possible molecular basis of mutagenic action by Y and Z.

(b) Name one mutagen expected to produce an effect like Y, and one expected to produce an effect like Z.

References

Bridges, C. B. 1916. Non-disjunction as proof of the chromosome theory of heredity. Genetics, 1: 1–52, 107–163.

Cooper, K. W. 1964. Meiotic conjugative elements not involving chiasmata. Proc. Nat. Acad. Sci., U.S., 52: 1248–1255. (Discusses collochores.)

Mendel, G. 1866. Experiments in plant hybridization. Translated in *Principles of Genetics, Fifth Edition,* Sinnott, E. W., Dunn, L. C., and Dobzhansky, Th., New York: McGraw-Hill Book Co., Inc. 1958, pp. 419–443; also in *Genetics, the Modern Science of Heredity,* Dodson, E. O., Philadelphia: W. B. Saunders Co., 1956, pp. 285–311. (Original proofs of segregation and independent segregation of gene pairs.)

Mendel, G. 1867. Part of a letter to C. Nägeli. Supplement I in *Genetics, Second Edition,* Herskowitz, I. H., Boston: Little, Brown and Co. 1965. (A summary of his discovery of segregation and independent segregation.)

Morgan, T. H. 1910. Sex limited inheritance in Drosophila. Science. 32: 120–122.

Peters, J. A. (Editor) 1959. *Classic Papers in Genetics.* Englewood Cliffs, N.J.: Prentice-Hall, Inc.

CHAPTER 13

Recombination of Nuclear Genes – Crossing Over

Recombination between chromatids is by no means a rare event. For, as we noted earlier, the chiasmata which hold together the strands of a tetrad are cytological evidence that recombination between chromatids has taken place at some previous time during meiosis. In this chapter we look at genetic evidence of such exchanges and consider the molecular basis for this kind of recombination.

13·1 *An exchange of genetic material between homologous chromosomes takes place in a process called crossing over.*

In Drosophila the genes for white eye (*w*) and cut wings (*ct*) are both X-limited and thus are linked to one another. Using pure lines, let us cross a white-eyed female with long wings to a cut-winged male with dull red eyes. Subsequently, we mate F_1 females, $w\ ct^+ / w^+\ ct$, with *any* males and score the phenotypes of sons. (Because we are scoring sons only, any male can serve as parent, since it contributes its Y, which does not carry the X-limited *w* and *ct* loci.) Of the male progeny 40% are white * ($w\ ct^+ / Y$), 40% cut ($w^+\ ct / Y$), 10% white and cut ($w\ ct / Y$), and 10% wild type ($w^+\ ct^+ / Y$). We expect the F_1 female, $w\ ct^+ / w^+\ ct$, to produce equal numbers of $w\ ct^+$ and $w^+\ ct$ gametes and thus to give rise to equal numbers of the two types of sons: half $w\ ct^+ / Y$, half $w^+\ ct / Y$. We do obtain equal numbers, but they make up only 80% of the male progeny. The other sons arose from the female gametes $w\ ct$ and $w^+\ ct^+$ – new combinations of parental genetic material. These gametes were produced by an exchange of genetic material between the two X homologs in a process of *crossing over*. The result of crossing over is two reciprocal recombinant, *crossover* chromosomes, which occur with equal frequency.

If $w\ ct / w^+\ ct^+$ females are mated with males of unspecified genotype as before, we get results similar to those above. About 80% of the sons carry parental combinations of the two genes, 40% $w\ ct$ and 40% $w^+\ ct^+$;

* By convention, the progeny are referred to by their mutant traits only.

and 20% carry nonparental combinations, 10% *w* ct^+ and 10% w^+ *ct*. Since the frequency of recombinant sons is the same for either type of female parent, the distance between the loci for *w* and *ct* on the X chromosome seems to be the same for all Drosophila females. We expect crossing over (hence, recombinant progeny) to be more frequent when two loci are further apart, and less frequent when closer together. If the two loci are not in the same chromosome, half the gametes will have the same combination of these genes as the parent; half will be recombinant for the two loci (see Section 12·2).

13·2 *Crossing over may occur between two nonsister strands at a four-stranded stage before diplonema.*

A possible mechanism for crossing over is shown in Figure 13-1. In stage I we see a pair of homologous chromosomes; one carries the mutant genes *a* and *b*, and the other their normal alleles, + and +. The homologs synapse to form a tetrad in which each univalent consists of two *sister strands*. At this time crossing over occurs, so the tetrad later seen at diplonema appears as in stage II with a chiasma between the *a* and *b* loci. Univalents whose strands initially were genetically identical now contain nonidentical strands as the result of exchange of equal segments between two *nonsister strands*. Stage III shows the recombinant dyads present after completion of the first meiotic division. In stage IV we see the four haploid nuclei of different genotypes produced at the end of the second meiotic division. In summary, if one chiasma (corresponding to one crossing over event) occurs anywhere between the *a* and *b* loci, two of the resultant four nuclei will contain parental combinations of these genes, and the other two will contain new combinations.

13·3 *Studies of gene linkage in Neurospora prove that crossing over occurs at a four-stranded stage.*

We can use Neurospora to test our hypothesis that crossing over occurs at a four-stranded stage. The "fruiting" bodies of the mold contain cells with two haploid nuclei apiece, each of which came from a different parent (Figures 11-7 and 13-2). These two nuclei fuse to form a diploid nucleus with seven pairs of chromosomes. The cell then elongates to form a sac, or ascus. Soon after its formation, the diploid nucleus undergoes meiosis, as in Figure 13-2, to produce four haploid nuclei arranged in tandem; the two uppermost nuclei come from one first-division nucleus, the bottom two from the other first-division nucleus. Each haploid nucleus subsequently divides once, so each meiotic product is present in duplicate within the ascus. We can remove each haploid ascospore from the ascus,

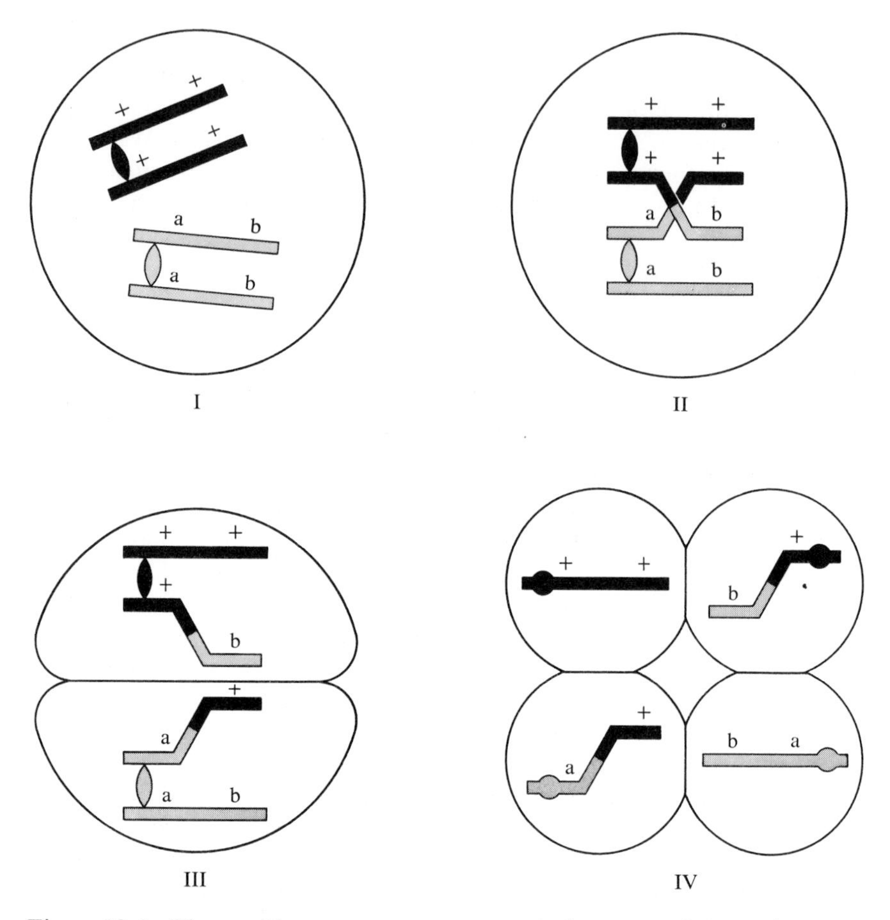

Figure 13-1. The genetic consequences expected after a crossing over between linked genes.

grow it by itself, and determine its genotype. Thus, all of the meiotic products derived from a single diploid nucleus can be identified.

In Figure 13-3 we see the hypothesized genetic consequences of a single crossing over between two given loci. (Only one of the seven chromosome pairs is represented.) As shown, a single crossing over in a four-stranded stage would result in two crossover and two noncrossover meiotic products. When many asci of a particular dihybrid for linked genes were scored, 90% had all eight spores noncrossovers for the two loci; in the remaining 10%, four of the eight spores were crossovers. Never were all eight spores from a single sac crossovers. It appears, therefore, that crossing over occurs only in a four-stranded stage, as depicted in Figures 13-3 and 13-4.

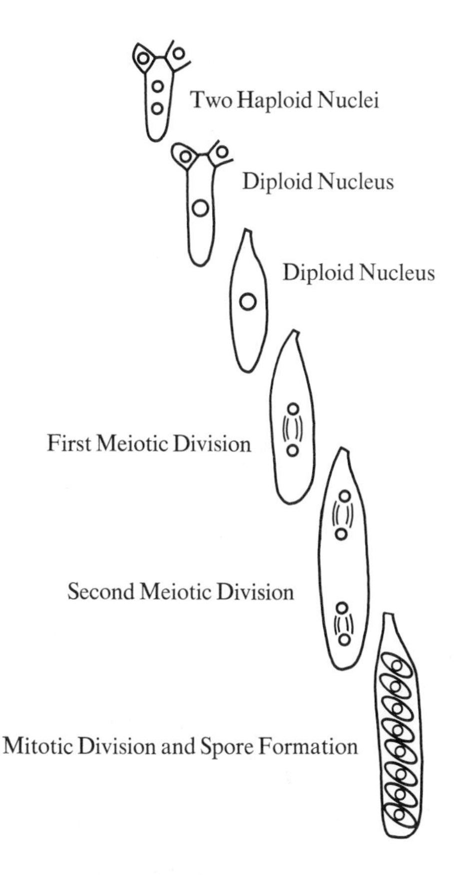

Figure 13-2. Meiosis in Neurospora.

Further evidence that crossing over takes place at a four-stranded stage is supplied by cytological observations of chiasmata.

13·4 *Genetically-detected crossovers are in a one-to-one correspondence with cytologically-detected recombinant chromosomes.*

If crossing over involves two homologous chromosomes (essentially identical in appearance under the microscope), we can tell by genetic analysis, that is, by growing progeny and scoring their phenotypes, that recombination has taken place. Crossover strands, however, have the same appearance as parental strands. We can detect crossing over by cytological means by using a dihybrid for linked genes in which one homolog differs physically from its partner on both sides of the loci being tested, as indicated in Figure 13-5. Consequently, cytological examination of noncrossover progeny shows that they retain the original chromosomal arrangement, but that crossovers have a nonparental combination of genetic material, as indicated by the special homologs used.

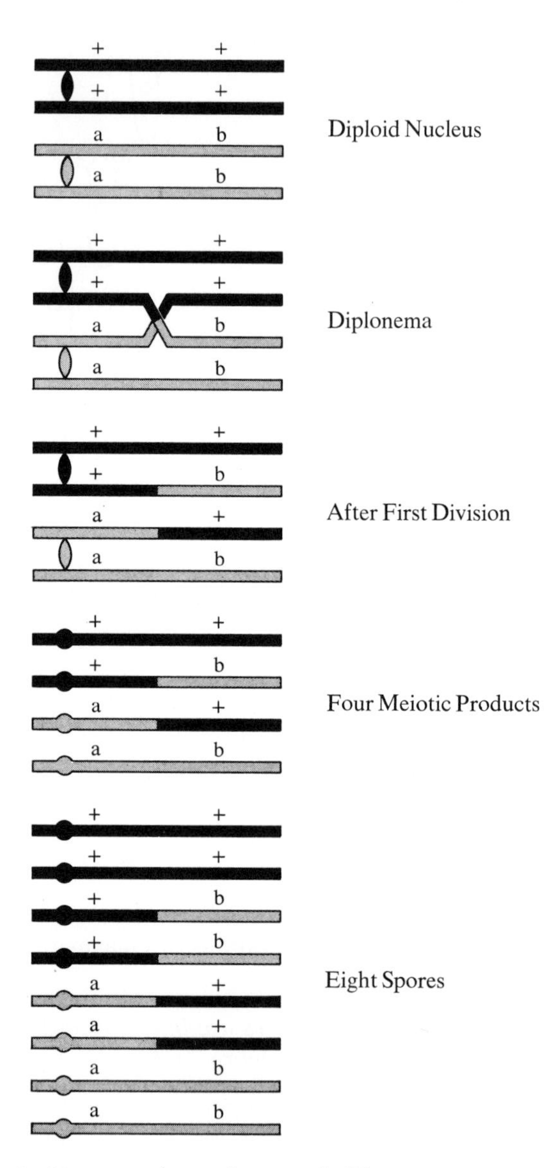

Figure 13-3. A chiasma and crossing over in Neurospora.

13·5 *Crossover frequencies can be used to measure the relative distances between linked loci.*

As implied earlier, the greater the distance between two loci, the greater the chance for crossing over to occur between them and the greater the frequency of crossover strands. Conversely, relative frequencies of crossovers indicate relative distances between linked loci. For instance, a chiasma frequency of 10% between *a* and *b* loci in Neurospora tetrads

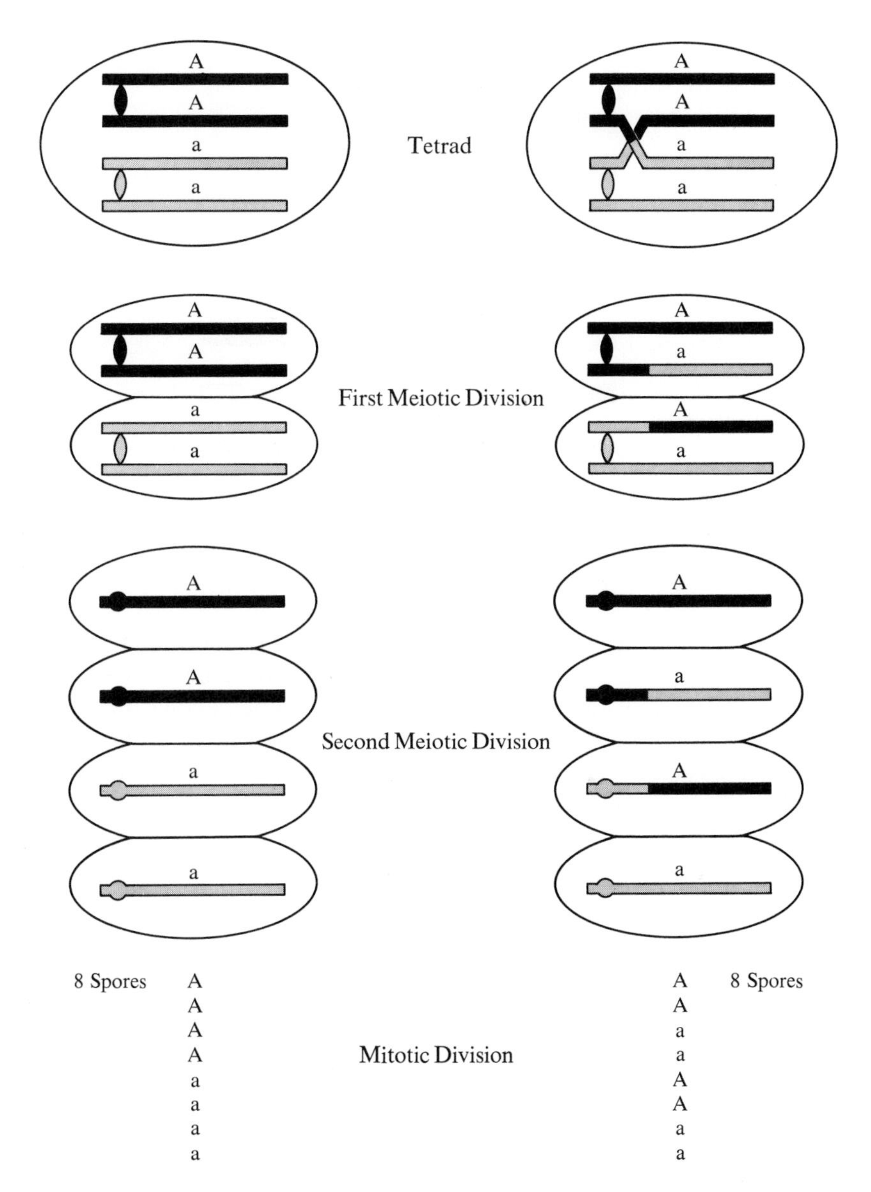

Figure 13-4. Arrangement of spores in the Neurospora ascus when segregation occurs at the first meiotic division (left) and at the second meiotic division (right), as determined by the absence and presence, respectively, of a chiasma between the segregating genes and the centromere. (Note that in Figure 13-3 the alleles at the *a* locus segregated in the first meiotic division whereas those at the *b* locus segregated in the second.)

results in 5% of all spores containing crossover strands. (Note that 5% of the spores – not 10% – contained crossover strands because only half the strands in a tetrad are crossovers.) By definition, a *crossover unit* is that distance between linked genes which results in one crossover per

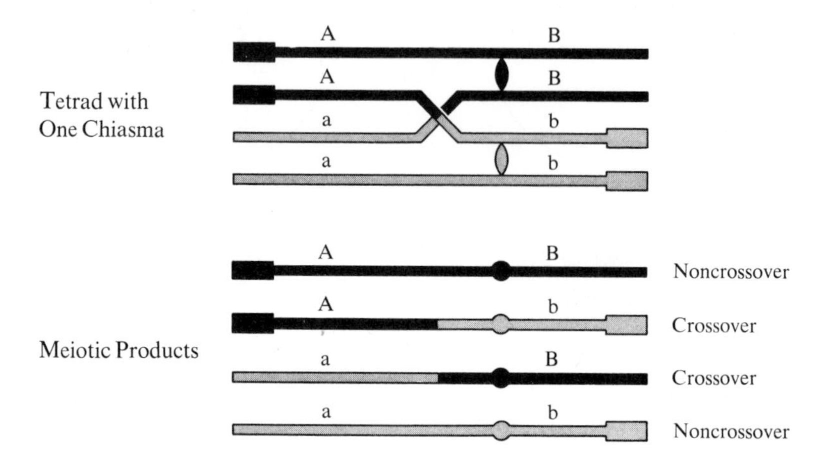

Figure 13-5. Correlation between genetic and cytological crossovers.

one hundred postmeiotic products. Thus, the distance between *a* and *b* loci is five crossover units. In general, when loci are sufficiently close together (as in the preceding example), the crossover percentage, hence, the distance between genes in crossover units, is one-half the chiasma frequency. This correlation supports the conclusion that one chiasma corresponds to a previous crossing over.

13·6 *Crossover frequencies can be used to construct a linear genetic map.*

In Drosophila the arrangement of three X-limited genes — *y* (yellow body color), *w* (white eyes), and *spl* (split bristles) — can be determined from recombination data. Dihybrid females *y w* / ++, *y spl* / ++, and *w spl* / ++ are crossed to appropriate double mutant males, and the following crossover distances are obtained: *y* to *w*, 1.5; *y* to *spl*, 3.0; and *w* to *spl*, 1.5. Since the crossover distance between *y* and *spl* equals the sum of the crossover distances from *y* to *w* and from *w* to *spl*, the genetic map thus defined is linear, namely, *y w spl* or *spl w y*. When the positions of other X-linked genes are mapped relative to the three studied above, with *y* arbitrarily assigned the position zero, all are found to be arranged in a linear order.

Since a linkage map for the X chromosome of Drosophila shows the genes *y*, *w*, *spl*, and *ct* (cut wings) taking their respective positions at 0, 1.5, 3.0, and 20 map units, *ct* and *spl* are 17 map units apart. The *spl*+ / +*ct* dihybrid thus should produce 17% recombinant, or crossover, progeny (8.5% ++ and 8.5% *spl ct*). Such a result is obtained, but only under special conditions. Observed crossover frequencies fluctuate considerably because of variations in sample size and in genetic and environmental factors which act during or after crossing over.

13·7 *The frequency of a second chiasma in a given region decreases with its proximity to the first. The choice of strands involved in a second chiasma, however, does not seem to be affected by those involved in the first.*

Since several chiasmata usually hold together the univalents of a bivalent, two (or more) chiasmata may occur between two loci. To see the types of recombinations possible, let us first label the strands in a tetrad 1, 2, 3, and 4, where 1 and 2 are sister strands with the normal alleles, and 3 and 4 are sister strands with the mutant alleles (Figure 13-6). We will consider genetic exchange between nonsister strands only. If one chiasma involves an exchange between strands 2 and 3 in the *a-b* region, a second chiasma in the *b-c* region theoretically can involve strands 2 and 3, 2 and 4, 1 and 3, or 1 and 4 (Figure 13-6). Thus, three types of *double-chiasmata* are possible: two-strand, three-strand, and four-strand. Note that two different three-strand double chiasmata are possible.

Figure 13-6 also shows the genetic consequences of double chiasmata in these tetrads. From two-strand double chiasmata, two of the four meiotic products are of the parental type, i.e., noncrossovers (+++ and *a b c*), and two are *double crossovers* (+ *b* + and *a* + *c*). (A double crossover is characterized by a switch in the position of the middle gene relative to the end genes.) Three-strand double chiasmata produce one double crossover, two *single crossovers,* and one noncrossover. (A single crossover is characterized by a switch in the position of one end gene relative to the other two.) Four-strand double chiasmata yield four single crossover strands. Thus, each type of double-chiasmata gives rise to a characteristic set of crossover and noncrossover strands. Furthermore, each set differs from the set of products resulting from a single chiasma: two single crossovers and two noncrossovers.

A chiasma in one region of the tetrad can sometimes interfere with the occurrence of another in the same tetrad; that is, in some regions the frequency of double chiasmata is less than might be expected. For example, if the frequency of a single crossing over in a given region is 0.10, then the frequency of two such events should be 0.10×0.10, or 0.01 – if the chiasmata do not affect each other. When the observed frequency of double chiasmata for this region is less than 0.01, we say that *crossing over interference* or *chiasma interference* has occurred. Such interference increases as the distance between the two chiasmata decreases. For example, in Drosophila crossing over interference is 100% for distances up to 10 to 15 map units; in other words, no chiasmata or crossovers occur within about 15 map units of each other.

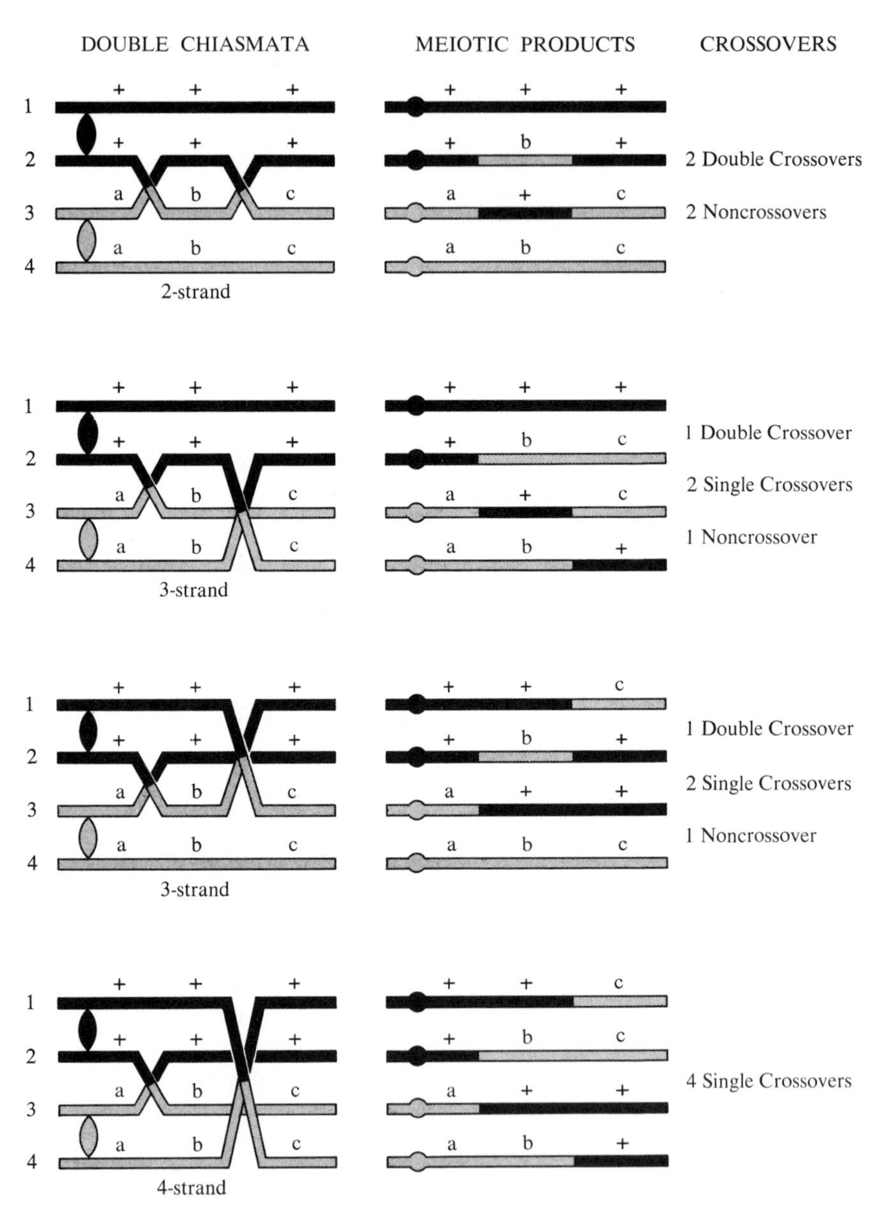

Figure 13-6. Types of double chiasmata and their genetic consequences.

In some experiments with Neurospora, all four types of double chiasmata are found to occur with equal frequency. From this result we can see that the strands forming one chiasma are not affected by those which form the other. In other words, there seems to be no *chromatid interference* in chiasma formation.

+++	0.31	+++	0.31
a b c	0.31	a c b	0.31
+ b c	0.14	+ c b	0.14
a++	0.14	a++	0.14
++ c	0.01	+ c+	0.01
a b+	0.01	a+ b	0.01
+ b+	0.04	++ b	0.04
a+ c	0.04	a c+	0.04
	1.00		1.00

Figure 13-7. Results of a cross of a trihybrid with a homozygote for *a*, *b*, and *c*.

13·8 *The order of three linked genes can be determined from their double crossover frequencies.*

Let us consider a cross in Drosophila of a heterozygote for three linked autosomal genes, +++ / *a b c* ♀ with *a b c* / *a b c* ♂. The frequencies of the various types of progeny are shown at the left in Figure 13-7. These values correspond to frequencies of the different genotypes in the gametes of the trihybrid parent. By merely scanning this table, we can tell which is the middle gene in the sequence: it is the one which switches least often from the original gene combinations (+++ and *a b c*), since only the middle gene requires two chiasmata for a switch. Consequently, *c* is the middle gene; and the sequence is *a c b* or *b c a*. At the right in Figure 13-7, the data are presented with the genes listed in their correct order so that the conclusion may be more apparent.

13·9 *The number of linkage groups for segregating genes approaches and sometimes equals the number of different kinds of chromosomes.*

Whenever the number of segregating gene pairs under study is considerably larger than the number of chromosome pairs, the number of groups of linked genes approaches (and often equals) the number of chromosome pairs. Hence, the maximum number of *linkage groups* often equals the haploid chromosome number (N). When, however, the sex chromosomes are heteromorphic (as are the X and Y chromosomes), each chromosome has unique loci; so the maximum number of linkage groups equals the haploid chromosome number plus one.

13·10 *In rare instances, crossing over occurs in nuclei entering mitosis.*

Drosophila females (*y*+ / + *sn*) carry the mutant gene for yellow body color (*y*) in one X chromosome and the mutant gene for singed bristles (*sn*) in the other; they normally have gray body color and straight bristles.

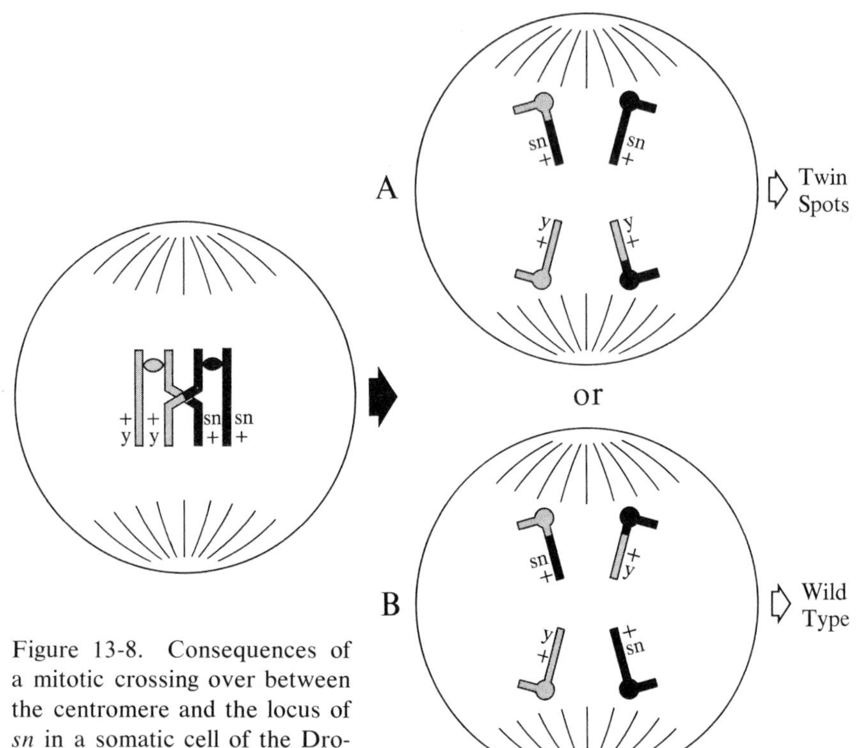

Figure 13-8. Consequences of a mitotic crossing over between the centromere and the locus of *sn* in a somatic cell of the Drosophila dihybrid *y* +/+ *sn*.

On rare occasions, however, a pair of adjacent spots of tissue in a wild-type background will be yellow with straight bristles, and gray with singed bristles. Such recombination proves to be the result of *mitotic crossing over* in a somatic cell. Figure 13-8 illustrates the result of exchange between nonsister chromatids of a pair of homologs that are synapsed in mitosis. If the chromatids separate at anaphase as in A, subsequent mitoses will give rise to spots of different appearance. If separation occurs as in B, though, no such difference will result.

Mitotic crossing over is not restricted to sex chromosomes and can also occur in germ line nuclei that undergo mitosis. It also occurs in corn, yeast, and fungi such as Aspergillus, which undergoes meiosis and has a definite sexual cycle. Mitotic crossing over also occurs in fungi that are not known to undergo meiosis; it occurs, for example, in the mold *Penicillium notatum* after haploid nuclei in a heterocaryon fuse to form a diploid nucleus. The frequency of recombinants produced by mitotic crossing over can sometimes be used to map the chromosomes of organisms without meiosis. We should keep in mind, though, that the rarity of such crossing over indicates that it is an abnormal genetic event, perhaps a type of mutation.

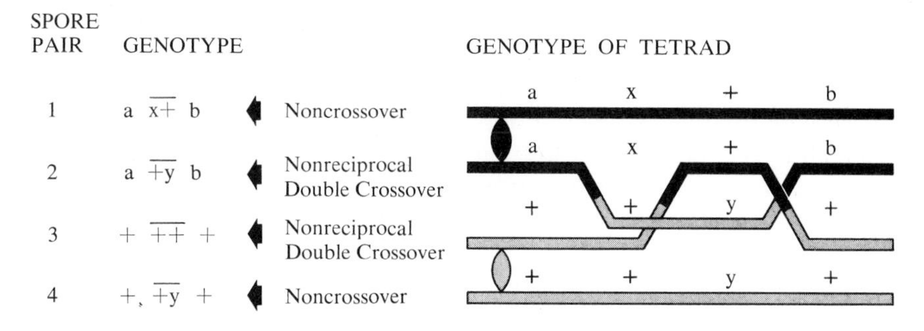

Figure 13-9. A tetrad showing nonreciprocal double crossovers.

13·11 *Postmeiotic segregation occurs in fungi.*

After meiosis occurs in the Neurospora heterozygote *A a*, each of the four meiotic products usually gives rise to identical daughter nuclei by mitosis. Consequently, the spores in the mature ascus are in the relative order *A A A A a a a a* when segregation occurs in the first meiotic division (as occurs, for instance, when there is no crossing over between the centromere and the marker locus); or *A A a a A A a a*, *A A a a a a A A*, or *a a A A A A a a* when segregation occurs in the second meiotic division (as when, for instance, a single crossing over occurs between the *A* locus and the centromere) (see Figure 13-4).

Sometimes asci are found to have an ascospore sequence of *A A a A a A a a*. Such an ordering indicates that the two middle meiotic products of the four were genetically hybrid; and each segregated in the next *mitotic* division to produce *A* and *a* daughter nuclei. Such postmeiotic segregation is also found to occur in other fungi.

13·12 *In rare instances, nonreciprocal recombinant strands arise during meiosis or mitosis.*

In Neurospora the exchange of genetic material between chromatids is nearly always a reciprocal exchange. Very rarely, however, nonreciprocal recombinant strands are found. To find out how this comes about, let us examine recombination in the diploid $a\,\overline{x+}\,b\,/+\overline{+y}+$, where $\overline{x+}$ and $\overline{+y}$ are different mutant alleles at a locus bordered by the closely linked loci *a* and *b*. Since $\overline{x+}\,/\,\overline{+y}$ heterozygotes occasionally give rise to normal $(\overline{++})$ progeny, whereas $\overline{x+}\,/\,\overline{x+}$ or $\overline{+y}\,/\,\overline{+y}$ individuals do not, it appears that *x* and *y* are mutant sites in the same gene between which recombination can occur to produce the normal allele. Occasionally, asci that contain recombinants in the *a-b* region are of the type shown in Figure 13-9. This tetrad contains two noncrossover strands ($a\,\overline{x+}\,b$ and $+\overline{+y}+$) and two double crossover strands ($a\,\overline{+y}\,b$ and $+\overline{++}+$). Note that since the *a-b* distance is short, more double crossing over occurred than expected, hence, *negative crossing over interference* is said to have occurred. The two double crossover strands here are nonreciprocal. Other exceptional asci that contain nonreciprocal crossovers have one double crossover and three noncrossover strands. Formation of these nonreciprocal recombinant strands appears to involve multiple crossing over. Nonreciprocal exchanges also occur in yeast nuclei undergoing mitotic as well as meiotic divisions.

13·13 *A molecular model can account for many aspects of reciprocal and nonreciprocal recombination in higher organims.*

In Section 10·7 we hypothesized that recombination between chromosomes of bacteria involves strand breakage, digestion, and repair. We can extend this hypothesis to explain various types of recombination involving homologs of higher organisms, since a limited amount of DNA synthesis (required by this hypothesis) has been found to occur at the late leptonema-pachynema stage of meiosis. Such a model for genetic recombination (Figure 13-10) supposes that each chromatid consists of a single DNA duplex, and that the recombination process starts at a tetrad stage, when homologs are synapsed (A). A strand of one chromatid breaks, and so does the complementary strand of a nonsister chromatid at the corresponding position (B). This event is followed by strand separation on one or both sides of the break point, and by DNA synthesis starting from the break point and proceeding in either direction or both (C). The newly synthesized DNA strands then separate from their templates (D), and "hybrid" duplexes are formed by base pairing with their nontemplate complements (E). Now unpaired, single-stranded DNA is digested (F), and all ends of the duplexes are properly joined enzymatically (G).

If the genetic recombination does occur as described, short homologous segments of each of the two nonsister chromatids will be hybrid in derivation; that is, they will be composed of the complements of nonsister templates. When the recombination occurs only to the left of *b* (between the *a* and *b* loci, as shown in the column at the left of the Figure), the crossover strands are *a* + + and + *b c*. Recombination only to the right of *b* results in the crossover strands *a b* + and + + *c*, as shown in the column at the right of the Figure. When recombination occurs at both positions (center column), double crossover strands *a* + *c* and + *b* + are produced. (With respect to *a* and *c* regions, however, the double-crossover strands would appear as noncrossovers if the DNA segment were unmarked in the *b* region). If marker *d* were present between *a* and *b* with its + allele on the partner chromatid, and recombination occurred between *a* and *b* as shown, the two crossover strands would contain corresponding short regions that are not only hybrid in derivation but genetically "heterozygous" – each containing one strand *d* and its complement +. At the next mitosis

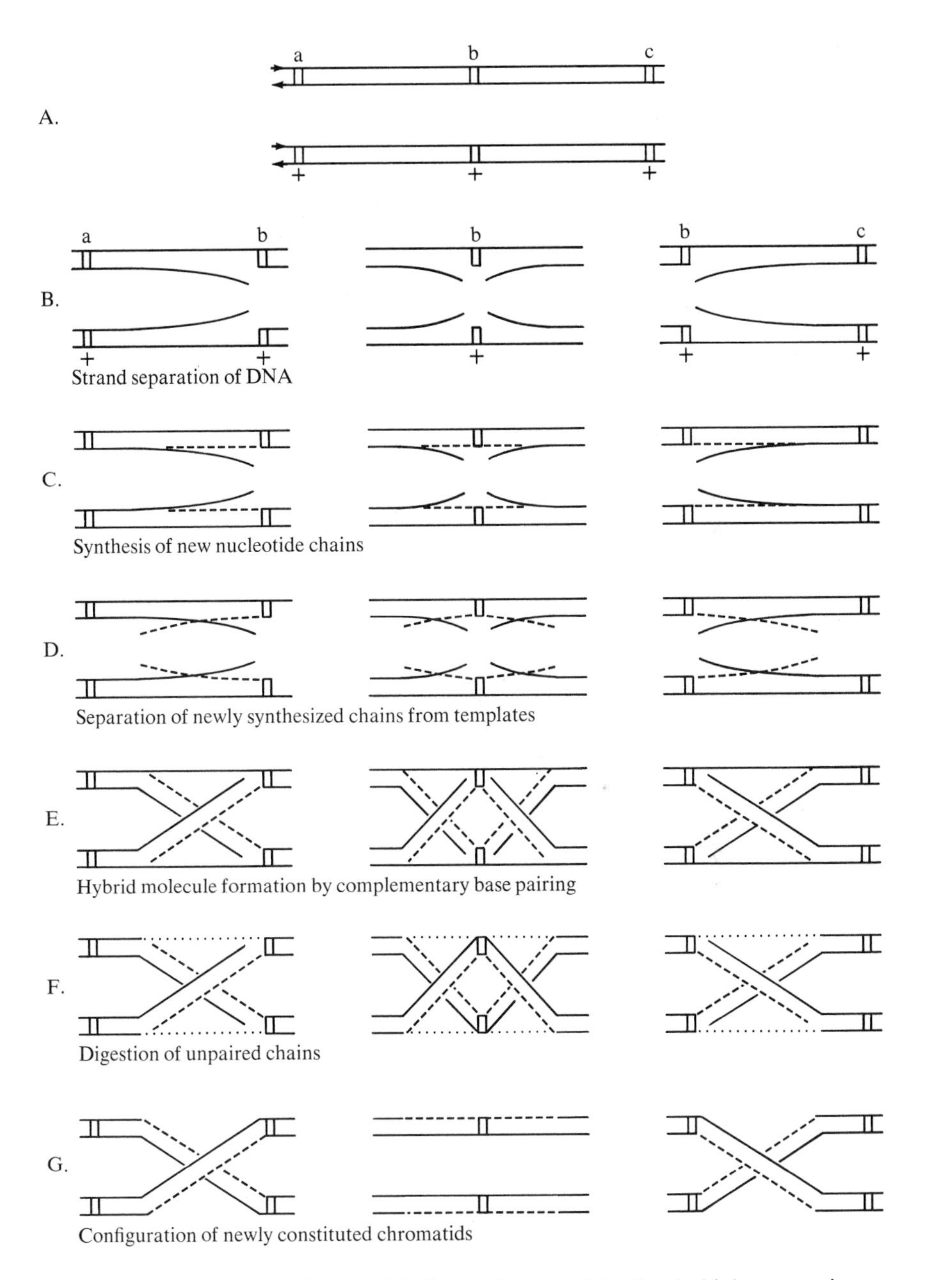

Figure 13-10. A molecular model of genetic recombination in higher organisms. Only two nonsister chromatids of the tetrad are shown. Unbroken lines represent the single strands of two corresponding DNA duplexes. The polarity of the strands is shown by arrows in the top diagram. The rectangles labeled *a*, *b*, and *c* indicate the fixed points of primary breakage from which the recombination is initiated. The broken lines represent newly-synthesized DNA strands, and the dotted lines DNA strands that are being broken down. (After H. L. K. Whitehouse and P. J. Hastings)

each such heterozygous chromosome would produce one daughter chromosome "homozygous" for *d* and the other "homozygous" for +. We see, therefore, that such a mechanism can account for post-meiotic segregation. At other times, when the hybrid segments are genetically heterozygous, a repair process could occur to correct the mispairing in the heterozygous region, and thus make one (or both) hybrid molecules genetically homozygous; as a result, nonreciprocal recombination could occur.

This model can also account for instances of negative crossing over interference (see middle column of Figure 13-10). Furthermore, it helps explain experimental results in which the frequency of crossing over is different for different points along a short region of a chromosome. According to the above model, the markers closest to a point of breakage would be more likely to cross over than those further away.

Questions and Problems

13·1 What should be the male genotype and which kinds of progeny should you score if you wish to determine the crossover distance between two X-limited loci? Two linked autosomal loci?

13·2 What frequencies of gametes do you expect from a dihybrid for two linked loci 50 map units apart? How can you prove these loci are linked?

13·3 If the chromatids of a chromosome at the tetrad stage are so coiled about each other that they act as a single strand, what are the consequences of a single crossing over between the *a* and *b* loci in the Neurospora dihybrid *a* + / + *b*?

13·4 In mapping the *y-spl* region of the Drosophila X chromosome in this chapter, two marker loci were studied in each of three crosses. Was it possible to detect double crossovers had they occurred? Explain. Had any double crossovers occurred? Explain.

13·5 A wild-type Drosophila female whose father had cut wings and whose mother had split bristles is mated to a male with cut wings. Give the relative frequencies of genotypes and phenotypes expected in the F_1.

13·6 A female Drosophila mated to a wild-type male produced 400 progeny in the F_1. Of the F_1 progeny, only three had white eyes and split bristles. Of what sex were these three flies? Give the genotype of the mother and the genotypes and frequencies of her gametes. What is the map distance involved?

13·7 In tomatoes the genes for tall (+) and short (*s*) are alleles, and the genes for smooth epidermis (+) and rough (*r*) are alleles. A cross between two plants produces 204 tall, rough; 180 short, smooth; 10 tall, smooth; and 6 short, rough. How do you know that the gene pairs are linked? Give the genotypes of both parents. What is the crossover map distance between the two loci?

13·8 Calculate the number of crossover units between *black body* (*b*) and *dumpy wings* (*dp*) in the following Drosophila crosses:

(a) P_1 pure black × pure dumpy
P_2 F_1 wild-type ♀♀ × black dumpy ♂♂
F_2 wild-type 27
black 79
dumpy 70
black dumpy 24

(b) P_1 black dumpy × pure wild-type
P_2 F_1 wild-type ♀♀ × black dumpy ♂♂
F_2 wild type 314
black 103
dumpy 89
black dumpy 294

13·9 The reciprocal P_2 mating in Question 13·8(a), F_1 wild-type ♂♂ × black dumpy ♀♀, produced in F_2 85 black and 90 dumpy only. The reciprocal P_2 mating in 13·8(b), F_1 wild-type ♂♂ × black dumpy ♀♀, produced in F_2 133 wild-type and 110 black dumpy only. How can you explain these results?

13·10 A trihybrid, $+a+b+c$ is crossed to $a\,a\;b\,b\;c\,c$. The F_1 show that the trihybrid produced the following gametes:

28	$+++$	22	$a\,b\,c$
230	$++c$	220	$a\,b+$
206	$+b\,c$	244	$a++$
23	$+b+$	27	$a+c$

(a) Which loci are linked and which segregate independently?
(b) Write the genotypes of both parents in light of your answer to (a).
(c) Give the map distances between the three loci wherever applicable.

13·11 In Neurospora, how many ascospores need be tested from a single ascus to determine whether crossing over occurred between two closely linked genes?

13·12 Suppose a pair of homologs in a diploid nucleus of Neurospora have the genotype $++/a\,b$. Draw an eight-spore ascus derived from a diploid nucleus that had
(a) no chiasma between these loci;
(b) one chiasma between the centromere and the nearest marked locus;
(c) one chiasma between the two marker loci;
(d) one two-strand double chiasmata between the marked loci.

13·13 How many gene pairs must be heterozygous to detect a single crossover in Drosophila and in Neurospora? Explain.

13·14 Map gene x relative to its centromere when a heterozygous Neurospora produces asci with the following spore orders:

% Asci	Spore Pair			
	1	2	3	4
92	x	x	+	+
4	x	+	x	+
1	+	x	x	+
3	x	+	+	x

13·15 In Neurospora, *arg* individuals are auxotrophs for arginine; *thi* individuals are auxotrophs for thiamin. Dihybrid nuclei for these mutants produce asci with the following spore orders:

% Asci	Spore Pair			
	1	2	3	4
51	*arg thi*	*arg thi*	+ +	+ +
49	*arg* +	*arg* +	+ *thi*	+ *thi*

Discuss the positions of these loci with respect to each other and their centromere(s). How would you determine the genotypes of these spores?

13·16 Suppose a given Neurospora cross produced asci with the following spore orders.

% Asci	Spore Pair			
	1	2	3	4
88	*a b*	*a b*	+ +	+ +
3	*a b*	+ +	*a b*	+ +
3	*a b*	+ +	+ +	*a b*
1.5	*a b*	*a* +	+ *b*	+ +
1.5	*a b*	*a* +	+ +	+ *b*
1.5	*a* +	*a b*	+ *b*	+ +
1.5	*a* +	*a b*	+ +	+ *b*

(a) Are *a* and *b* linked?

(b) If they are not linked, give the crossover distance of *a* and *b* from their centromeres. If they are linked, give the crossover distances between *a*, *b*, and the centromere.

13·17 Explain the genetic result in Section 13·12 using the molecular model discussed in Section 13·13.

References

Creighton, H. S., and McClintock, B. 1931. A correlation of cytological and genetical crossing-over in *Zea mays*. Proc. Nat. Acad. Sci., U.S., 17: 492–497. Reprinted in *Classic Papers in Genetics,* Peters, J. A. (Editor), Englewood Cliffs, N.J.: Prentice-Hall, Inc. 1959, pp. 155–160; also in *Great Experiments in Biology,* Gabriel, M. L., and Fogel, S. (Editors), Englewood Cliffs, N.J.: Prentice-Hall, Inc., 1955, pp. 267–272.

Fincham, J. R. S., and Day, P. R. 1963. *Fungal Genetics.* Oxford University Press: Blackwell Scientific Publications.

Herskowitz, I. H. 1965. *Genetics, Second Edition.* Boston: Little, Brown and Co. (Contains crossover maps for Neurospora, Drosophila, man, mouse, and corn.)

Hotta, Y., Ito, M., and Stern, H. 1966. Synthesis of DNA during meiosis. Proc. Nat. Acad. Sci., U.S., 56: 1184–1191.

Stern, C. 1931. Zytologisch-genetische Untersuchungen als Beweise für die Morgansche Theorie des Faktorenaustauschs. Biol. Zbl., 51: 547–587. (Correlates genetic and cytological crossovers.)

Sturtevant, A. H. 1913. The linear arrangement of six sex-linked factors in Drosophila, as shown by their mode of association. J. Exp. Zool., 14: 43–59. Reprinted in *Classic Papers in Genetics,* Peters, J. A. (Editor), Englewood Cliffs, N.J.: Prentice-Hall, Inc., 1959, pp. 67–78.

Whitehouse, H. L. K. 1965. *Towards an Understanding of the Mechanism of Heredity.* New York: St. Martin's Press. (Chapter 15 discusses the molecular basis of crossing over.)

Whitehouse, H. L. K., and Hastings, P. J. 1965. The analysis of genetic recombination on the polaron hybrid DNA model. Genet. Res., Cambridge, 6: 27–92. (Molecular basis of recombination between partner chromosomes in nucleated cells.)

CHAPTER 14

Recombination of Nuclear Genes — Gross Chromosomal Changes

We have already considered cytologically-detectable genetic recombinations associated with mitosis, meiosis, and fertilization. Chromosomes can undergo other natural, or unnatural, changes that are detectable cytologically. These changes involve the rearrangement of large chromosome segments produced by breakage as well as the gain or loss of entire chromosomes or chromosome sets. In this chapter we will consider the causes and the consequences of such gross chromosomal changes.

CHANGES INVOLVING BROKEN CHROMOSOMES

14·1 *Pieces of fragmented chromosomes can join with pieces from the same or from different chromosomes. Most single breaks rejoin as before, since the proximity of ends at a point of breakage favors their union.*

A chromosome broken into two or more pieces has "sticky" ends at the points of breakage, each of which can rejoin with another "sticky" end but not with a normal end. Ordinarily, terminal genes called *telomeres* seal off the ends of a normal chromosome so that they cannot join with others. The two ends produced by a single break usually rejoin as before even when other sticky chromosome ends occur in the same nucleus. It appears that the proximity of sticky ends favors their rejoining in a *restitutional union,* which restores the original linear order of the chromosome segments. When, however, the ends which unite come from different breaks (from the same or different chromosomes), a new chromosomal arrangement results. Such unions are of the *nonrestitutional,* or *exchange,* type. The number of unions is related, of course, to the number of breaks.

Although high-energy radiations produce many chromosome breaks, the number of breaks they cause is influenced by the metabolism of the cell. Thus, the number of breaks (1) increases when, during irradiation, the cell's oxygen supply is increased or its reducing substances are destroyed; and (2) decreases when, during irradiation, nitrogen replaces air. The joining of two sticky ends is a metabolic reaction that apparently involves adenosine triphosphate, appropriate enzymes, and protein synthesis (see p. 85). Replacing air by oxygen after irradiation enhances joining; replacing air by nitrogen after irradiation inhibits joining. Consequently, restitution is less likely if nitrogen replaces air after irradiation, since ends from the same break stay open for a longer time. Oxygen thus has two contrary effects on rearrangement frequency – it increases the number of breaks during irradiation, but afterwards promotes restitution.

14·2 *A single chromosome break can result in chromosome segments without a centromere, and can lead to the formation of chromosomes with two centromeres. The acentric segments are usually lost, but the dicentric chromosomes can block nuclear division or enter a special chromosomal cycle.*

Let us consider the consequences of a single *chromosome break,* that is, a break through both chromatids (Figure 14-1). Diagram 1 shows a normal chromosome (its chromatids are not shown) whose centromere is indicated by a black dot. In diagram 2 the chromosome is broken; and in diagram 3, the broken chromosome has replicated to form an identical daughter chromosome. The union of a and b, a′ and b′, a′ and b, or a and b′ would be restitutional. In diagram 4 we see the results of nonrestitutional unions: one *acentric chromosome* (without a centromere) and one *dicentric chromosome* (with two centromeres). Diagram 5 shows the acentric chromosome being pulled toward neither pole in anaphase while the dicentric one is pulled toward both poles at once. Consequently, the acentric chromosome is not included in either daughter nucleus, and is lost to both. The dicentric chromosome forms a *bridge* which by hindering migration to the poles can prevent both daughter nuclei from receiving any of its chromosomal material. Thus, the dicentric chromosome, too, may be lost. Sometimes, however, the bridge snaps (usually into unequal pieces) so that a piece with one centromere goes to each pole; after replication, a new dicentric chromosome can form in one or both daughter nuclei, and once again make a bridge at the next anaphase. In this manner, a *bridge-breakage-fusion-bridge cycle* can occur in successive nuclear generations. (Under similar conditions, shorter dicentrics break more often than longer ones.) A bridge which fails to break can tie the two daughter nuclei together and interfere with subsequent nuclear division. Such interference may have a much greater effect than the unequal distribution of the genes located in the bridge.

Detriment or death to daughter cells can result from the loss of genetic material when an acentric or dicentric fragment is left out of a daughter nucleus. Furthermore, a succession of bridge-breakage-fusion-bridge

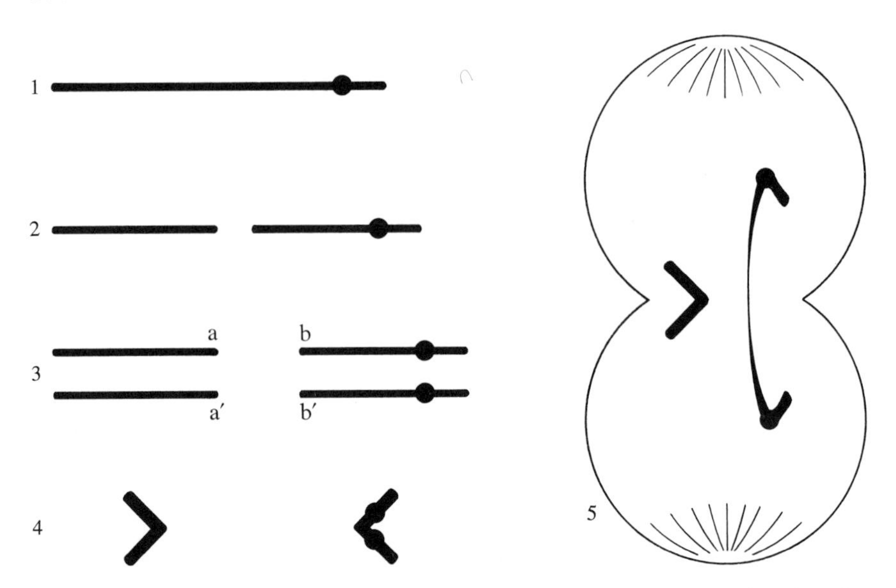

Figure 14-1. Consequences of a single nonrestituting chromosome break. Diagram 4 shows the chromosomes as they are contracted prior to metaphase.

cycles may be harmful to future cell generations because of abnormal quantities of chromosomal regions received.

Such chromosome breaks as those above can occur in either the somatic or the germ line. Consequently, *aneuploid* gametes, that is, those with some genes of incorrect ploidy, may arise. Since genes are physiologically inactive in the gametes of animals, an aneuploid gamete can join with a normal gamete to form a zygote which may subsequently suffer harmful or lethal effects. In many plants, on the other hand, the meiotic products form a gametophyte generation during which genes are active, so the detrimental effects of aneuploidy are usually seen before fertilization.

14·3 *Most unions occur during interphase. After replication, a nonrestituted chromatid becomes a nonrestituted chromosome.*

Sometimes a break involves only one chromatid of a chromosome. For such *chromatid breaks* restitution is more likely than for chromosome breaks, since the unbroken strand serves as a splint to hold the newly produced ends close to each other. We should note, however, that what appears under the microscope as a break involving only one chromatid may be a chromosome break which at that time has restituted one chromatid.

When restitution of chromatid fragments does not take place, nonrestitutional chromosome fragments result if the fragments last long enough to replicate. To be detected cytologically, a chromatid or chromosome break produced during interphase usually has to persist without restitution until

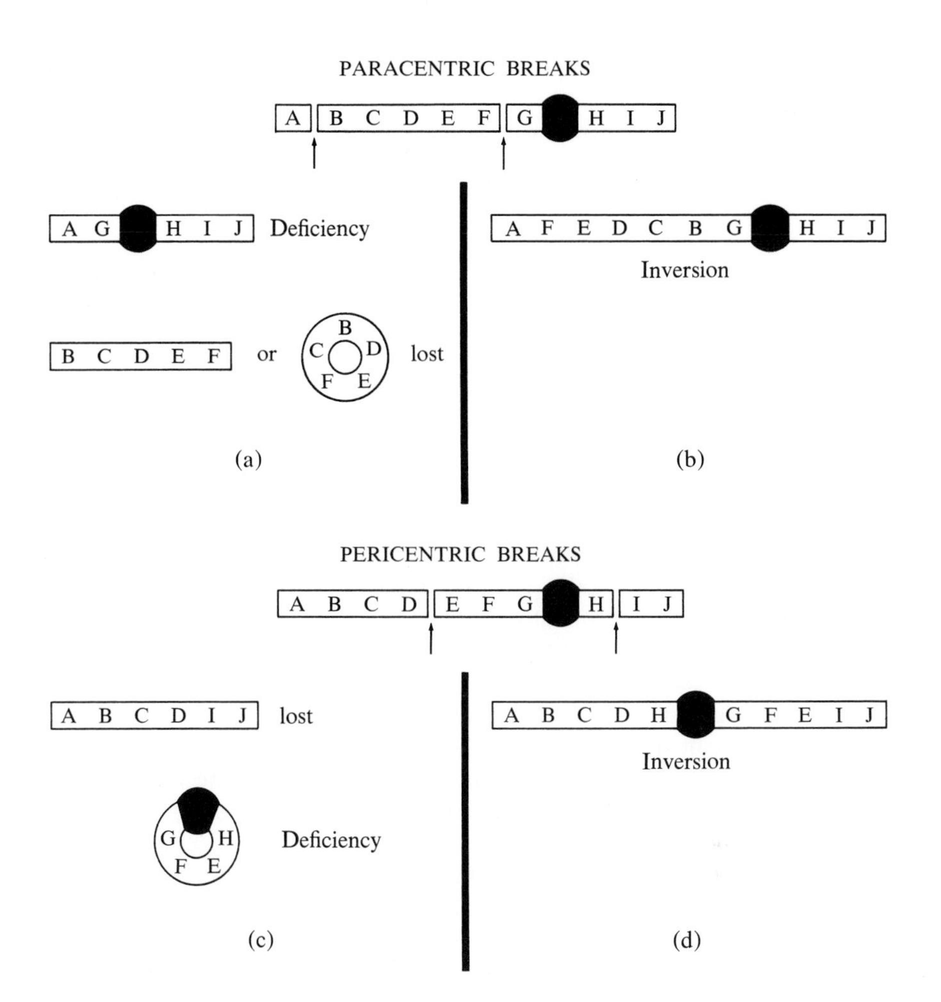

Figure 14-2. Some consequences of two breaks in the same chromosome.

nuclear division occurs. Some breaks induced in metaphase chromosomes may not be visible, because fragments can be held together by the nongenetic material in a chromosome, To detect such breaks, we would have to wait until the next division. Since nearly all ends resulting from breaks are not sticky when the chromosome is contracted (as it is during nuclear division) union is less likely at this time than between late telophase and early prophase. The later a break occurs in the late-telophase–early-prophase period, the less likely that its ends will join. Broken ends produced from early prophase to late telophase have the maximum time for joining and probably also the greatest chance for crossunion, that is, nonrestitutional union.

As mentioned earlier, the consequences of single nonrestituted chromatid breaks are similar to those of single nonrestituted chromosome breaks. Hence, the following discussion will be restricted to chromosome breaks that fail to restitute. We should not think, however, that chromatid breaks are less frequent or less important than chromosome breaks.

14·4 *Two nonrestituted breaks in one chromosome can result in deficiency, inversion, or duplication.*

In a chromosome with two breaks, the two points of breakage may be *paracentric* (to one side of the centromere) or *pericentric* (with the centromere between them) as shown in Figure 14-2.

(1) *Deficiency.* Let us consider a chromosome with segments in the order ABCDEFG.HIJ, where the centromere is represented by the period between G and H (Figure 14-2). Paracentric breaks (say, between A and B, and between F and G) give rise to a centric chromosome, AG.HIJ, deficient for the piece BCDEF after the sticky ends at A and G join. The ends of the acentric fragment can join to form a ring chromosome. The acentric piece is usually lost before the next nuclear division. When the breaks are pericentric (for instance, between D and E, H and I) the acentric end pieces are lost even if they join together (Figure 14-2c). The centric piece can survive if its ends join to form a ring and if the deficient sections are not essential. Such a ring is at a disadvantage because a single crossing over with another chromosome (in rod or ring form) results in a dicentric chromosome.

A nondividing nucleus in which breakage or another structural change occurs is still *euploid* (that is, its genes remain in the normal ratio) since it neither gains nor loses any genetic material. The daughter nuclei formed by such a nucleus, however, will likely be aneuploid: *hyperloid* if chromosomes or chromosome parts are in excess; *hypoploid* if segments are missing.

(2) *Inversion.* Two breaks in the same chromosome can lead to the inversion of a chromosomal segment (Figure 14-2b, d). We can see in the figure that the middle piece becomes inverted with respect to the end pieces. In this manner, paracentric or pericentric inversions (both euploid rearrangements) result.

(3) *Duplication.* If the joining of ends made by two breaks is delayed until after the chromosome is replicated, the pieces can join to form a chromosome with an internal region repeated, or duplicated (Figure 14-3); neither, either, or both of the regions involved in the duplication may be inverted with respect to the original arrangement. The remaining pieces may join to form a deficient chromosome. If the duplicated region is small and does not contain a centromere, the chromosome may survive.

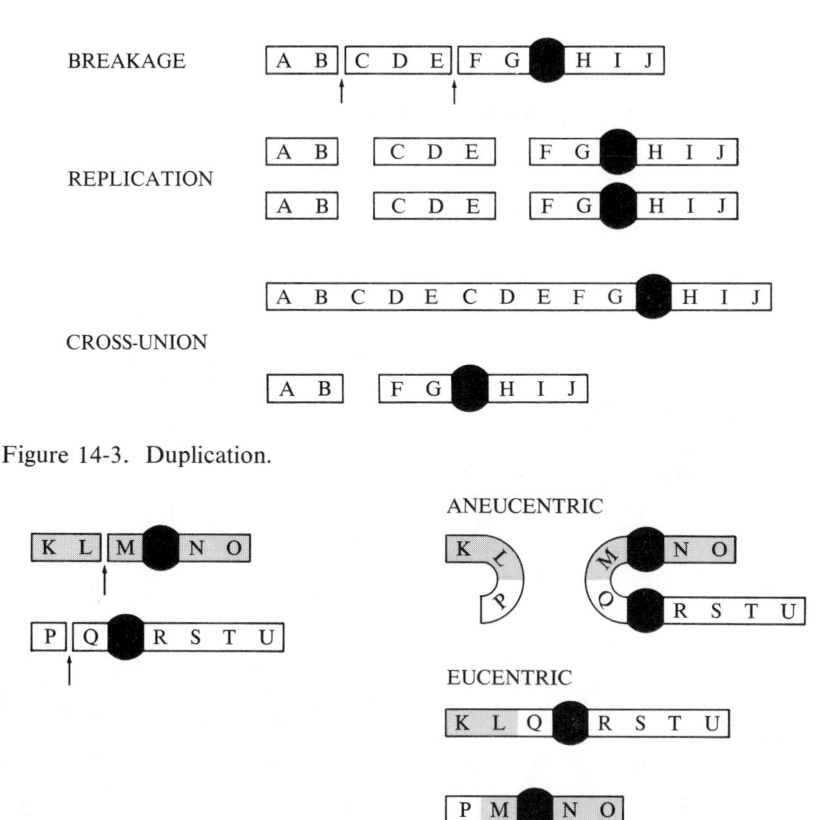

Figure 14-3. Duplication.

Figure 14-4. Reciprocal translocation between nonhomologous chromosomes.

14·5 *A nonrestituted break in each of two chromosomes can result in a reciprocal translocation or a half-translocation.*

If two nonhomologous chromosomes are each broken at one point, the two centric pieces can unite to form a dicentric chromosome (Figure 14-4). The two acentric pieces (which may join together) are lost in the next division. The product of such a mutual exchange of chromosomal segments is called a *reciprocal translocation;* the *aneucentric type* is often lethal. Reciprocal translocations of *eucentric type* are equally likely to occur, and are less frequently lethal. In individuals heterozygous for this kind of exchange (Figure 14-5), that is, with one eucentric reciprocal translocation between two pairs of chromosomes, gametes are formed with deficiencies and duplications if they receive one but not both members of the reciprocal translocation.

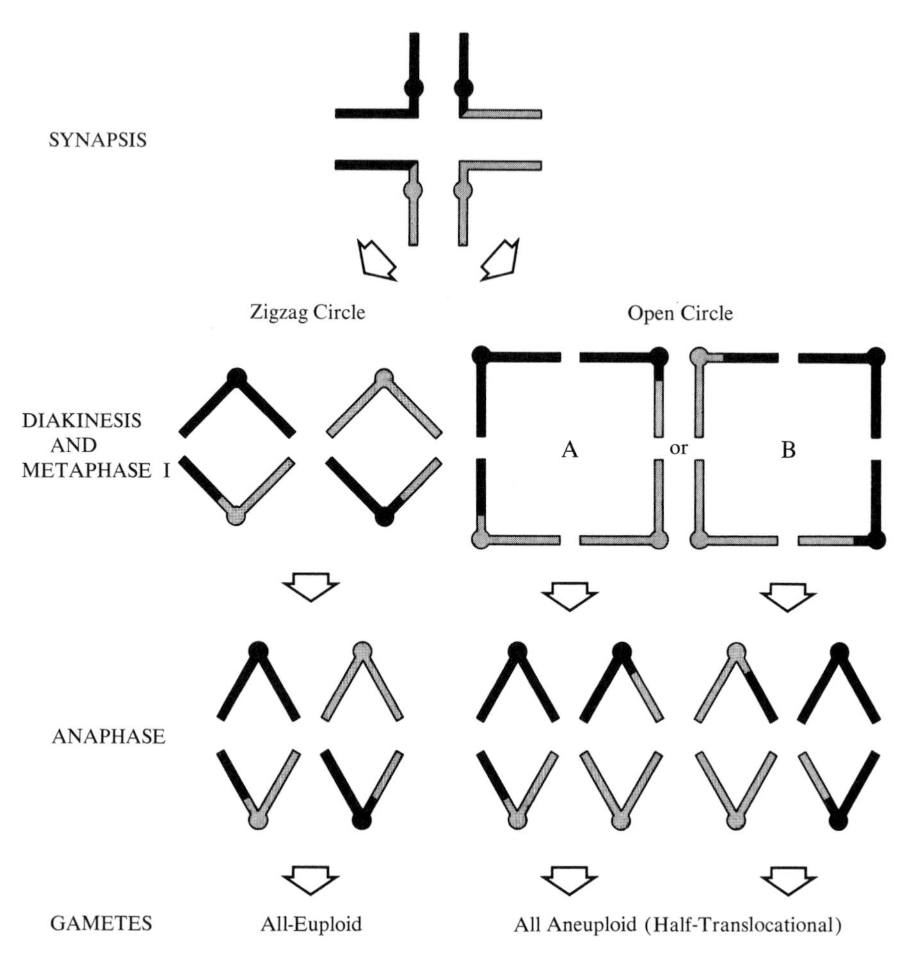

Figure 14-5. Diagrammatic representation of segregation in eucentric reciprocal translocation heterozygotes. (Chromatids not shown; the spindles – also not shown – have their poles oriented vertically.)

When chromosomes are located in a relatively small nuclear volume, no broken end is far from any other. Hence, if one of the two unions needed for reciprocal translocation occurs, the other usually does also. (Such is the case in the nucleus of Drosophila sperm just after fertilization.) In cells which have a relatively large nuclear volume (like oocytes), however, the distance between the broken ends of nonhomologs is so great that reciprocal translocation is a rare event. Even if one cross-union occurs, the two other broken ends usually fail to join to each other, and a *half-translocation* results. As we might expect, the unjoined fragments can cause descendant cells to die or to develop abnormally. Half-translocations can also occur when heterozygotes for a eucentric reciprocal translocation undergo segregation and only one of the two rearranged chromosomes is present in a gamete (Figure 14-5).

When each member of a pair of homologs is broken once, the breaks are usually at different places. Hence, reciprocal translocation of the aneucentric type will result in a dicentric and an acentric chromosome; on the other hand, a eucentric reciprocal translocation will produce two eucentric chromosomes, one with a deficiency and the other with a duplication.

CHANGES INVOLVING UNBROKEN CHROMOSOMES

14·6 *The nucleus of a euploid cell contains one or more whole chromosome sets, or genomes.*

Most sexually-reproducing species are diploid. Each gamete contributes one *genome,* or set of chromosomes, to the zygote to maintain the diploid chromosome number. Oenothera, the evening primrose, is one such sexually-reproducing organism. Cytological examination of a giant type of Oenothera called *gigas,* however, shows that it has three genomes; in other words, it is *triploid.* Other plants, with four chromosome sets, are *tetraploids;* and still others have six or eight genomes. The occurrence of extra genomes is called *polyploidy.* Changes in genome number are euploid since normal gene and chromosome ratios are maintained.

14·7 *The number of genomes can increase by allopolyploidy.*

Ploidy can increase when two species are crossed and each contributes two or more genomes to form a third species, which is said to be *allopolyploid* (Figure 14-6). Cultivated wheat is an allopolyploid organism. As we might expect, allopolyploids often show characteristics of both parent species.

14·8 *The number of genomes can increase by autopolyploidy.*

The ploidy of a nucleus can also increase by the addition of genomes of the same kind as those already present – resulting in *autopolyploidy.* Autopolyploidy can arise in several different ways.

(1) If anaphase of mitosis is abnormal, the doubled number of chromosomes may be included in a single nucleus. Subsequent normal divisions thus will give rise to polyploid daughter nuclei. Autopolyploidy can be artificially induced in a number of plants and animals by colchicine or its synthetic analog, colcemide, drugs which destroy the spindle and thereby prevent chromosome movement during anaphase. Mechanical injury, ir-

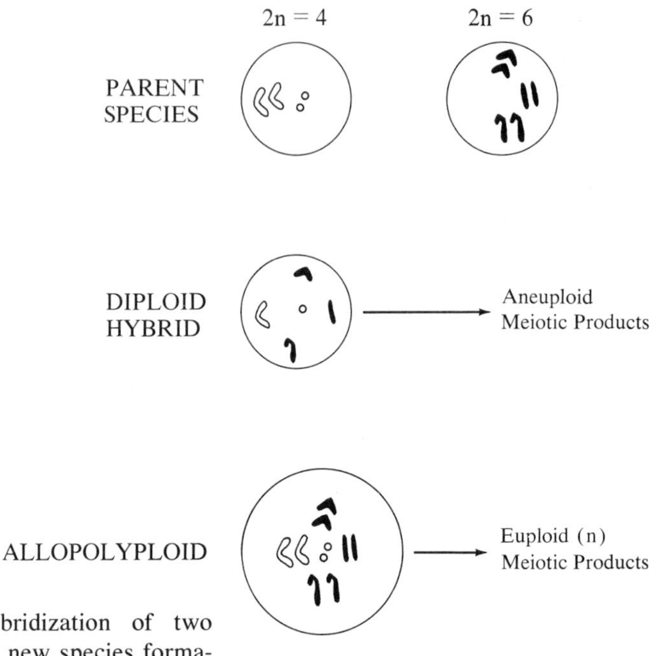

Figure 14-6. Hybridization of two species leading to new species formation by means of allopolyploidy.

radiation, and environmental stresses like starvation, and extremes of temperature can also cause autopolyploidy.

(2) Sometimes two of the haploid nuclei produced by meiosis fuse to form a diploid gamete. After union with a haploid gamete, it forms a triploid zygote.

(3) Some haploid organisms undergo meiosis. Although the gametes formed usually contain only part of a genome, some contain a complete genome. Fertilization between two haploid gametes produces a diploid zygote.

(4) Females of certain moths produce haploid eggs; others produce diploid eggs. Both types start development *parthenogenetically,* that is, without fertilization. During development, however, nuclei fuse in pairs to establish the diploid and tetraploid conditions. In such organisms, normal parthenogenesis leads to normal diploidy and tetraploidy.

The Jimson weed, Datura, shows autopolyploidy: some forms are haploid; others diploid, triploid, or tetraploid. Autopolyploidy also occurs in animals. For example, the water shrimp (Artemia), the sea urchin (Echinus), the roundworm (Ascaris), and the moth (Solenobia) have autotetraploid species. Triploid and tetraploid embryos are found in a variety of mammals. Polyploid larvae of salamanders and of frogs also have been found. Triploid and tetraploid females occur in Drosophila (normally diploid); haploid somatic parts have been found in some fruit flies.

As we saw in earlier chapters, changes in ploidy usually occur during gametogenesis and fertilization. Autopolyploidy is a normal process in certain somatic tissues of man (liver cells, for instance). This kind of autopolyploidy is accomplished by means of *endoreplication,* in which the products of replication remain in one nucleus.

14·9 *The salivary gland cells of Dipteran larvae contain giant chromosomes resulting from endoreplication and the synapsis of homologous strands.*

After endoreplication in some cells, all daughter chromosome strands remain synapsed, so the number of separate chromosomes does not increase. An example of this condition is found in the chromosomes of giant salivary gland cells of Dipteran larvae; these chromosomes are so thick that they can be seen easily under a light microscope. Although the chromosomes of Drosophila are highly coiled at metaphase (see Figure 12-4), they are relatively uncoiled during interphase. The chromosomes in the larval salivary gland nuclei are also in an uncoiled state at interphase, but differ in at least the following three ways.

(1) Each chromosome endoreplicates several times in succession: one chromosome gives rise to two; two to four; four to eight; and so forth. Endoreplication of a single chromosome has been found to occur as much as nine times, thereby producing 512 daughters.

(2) The daughter strands, instead of separating, all remain together with homologous loci side-by-side. The resulting chromosome looks like a many-threaded (polynemic) cable. Polynemic chromosomes are usually found in cells which never divide again.

(3) The original pair of homologs are paired at corresponding loci in what is called *somatic synapsis.* Consequently, the double cable can contain as many as 1024 chromosome strands.

Under the microscope these double cables appear cross-banded as a result of differences in density along their length (Figure 14-7). Bands (and interbands) are formed by the synapsis of similarly-dense regions in all the strands. The pattern of bands is so constant and characteristic that it is possible to identify not only each chromosome but particular regions within a chromosome on the basis of the banding pattern (Figure 14-8). Note also in the figure that in Drosophila the regions nearest the centromeres of all larval salivary gland chromosomes synapse to form a light-staining mass, the *chromocenter,* from which the double cables radiate.

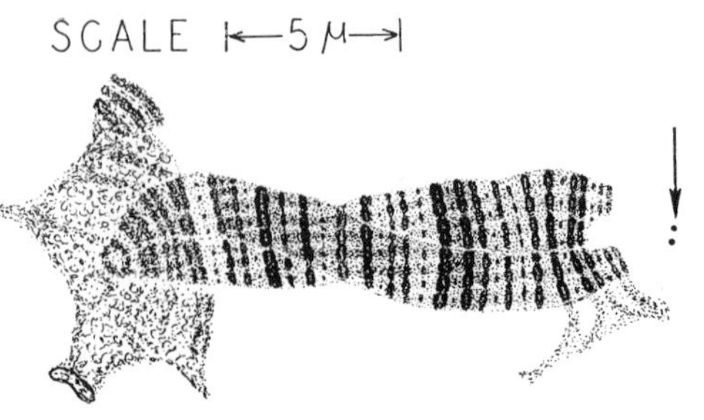

Figure 14-7. The pair of fourth chromosomes as seen in salivary gland nuclei (each homolog is highly polynemic) and at mitotic metaphase (arrow), drawn to the same scale. (By permission of The American Genetic Association, C. B. Bridges, "Salivary Chromosome Maps," Journal of Heredity, vol. 26, p. 62, 1935.)

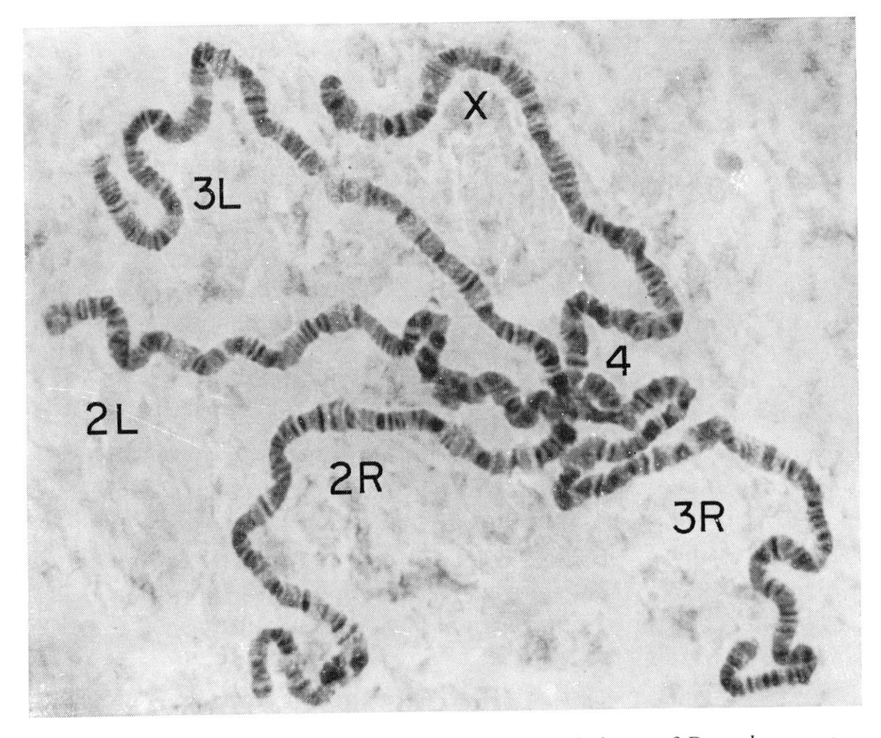

Figure 14-8. Salivary gland chromosomes of a female larva of *D. melanogaster*. Note the chromocenter, from which the giant chromosomes radiate. (Courtesy of B. P. Kaufmann; by permission of The American Genetic Association, Journal of Heredity, Frontispiece, vol. 30, No. 5, May, 1939.)

14·10 *Chromosomes in a genome can be added or lost.*

The addition or subtraction of chromosomes from a genome upsets the normal chromosomal and gene balance and results, therefore, in aneuploidy.

Nondisjunction of the small fourth chromosome in Drosophila can give rise to individuals with only one fourth chromosome or with three. One individual is said to be *monosomic* and the other, *trisomic*, instead of both being *disomic*. The incidence of nondisjunction in Drosophila can be increased by high energy radiations as well as by carbon dioxide and other chemical substances. Certain mutants have an increased frequency of nondisjunction. In human beings the evidence that older women are more likely to have trisomic children indicates that a metabolic defect associated with increased age increases the chance for nondisjunction.

As we noted earlier, chromosomes can also be lost after breakage.

14·11 *The loss of a chromosome is usually more detrimental to a diploid organism than the gain of one.*

A diploid individual contains in its two sets of chromosomes a balance of genes which is responsible for the proper functioning of that organism. The gain or loss of a chromosome will affect this balance; but the loss of a chromosome is likely to be of greater consequence to the individual since it brings about more of an imbalance. As we might expect, autopolyploids usually survive whole chromosome additions and subtractions better than diploids.

14·12 *A mutation in one cell of a multicellular organism can make that individual a mosaic with respect to chromosome number.*

A human being has been found who was diploid in some tissues and triploid in others (normally diploid). Such *mosaicism* for ploidy occurs both in plants and in animals, and can involve tissues of both the germ and somatic lines. If nondisjunction occurs in later development, monosomic and trisomic patches will occur in a diploid background. Such patches are often detrimental and sometimes lethal to the organism.

14·13 *Somatic cell mating gives rise to polyploid cells which subsequently undergo chromosome losses.*

Several mouse tissue culture lines are unique in that each has a number of morphologically distinct chromosomes. After certain pairs of such cell lines are mixed and grown together, hybrid cells with a single nucleus are produced in which the chromosome number is approximately equal to the sum of those of the two parent lines and in which chromosomes morphologically characteristic of each line are found. Over a period of several months, colonies of these hybrid cells show a reduction in chromosome number – probably due to nondisjunction. Similar results have been obtained with hybrid nuclei produced by the fusion of human cells with mouse cells. Although the *in vivo* frequency of such *somatic cell mating* in mammals is unknown, one possible instance has been reported in cattle.

Both members of a pair of twins were mosaic: each had the same two genetically-different types of erythrocytes. At three years of age twin A had blood of which 10% was of his own genotype and 90% of his twin's genotype. At eight years of age, however, twin A had blood corpuscles of three types: the two "parental" types (each making up 2% and a "hybrid" type (constituting 96% of the erythrocyte population).

Somatic cell mating also occurs in filamentous fungi such as Aspergillus and Penicillium (see Section 13·10). This process involves the formation of diploid nuclei by rare (probably accidental) nuclear fusions in a multinucleate mycelium containing haploid nuclei. The diploid nuclei that are formed multiply side-by-side with the haploid nuclei, and undergo chromosome loss by nondisjunction. (Recombination can also occur by means of mitotic crossing over.)

Questions and Problems

14·1 At least seven viral infections in man are associated with an increased incidence of chromosome rearrangements in white blood cells, e.g., chromosome loss, chromosome breakage, and other gross structural rearrangements. Apparently, the frequency with which these mutations involve different chromosomes is not random. What molecular explanation can you offer for such viral effects?

14·2 What are some causes of nonrestitution of sticky ends?

14·3 For an ordinarily diploid individual, parthenogenetic development as a haploid usually produces abnormalities. Development is sometimes less abnormal, however, if chromosome doubling occurs at an early developmental stage. Explain both observations.

14·4 Why are salamanders and rabbits resulting from parthenogenesis always female?

14·5 Is a diploid ever a polyploid? Explain.

14·6 How would you use an organism with giant polynemic chromosomes to correlate genetic and cytological events?

14·7 What role does the placenta play in the production of cattle twins with erythrocyte mosaicism?

14·8 Drosophila that are monosomic for either large autosome die in the egg stage. What do you expect of trisomics for either large autosome? Why?

14·9 Explain in molecular terms why in a diploid the loss of a chromosome is more detrimental than the addition of this chromosome.

14·10 Locate the chromocenter in Figure 14-7.

14·11 Which is more likely to have an abnormal distribution of chromosomes during meiosis, an autotetraploid or an allotetraploid? Explain.

14·12 Defend the statement that sex type in Drosophila depends on the balance between X's and autosomes.

14·13 What explanation can you give for the appearance of the Drosophila salivary gland chromosomes pictured below in A (courtesy of M. Demerec)? In B (courtesy of B. P. Kaufmann)?

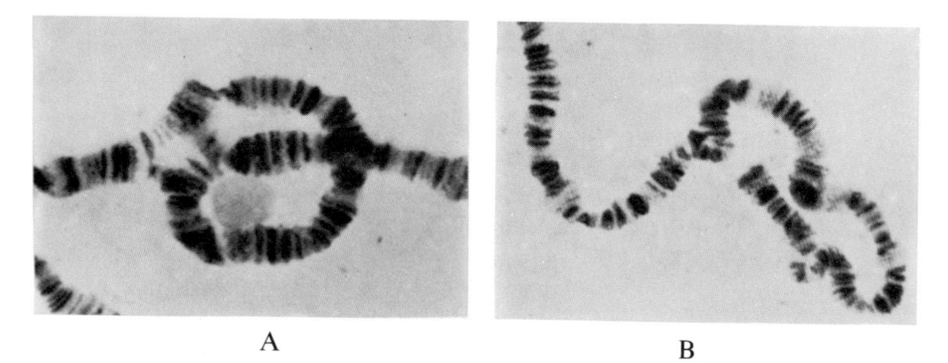

14·14 How can you explain the appearance of the corn chromosomes at pachynema pictured below in A (courtesy of M. M. Rhoades)? In B (courtesy of D. T. Morgan, Jr.)?

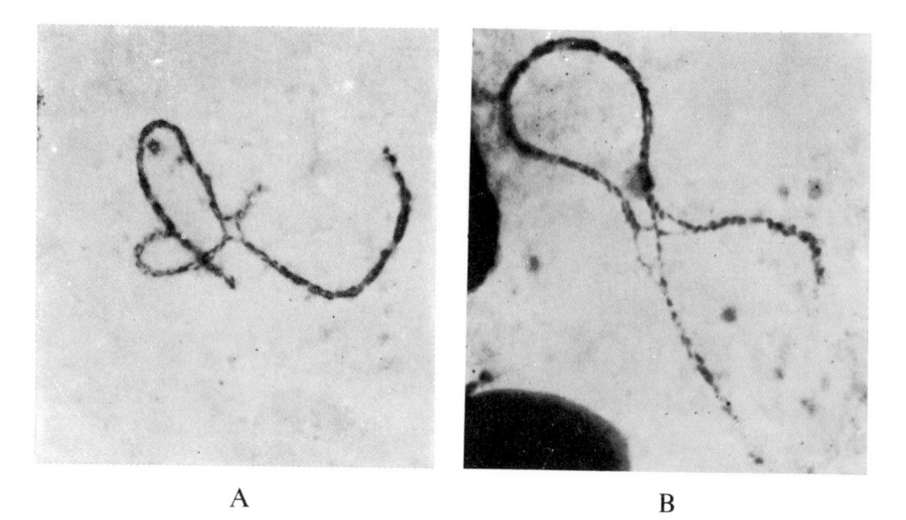

14·15 Diagram a single crossing over between two homologs, if they are
(a) both rod chromosomes;
(b) one a rod, one a ring;
(c) both rings.

14·16 Do you suppose the "mitotic crossing over" discussed in Section 13·10 occurs during mitosis? Explain.

References

Ephrussi, B., and Sorieul, S. 1962. Mating of somatic cells in vitro, in *Approaches to the Genetic Analysis of Mammalian Cells,* Merchant, D. J., and Neel, J. V. (Editors), Ann Arbor: University of Michigan Press, pp. 81–97.

Harris, H., and Watkins, J. F. 1965. Hybrid cells derived from mouse and man: artificial heterocaryons of mammalian cells from different species. Nature, Lond., 205: 640.

Kevin, P., Witkus, E. R., and Berger, C. A. 1966. Effects of kinetin on cell division in *Triturus viridescens.* Exp. Cell. Res., 41: 259–264. (Autopolyploid cells photographed at metaphase.)

Muller, H. J. 1954. The nature of the genetic effects produced by radiation, in *Radiation Biology,* Hollaender, A. (Editor), New York: McGraw-Hill Book Co., Inc., Chap. 7, pp. 351–473.

Nichols, W. W. 1966. Studies on the role of viruses in somatic mutation. Hereditas, 55: 1–27.

Nichols, W. W. 1966. The role of viruses in the etiology of chromosomal abnormalities. Amer. J. Human Genet., 18: 81–92.

Patau, K. 1963. The origin of chromosomal abnormalities. Pathologie-Biologie, 11: 1163–1170.

Russell, L. B. 1962. Chromosome aberrations in experimental animals. Progress in Medical Genetics, 2: 230–294.

Stone, W. H., Friedman, J., and Fregin, A. 1964. Possible somatic cell mating in twin cattle with erythrocyte mosaicism. Proc. Nat. Acad. Sci., U.S., 51: 1036–1044.

CHAPTER 15

Extranuclear Genes

In the first chapter we noted that DNA and RNA are found not only in nuclei and nuclear areas, but in other parts of the cell also. We decided that before we can consider such nucleic acids to be genetic material, they must be shown to contain information that is used for their own replication or to be transcripts that are themselves transcribed (p. 35). Let us now consider the occurrence, function, and properties of nucleic acids in organelles outside the nucleus to see whether they are genetic material.

15·1 *The genes of some microorganisms are nonmendelian since they are not distributed to progeny cells by means of a spindle during mitosis and meiosis. Other nonmendelian genes may be in the DNA of extranuclear organelles.*

We have seen that nucleated cells use a spindle mechanism in mitosis and meiosis to distribute the chromosomes in specific ways. The genes of these nuclear chromosomes, therefore, are also distributed in specific ways; for example, they undergo segregation during meiosis. Such genes are called *mendelian genes* since their distribution follows the segregation principle first discovered by Mendel for nuclear genes in meiotic organisms. Because *E. coli* does not have a spindle for such segregation, its chromosomes are said to carry *nonmendelian genes,* which nonetheless are distributed in a regular manner during bacterial division and can segregate from a diploid to a haploid condition.

When some microorganisms infect a cell, their genetic material can be considered extranuclear and nonmendelian since it is restricted to the cytoplasm and does not utilize the host's spindle apparatus. Rabbit poxvirus (a DNA virus), certain rickettsiae, and some RNA viruses are in this category. The endosymbionts found in the cytoplasm of Paramecium (kappa, lambda, and mu) are other sources of extranuclear nonmendelian genes. The genetic material of viruses located in the nucleus (TMV, for example) may not be integrated into a normally-segregating host chromosome; in such cases, the new genes within a host are considered to be nonmendelian even though they are nuclear. It was noted earlier that a particular mRNA of Paramecium behaves like a gene when in Didinium. We cannot yet classify this genetic material as mendelian or nonmendelian, however, until more is known about its mode of transmission. Although the RNA genetic material of Rous sarcoma virus seems to be nonmendelian, its DNA transcript is apparently integrated into a host chromosome where it probably acts as a mendelian gene.

We should note that a gene which does not segregate from an allele during meiosis is not necessarily an extranuclear or a typical nonmendelian gene, since certain loci (e.g., loci that are X- or Y-limited) occur in nuclear chromosomes and have no alleles from which to segregate. Furthermore, a nuclear chromosome with a centromere abnormality may be distributed in a nonmendelian manner. In organisms still evolving a meiotic mechanism or ones in which meiosis has degenerated, gene distribution may be somewhat irregular as compared with normal meiosis.

Various organelles outside the nucleus, some of which contain DNA, are not distributed to daughter cells by the spindle mechanism. Such DNA may be extranuclear nonmendelian genetic material.

15·2 *Plastids, cytoplasmic bodies, contain genetic material which is probably DNA. Nuclear and plastid genes interact and can affect chlorophyll production.*

Many plant cells contain cytoplasmic bodies called *plastids*. Some, the *chloroplasts*, are green because they contain chlorophyll; others, the *leucoplasts*, are white. Chloroplasts lose their pigment in the dark to become leucoplasts, but revert to chloroplasts upon exposure to sunlight. In corn, several mutations of nuclear genes affect the sequence of reactions leading to the manufacture of chlorophyll. One such mutation prevents plastids from producing any chlorophyll at all, so they become leucoplasts, which cannot function in photosynthesis.

Certain corn plants have mosaic leaves; that is, some leaves are striped green and white. The white parts, which contain leucoplasts that cannot become green, can survive by receiving nourishment from the green parts. This mosaic phenotype is apparently not due to a nuclear gene transmitted through a gamete, since striping persists even when all paternal and maternal nuclear chromosomes are replaced by means of matings with nonstriped individuals. The cause of this mosaicism is indicated by the following experiment. Sometimes a green-and-white striped portion of a plant gives rise to an ovary which develops into an ear of corn. When the kernels in such an ear are planted in rows which correspond to their positions in the cob, white and green seedlings occur in groups (Figure 15-1) as though a pattern of striping that occurred in the ovary had persisted in the cob. The greenness or whiteness of a seedling thus seems to be maternally determined. Support for this hypothesis is that the color of the par-

Figure 15-1. Groups of albino and non-albino seedlings from kernels planted in rows corresponding to their positions in a cob produced by a green-white striped plant.

ental part which forms the pollen (and, hence, the male gamete) has no influence on seedling color. Since pollen grains are not known to carry plastids and since the one key factor proves to be the color of the tissue giving rise to the ovary, it appears that only the plastids within an ovum determine seedling color.

Cells located at the border between green and white tissues contain plastids of both fully green and completely white types. These two kinds of plastids within the same cell seem to have no influence upon each other, and appear to develop according to their intrinsic capacities. When a zygote (or other cell) containing both kinds of plastids produces daughter cells which receive only white or only green plastids, these daughter cells give rise to sectors only of white or only of green tissue. Plastids thus seem to arise only from pre-existing plastids; and daughter plastids appear to be of the same color type as their parent. Since they are self-replicating, mutable (capable of being changed), and capable of replicating their mutant condition, plastids seem to contain at least one cytoplasmic gene. We should keep in mind, however, that chlorophyll formation (hence, striping) is influenced by nuclear as well as plastid genes, and that we have no evidence that the plastid gene (or genes) for chlorophyll consists of chloroplast DNA.

In another study, a cross of two all-green corn plants produced some green-and-white striped progeny. These striped plants prove to be homozygous for a mutant nuclear gene, *iojap* (*ij*), for which their parents were heterozygous. Since colorless plastids in ova of striped plants remain colorless in subsequent generations, even in homozygotes for the normal nuclear allele, the plastids' lack of color is not due to interference by *ij ij* in the biosynthetic pathway leading to the production of chlorophyll pigment. One possible explanation for this effect is that, in the presence of *ij ij*, a plastid gene essential for chlorophyll production is made permanently nonfunctional.

15·3 *Chlamydomonas seems to possess an extensive system of genes that (1) are transmitted usually by one sex type only, (2) do not segregate during meiosis, (3) can recombine postmeiotically, and (4) may be, in part, located in chloroplast DNA.*

Chlamydomonas reinhardi is a haploid, one-celled alga with two flagella and a single chloroplast. It can reproduce asexually by means of mitotic cell division to produce a colony. No sexual reproduction is observed between members of a single colony, which are all of the same mating type (either + or −). When individuals of different mating type are mixed together, they can pair, fuse, and produce zygotes. After two meiotic divisions, the zygote produces four cells which, when isolated, give rise to two colonies of the + mating type and two of the − mating type. It thus appears that the determinants for mating type are single mendelian genes (called mt^+ and mt^-).

The wild-type Chlamydomonas (*ss*) is sensitive to streptomycin, which also acts as a mutagen to induce streptomycin-resistant (*sr*) individuals. When *sr* individuals are crossed with *ss*, all progeny become streptomycin-resistant when the *sr* parent is mt^+. Essentially none of the progeny become *sr* when the *sr* parent is mt^-. Thus, *ss* and *sr* are not distributed to the zygote or its meiotic products as we might expect. These and other results indicate that the streptomycin resistance factor, *sr*, is produced by a nonmendelian gene. Streptomycin also causes a large number of Chlamydomonas prototrophs to become auxotrophs by mutating, apparently, other nonmendelian genes.

In rare cases, zygotes contain nonmendelian genes from both parents rather than just from the mt^+ parent. The progeny of such zygotes from crosses involving one or more nonmendelian genes show that (1) the nonmendelian genes can recombine postmeiotically; (2) some of the genes are linked to each other, others are unlinked; and (3) two different, seemingly allelic, mutants can recombine to produce either the wild-type allele or the corresponding "double" mutant.

Such studies indicate the existence of an extensive nonmendelian, though not necessarily extranuclear, gene system in Chlamydomonas. Some of its genes may be located in the chloroplast (whose DNA is reported to have a lower G + C content than cellular DNA as a whole).

15·4 *Mitochondria, which contain DNA, replicate themselves and some of their modifications.*

Mitochondria (Figure 15-2) are organelles consisting of a smooth outer membrane that is probably continuous with the endoplasmic reticulum and an inner membrane that forms double-layered folds, or cristae. The outer membrane seems to control the flow of materials in and out of the mitochondrion. The inner membrane, cristae, and elementary particles attached to it contain most of the respiratory enzymes involved in the process of oxidative phosphorylation – the main source of energy for the cell. Mitochondria have been seen to divide transversely, and probably arise from pre-existing mitochondria.

These organelles contain circular double-stranded DNA, composed of approximately 14,600 base pairs, which has a characteristic buoyant density. It does not pair with nuclear DNA when both are single-stranded. In Neurospora, mitochondrial DNA is conserved during vegetative multiplication and sexual reproduction. In the latter case, the DNA is transmitted predominantly by the maternal parent. Mitochondria contain a DNA polymerase and a DNA-dependent RNA polymerase which perhaps are used to transcribe mitochondrial DNA; at least some RNA found in mitochondria, however, is known to be a transcript of nuclear DNA. Some organisms with 80s ribosomes outside their mitochondria probably have 70s mitochondrial ribosomes (Euglena has 70s ribosomes in its chloroplasts, 80s ribosomes elsewhere).

Mitochondrial DNA may play a role in the genetics of yeast. Several mutant yeast strains (called "petite" mutants) form tiny colonies on agar. When such individuals are crossed with normal-sized ones, a 2:2 ratio of normal: petite results after segregation. These strains, which are caused by mutant nuclear genes, are called *segregational petites*. When normal yeast cells are treated with the acridine dye euflavin, numerous petite colonies arise which do not segregate regularly when crossed with normal yeast. The ease with which these *vegetative petites* are induced and the subsequent failure of the petite gene to segregate properly indicate that they are caused by a mutant nonmendelian gene. No change in mitochondrial morphology has been detected for petites; the slow growth of petites is due largely to the absence of respiratory enzymes known to reside in mitochondria. It has not yet been proved, however, that any of these enzymes are encoded in mitochondrial DNA.

In Neurospora a slow-growing strain, "poky," fails to show segregation when crossed with a wild-type strain. The trait is not linked to any nuclear

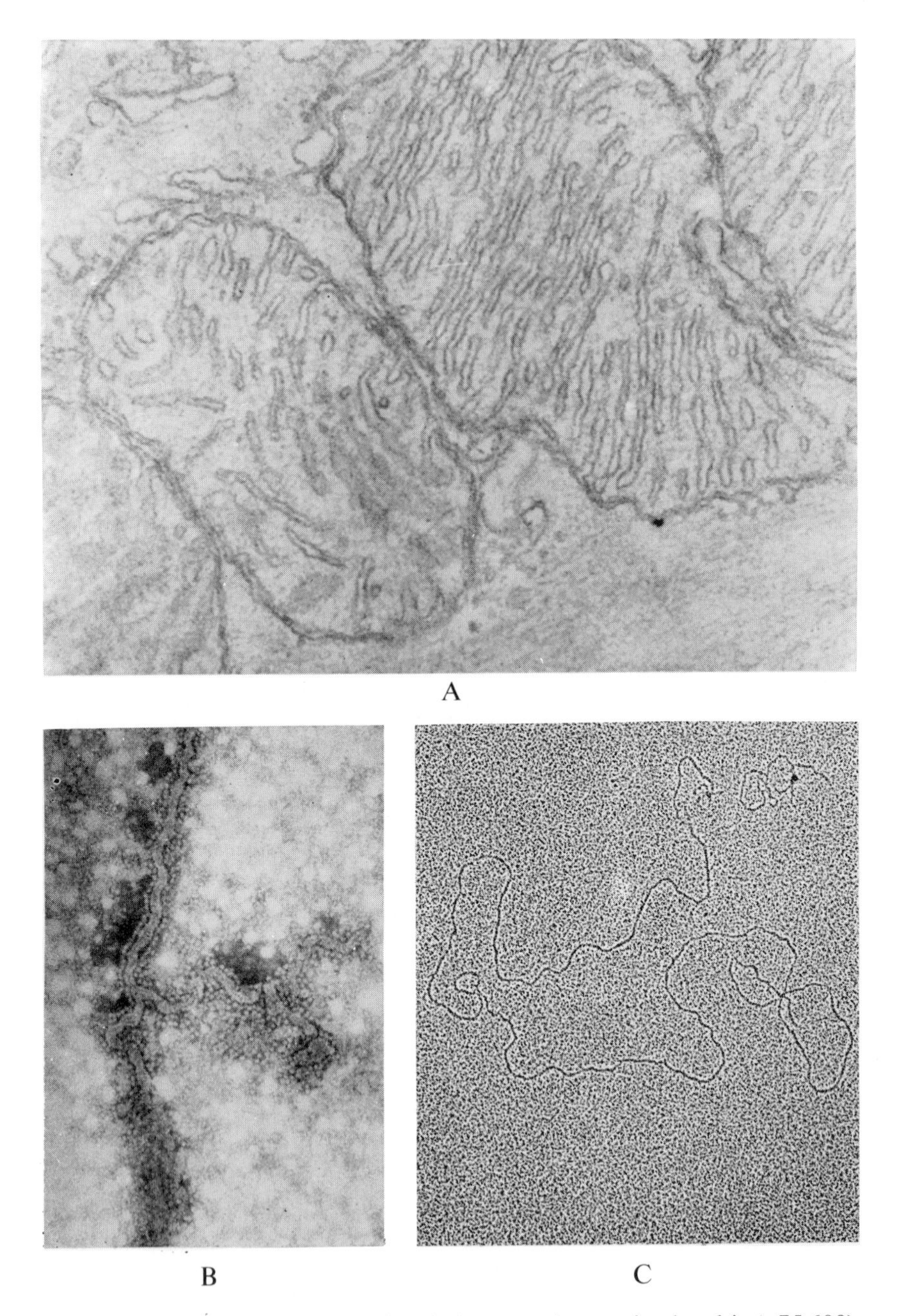

Figure 15-2. Electron micrographs of (A) mouse heart mitochondria (×75,600), (B) Neurospora mitochondria prepared to show cristae with elementary particles attached (×67,200), and (C) the outline of Neurospora mitochondrial DNA (×32,500). (Courtesy of Dr. Walther Stoeckenius, Rockefeller University, New York)

chromosome and is apparently due to a maternally-transmitted mutant nonmendelian gene. Poky individuals have morphologically abnormal mitochondria, in which an amino acid substitution has occurred in a structural protein. Young cultures of poky have no cytochromes a and b, but make an excess of a cytochrome c by derepression. As the culture ages, it starts producing cytochromes a and b, the excess cytochrome c is diluted out, and the phenotype approaches that of the wild type. The location of the nonmendelian genes responsible for poky is unknown.

Another maternally-transmitted mutant in Neurospora has a defective respiratory metabolism even though all the normal respiratory enzymes are present. This strain also has been found to have defective mitochondrial structural protein. Perhaps the gene encoding this protein will prove to be in mitochondrial DNA.

15·5 *The properties of centromeres, centrosomes, and kinetosomes indicate that they are structurally related. The DNA they contain seems to be episomal.*

A granular structure, the *centriole,* is sometimes seen within the *centrosome,* the organelle which serves as a pole at each end of the spindle in animal cells. Likewise, granules are sometimes seen within the *centromere,* an organelle structurally similar to the centriole. Furthermore, both centrosome and centromere granules appear to contain DNA. The DNA of the centromere is apparently a coiled thread which passes from one chromosome arm to the other.

Centromeres and centrosomes both are motile. Centromeres are sometimes attracted to each other, and are attracted to the centrosomes at anaphase. During the meiotic divisions preceding sperm formation in a particular mollusk, some chromosomes degenerate and release "naked" centromeres. These bodies group together at the centrosome and thereafter mimic centrosomal behavior and appearance exactly. Formerly part of a chromosome, the DNA of a centromere acts as an episome, since it now exists independently of that chromosome. Evidence indicates that the granular body at the base of each cilium or flagellum, the *kinetosome,* also contains DNA and is homologous to a centriole or centrosome. Perhaps kinetosomes – organelles responsible for ciliary and flagellar motion – also contain episomes or episomal derivatives.

The *kinetoplast* of Trypanosoma contains a significant amount of DNA as well as a histone-like protein. Such large cytoplasmic organelles, which are associated with mitochondria, are (like kinetosomes) involved with motility. DNA replication occurs synchronously in nucleus and kinetoplast; the latter can be damaged irreversibly by treatment with acridine dyes. The information stored in kinetoplast DNA is presently under investigation.

Questions and Problems

15·1 Criticize the statement that the same episome may be a mendelian gene at one time and a nonmendelian gene at another.

15·2 What is your opinion of the text's restriction of mendelian genes to nucleated cells that produce a spindle?

15·3 Should the "naked" centromeres referred to in the text be considered chromosomes that have been grossly deleted? Justify your answer.

15·4 In what respect does the episome F function like a centromere?

15·5 In what ways do you expect the properties of extranuclear genes to differ from the properties of nuclear genes?

15·6 Do you expect that RNA extranuclear genes will be found to be normal components of nucleated cells? Explain.

15·7 What evidence would you require for proof that the mitochondrion contains genetic material?

15·8 Account for the DNA reported in the cell membrane of red blood corpuscles, using your knowledge of the location of bacterial DNA and of cell structure.

15·9 Calculate the approximate molecular weight of mitochondrial DNA.

15·10 What are the theoretical and experimental implications of the finding that mitochondrial ribosomes may be 70s while extramitochondrial ribosomes in the same cell are 80s?

References

Barnett, W. E., and Brown, D. H. 1967. Mitochondrial transfer ribonucleic acids. Proc. Nat. Acad. Sci., U.S., 57: 452–458.

Brinkley, B. R., and Stubblefield, E. 1966. The fine structure of the kinetochore of a mammalian cell *in vitro*. Chromosoma, 19: 28–43. (Centromere structure.)

Chèvremont, M. 1963. Cytoplasmic deoxyribonucleic acids: their mitochondrial localization and synthesis in somatic cells under experimental conditions and during the normal cell cycle in relation to the preparation for mitosis. Sympos. Int. Soc. for Cell Biol., 2: 323–331.

Ephrussi, B. 1953. *Nucleo-Cytoplasmic Relations in Micro-Organisms.* Oxford: Clarendon Press.

Gillham, N. W. 1965. Linkage and recombination between nonchromosomal mutations in *Chlamydomonas reinhardi*. Proc. Nat. Acad. Sci., U.S., 54: 1560–1567.

Humm, D. G., and Humm, J. H. 1966. Hybridization of mitochondrial RNA with mitochondrial and nuclear DNA in agar. Proc. Nat. Acad. Sci., U.S., 55: 114–119.

Kroon, A. M., Borst, P., Van Bruggen, E. F. J., and Ruttenberg, G. J. C. M. 1966. Mitochondrial DNA from sheep heart. Proc. Nat. Acad. Sci., U.S., 56: 1836–1843.

Lima de Faria, A. 1956. The role of the kinetochore in chromosome organization. Hereditas, 42: 85–160. (Evidence that the centromere contains DNA.)

Macgregor, H. C., and Callan, H. G. 1962. The actions of enzymes on lampbrush chromosomes. Quart. J. Micr. Sci., 103: 173–203. (Evidence that the centromere contains DNA.)

Mitchell, M. B., and Mitchell, H. K. 1952. A case of "maternal" inheritance in *Neurospora crassa*. Proc. Nat. Acad. Sci., U.S., 38: 442–449.

Parsons, P., and Simpson, M. V. 1967. Biosynthesis of DNA by isolated mitochondria: Incorporation of thymidine triphosphate-2-C^{14}. Science, 155: 91–93.

Pollister, A. W., and Pollister, P. F. 1943. The relation between centriole and centromere in atypical spermatogenesis of viviparid snails. Ann. N.Y. Acad. Sci., 45: 1–48.

Reich, E., and Luck, D. J. L. 1966. Replication and inheritance of mitochondrial DNA. Proc. Nat. Acad. Sci., U.S., 55: 1600–1608.

Richards, O. C. 1967. Hybridization of *Euglena gracilis* chloroplast and nuclear DNA. Proc. Nat. Acad. Sci., U.S., 57: 156–163.

Rhoades, M. M. 1946. Plastid mutations. Cold Spring Harb. Sympos. Quant. Biol., 11: 202–207.

Rhoades, M. M. 1955. Interaction of genic and non-genic hereditary units and the physiology of non-genic inheritance, in (Vol. 1) *Encyclopedia of Plant Physiology,* Ruhland, W. (Editor), Berlin: Springer Verlag, pp. 19–57.

Sager, R. 1965. Genes outside the chromosome. Scient. Amer., 212 (No. 1): 70–79, 134.

Sager, R. 1966. Mendelian and non-Mendelian heredity: a reappraisal. Proc. Roy. Soc., B, 164: 290–297.

Sager, R., and Ishida, M. R. 1963. Chloroplast DNA in *Chlamydomonas*. Proc. Nat. Acad. Sci., U.S., 50: 725–730.

Sager, R., and Ramanis, Z. 1965. Recombination of nonchromosomal genes in *Chlamydomonas*. Proc. Nat. Acad. Sci., U.S., 53: 1053–1060.

Sherman, F., Stewart, J. W., Margoliash, E., Parker, J., and Campbell, W. 1966. The structural gene for yeast cytochrome c. Proc. Nat. Acad. Sci., U.S., 55: 1498–1504. (A protein in mitochondria encoded in the nucleus.)

Sinclair, J. H., and Stevens, B. J. 1966. Circular DNA filaments from mouse mitochondria. Proc. Nat. Acad. Sci., U.S., 56: 508–514.

Wilkie, D. 1964. *The Cytoplasm in Heredity*. London: Methuen & Co., Ltd.

Woodward, D. O., and Munkres, K. D. 1966. Alterations of a maternally inherited mitochondrial structural protein in respiratory-deficient strains of Neurospora. Proc. Nat. Acad. Sci., U.S., 55: 872–880.

CHAPTER 16

Regulation of Gene Synthesis and Distribution

In the preceding chapters we have looked at structural, functional, mutational, and recombinational properties of genetic material. We have not yet, however, dealt with all the kinds of information which must be contained in the genetic material of an organism. For the term "organism" implies an organization, an orderliness in structure and function, by which are coordinated not only the parts of a cell but the cells themselves. This ordering requires that genes act in specific patterns and sequences. We will now consider how genetic material is able to regulate its own function and shall look first at the genetic basis for the regulation of gene synthesis and distribution.

REGULATION OF GENE SYNTHESIS

16·1 *Genes contain information for making the enzymes which are involved in gene synthesis.*

In order to fully appreciate the regulation of gene synthesis *in vivo*, it is important to be familiar with the pathways for synthesizing the four most common deoxyribonucleoside 5′-triphosphates: dAPPP, dGPPP, dTPPP, and dCPPP (summarized in Figure 16-1). In uninfected *E. coli* the *ribo*nucleoside 5′-diphosphates of A, G, C, and U are converted by *deoxyribosidase*, or *reductase*, to the corresponding *deoxyribo*nucleoside 5′-diphosphates. ATP supplies energy for this reduction (loss of O from the 2′ position). Uracil is changed to thymine by *thymidylate synthetase*, which adds a methyl group to the pyrimidine at its 5 position. Since this enzyme can act only when the uracil is in the form of deoxyuridine monophosphate (dUP), dUPP (and dUPPP) must first be changed to this form in order to be used. The resulting dTP is phosphorylated by a specific dTP kinase in the following reaction: dTP + ATP $\xrightleftharpoons{\text{dTP kinase}}$ dTPP + ADP (adenosine 5′-diphosphate).

All four deoxyribonucleoside 5′-diphosphates become triphosphates through the action of other specific phosphorylating enzymes, *nucleoside*

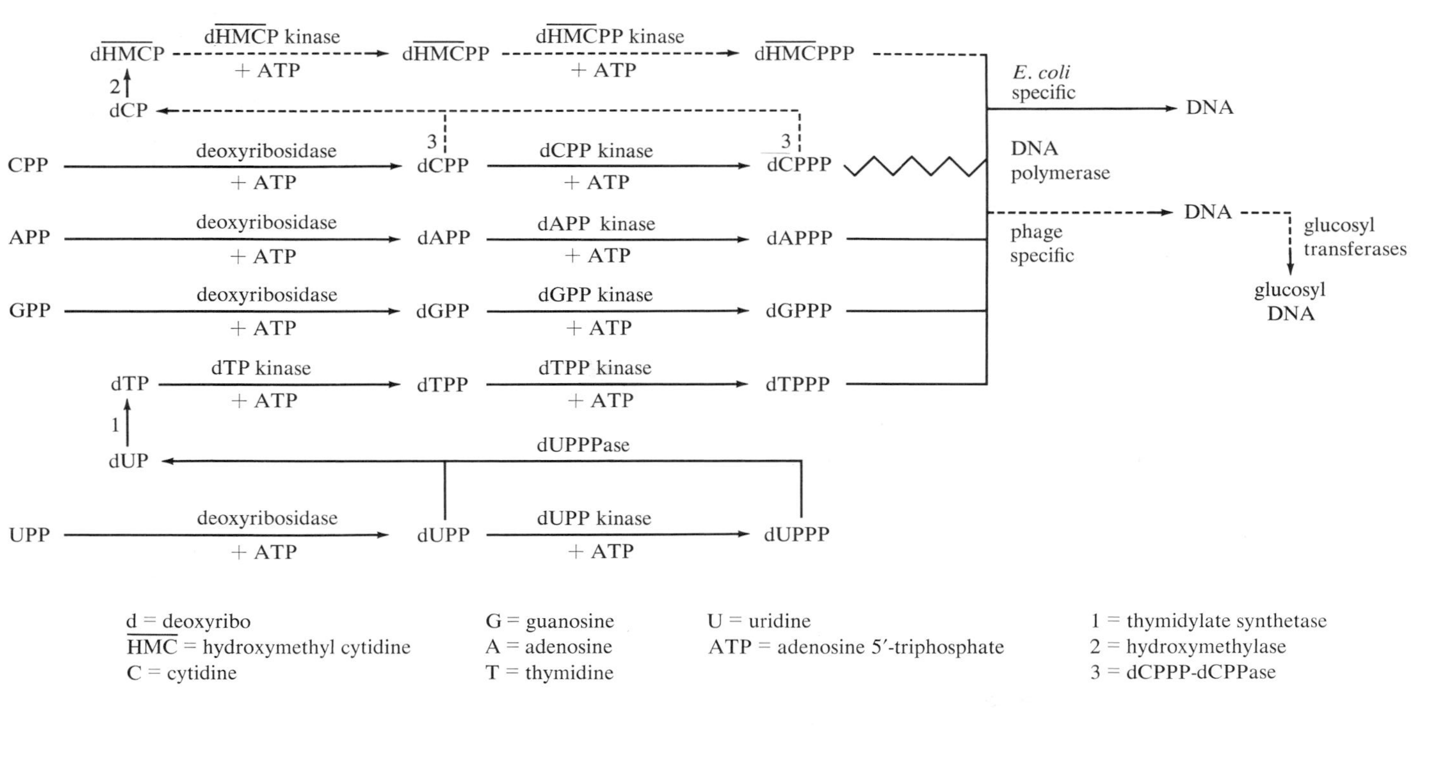

Figure 16-1. Enzymatic pathways leading to DNA synthesis in *E. coli.* Interrupted arrows denote reactions occurring and wavy line denotes reaction blocked in cells infected with T-even phages. (After M. J. Bessman, 1963)

diphosphate kinases, which catalyze the following general reaction: $\text{dXPP} + \text{ATP} \overset{\text{nucleoside diphosphate kinase}}{\rightleftharpoons} \text{dXPPP} + \text{ADP}$, where X is the nucleoside of C, A, G, or T. We should note that all these reactions in the organism require enzymes, which are themselves encoded in genes.

16·2 *The synthesis of phage DNA is regulated genetically in a T-even-phage–*E. coli *system by the DNA of the phage.*

Virulent phages carry instructions for making a number of specific proteins. Within two minutes after a T phage injects its DNA into *E. coli,* phage-specific RNA appears. Within four minutes phage-specific proteins appear; and within six minutes phage DNA is synthesized – at a rate five times that of bacterial DNA synthesis in uninfected cells. Roughly half an hour after infection 100 to 200 new phage are liberated by lysis of the host. It appears that after infection by a virulent phage, all DNA and mRNA synthesis in the bacterial cell is directed by the phage DNA.

The genetic material of T-even phages contains the information for making new enzymes, which (1) carry out syntheses unique to viral DNA production, (2) bypass host enzymes antagonistic to this process, (3) speed up synthesis of viral DNA by supplementing the action of the host's enzymes, and (4) degrade the host's DNA. The following examples demonstrate how DNA synthesis is regulated genetically in the T-even-phage–*E. coli* system.

We can detect the production of T-even phage DNA because instead of containing cytosine, as does *E. coli* DNA, it contains 5-hydroxymethyl cytosine ($\overline{\text{HMC}}$) to which glucose is attached (see Section 2·9). Within several minutes after infection by a T-even phage, dCP in the pathway of phage DNA synthesis is converted to d$\overline{\text{HMC}}$P by a *hydroxymethylase.* This enzyme is newly produced, since uninfected cells or cells infected with T5 (which has no $\overline{\text{HMC}}$ in its DNA) have no hydroxymethylase activity. Through the action of specific monophosphate and diphosphate kinases (likewise produced only in T-even infected cells), d$\overline{\text{HMC}}$P is phosphorylated to d$\overline{\text{HMC}}$PPP. In T2-infected cells another new enzyme appears which splits pyrophosphate from dCPPP and *orthophosphate* (*P*) from dCPP to form dCP, the substrate for making d$\overline{\text{HMC}}$P. This enzyme, *dCPPP-dCPPase,* has a high dephosphorylating activity but has no effect upon d$\overline{\text{HMC}}$PPP. Consequently, it is not surprising that C is not found in the DNA of T-even phages.

In cells infected with T-even phages, a DNA polymerase uses the d$\overline{\text{HMC}}$PPP, dAPPP, dGPPP, and dTPPP to make phage DNA. This enzyme appears to be phage-induced since it shows an especially high level of activity in phage-infected cells. Since the DNA polymerases from uninfected and T2-infected cells are different in various characteristics, a new DNA polymerase, *T2 DNA polymerase,* apparently is formed in

T2-infected *E. coli.* Another phage-induced enzyme, a DNase, is thought to destroy host DNA.

The proportion of $\overline{\text{HMC}}$ that has glucose attached to it differs in the different T-even phages. The glucose residues are added to $\overline{\text{HMC}}$ in already-formed DNA by *glucosyl transferases,* which transfer glucose from uridine diphosphate glucose (not shown in Figure 16-1) to the $\overline{\text{HMC}}$. Since such enzymes are not found in uninfected cells, they must be encoded in the phage DNA. The DNA of T-even phages also encodes a new thymidylate synthetase and a *DNA methylase* which converts some adenine to 6-methyl adenine in the completed DNA polymer. (ϕT3, on the other hand, contains no 6-methyl adenine because it produces an enzyme, *SAM-ase,* which digests the methyl donor S-adenosylmethionine.) The DNA of ϕT2 and ϕT4 apparently encodes a *polynucleotide kinase* which catalyzes the transfer of orthophosphate from ATP to the 5′-hydroxyl termini of DNA, RNA, short polynucleotides, and even nucleoside 3′-monophosphates.

16·3 *RNA viruses, like DNA viruses, contain information for their own replication.*

The genomes of RNA viruses serve as their own mRNA and encode the RNA-dependent RNA polymerases needed for replication *in vivo.* An exception is the satellite tobacco necrosis virus (STNV), which requires the presence of TMV in order to replicate. The polymerases of $\phi Q\beta$ and ϕMS2, on the other hand, cannot replicate the RNA of other phages. (The replication of STNV RNA by TMV RNA-dependent RNA polymerase indicates that these viruses are in part genetically homologous.)

RNA viruses can also affect the RNA's of their hosts. For example, poliovirus infection inhibits the synthesis of host RNA and induces the synthesis of poliovirus RNA. Furthermore, after a cell is infected with TMV, cytoplasmic rRNA is broken down and the ribonucleosides liberated are utilized in the synthesis of TMV RNA.

16·4 *DNA replication is regulated at the cellular, genomic, chromosomal, and intrachromosomal levels. Replication apparently occurs in units called replicons.*

One example of the regulation of DNA synthesis at the *cellular level* is that DNA replication occurs only during a particular part of interphase and early prophase I of meiosis. Another example of control at this level is seen in the lily, in which the microspore, which contains DNA, remains in interphase for several weeks. During this time *thymidine kinase* activity starts at a specific time and ends within 24 hours. Thus it appears that this enzyme, needed for DNA replication before mitosis, is formed for this purpose and is destroyed or inactivated after its task is completed.

An example of regulation at the *genomic level* is that DNA synthesis ceases when the nucleus is euploid for DNA – even if the nucleus fails to divide and contains one or more extra genomes. DNA synthesis is also regulated at the *chromosomal level* (certain chromosomes replicate later in interphase than others) and at the *intrachromosomal level;* that is, in some higher organisms, DNA synthesis begins at several places on a chromosome at once. (Remember that in bacteria, replication seems to be accomplished in a single sequential synthesis. Perhaps the chromosomes of higher organisms consist of fibers made up of a series of circular DNA duplexes – each one, say, about the size of the *E. coli* chromosome – joined linearly by means of polypeptide linkers.)

In our discussion of transformation (Chapter 8), we implied that donor DNA does not replicate unless it is integrated into the host chromosome. The host chromosome seems to be a complete replicating unit, or *replicon,* whereas the donor DNA fragment does not seem so. Episomes such as the DNA of temperate phages, sex factors, and substituted sex factors must also be replicons since they themselves contain the information necessary for their replication. In abortive transduction, however, the transducing phage contains genetic material that must be a defective replicon since the unintegrated loci cannot replicate. Mutant types of F are known which cannot replicate when free but can when integrated in the *E. coli* chromosome, where they are part of a functioning replicon. When a normal episome is integrated, apparently only the replicon of the host chromosome is operative.

REGULATION OF GENE DISTRIBUTION

16·5 *Some aspects of mitosis and, probably, amitosis are under genetic control.*

(1) *Unicellular organisms.* One-celled organisms such as bacteria and blue-green algae have nuclear areas with no nuclear membrane. Even such simple organisms seem to have a special mechanism for gene distribution to progeny cells. In *E. coli,* for example, chromosome replication and distribution apparently involve a replicon whose activity is synchronized with the replication of the portion of cell membrane to which it is attached. Single-celled organisms with a nucleus usually divide by mitosis, in which a spindle separates the chromosomes. A Paramecium usually contains, in addition to a diploid micronucleus which divides mitotically, a highly polyploid *macronucleus* (about 1000 N) which divides amitotically by pinching into two parts. Since the macronucleus apparently does not become aneuploid even after many successive divisions, some mecha-

nism must cause whole genomes to separate from one another when daughter macronuclei are formed. The mechanism and genetic control of such amitotic divisions are as yet unknown.

(2) *Multicellular organisms.* Nuclei of multicellular organisms usually divide mitotically. In such divisions the orientation of the spindle relative to other cells or nuclei is under genetic control. In the snail Limnaea, a single gene pair in the diploid mother determines the orientation of the spindle during the first two cleavage divisions of the fertilized egg. When the mother carries the normal allele, the spindle is oriented in one particular direction, and a snail is formed whose shell is coiled right-handedly. When the mother is homozygous for a mutant allele, however, the spindle is in the opposite direction and gives rise to a snail whose shell has a left-handed coil.

The control of gene distribution is clearly important in cells whose chromosomes become polyploid (as in the human liver) or polynemic (as in the Dipteran larval salivary gland). The strands of a polynemic chromosome may be prevented from separating by histones which bind them together. The rate of mitosis, an important aspect of gene distribution, is also under genetic control.

16·6 *Differences in gene distribution in somatic and germinal cells can occur for genetic reasons.*

In one species of the roundworm Ascaris, the nuclei in the germ line contain a single pair of chromosomes. These chromosomes each contain several centromeres, only one of which is functional. When germ-line nuclei first enter the somatic line, their chromosomes break up into a number of small, linear fragments whose ends are sealed off. Mitotic behavior, nevertheless, remains normal since each chromosome fragment retained in the somatic line has a centromere. Because chromosome fragmentation in Ascaris takes place only in somatic cells, there must be a physiological difference between cells entering the somatic line and those remaining in the germ line.

Other unusual phenomena associated with gene distribution are also under genetic control. Mutant genes are known in Drosophila and corn which give rise to spindles whose fibers do not converge at the poles during meiosis (but which converge normally during mitosis). The divergent spindles lead to chromosome loss. In Sciara, the fungus gnat, whole chromosomes are eliminated in somatic nuclei during early cleavage stages. Moreover, paternally-derived chromosomes are eliminated in males during meiosis.

In corn plants that have a particular rearrangement of chromosome 10, the centromeres of most chromosomes are nonfunctional during meiosis but not mitosis. These chromosomes are still able to migrate to the poles during meiotic anaphase because of new, functional centromeric regions which appear near each end. Such *neocentromeres* are also formed in mutant strains of rye and other cereal plants.

16·7 *Crossing over and synapsis are under genetic control.*

Crossing over usually occurs at exactly corresponding points in two non-sister strands. Consequently, no deficient or duplicated segments are produced and euploidy is maintained even though recombination between homologs occurs. Synapsis and chiasma formation in meiosis help distribute the homologs in such a way as to prevent the gain or loss of whole chromosomes.

Specific genes are known (one occurring in corn) which not only lack synaptic attraction for their alleles but also prevent or destroy synapsis at other loci. In contrast to such genes are those (collochores, for example) which assist the synapsis of homologs (see Section 12·7). In the Drosophila male, which has no crossing over and hence no typical chiasmata, the collochores serve to hold homologs together until anaphase I.

16·8 *Gene distribution during meiosis is influenced by meiotic drive.*

In organisms heterozygous for sufficiently large paracentric inversions (Figure 16-2), the partner chromosomes can synapse during meiosis at all regions except those adjacent to the points of breakage. Synapsis requires one partner to twist in the inverted region while the other partner does not. Should crossing over occur anywhere within the inverted region – for example, between C and D – the two noncrossover strands of the tetrad will each contain one centromere and will thus be *eucentric* – one with and one without the inversion. The two crossover strands will be *aneucentric;* that is, one will be acentric (duplicated for A and deficient for G.HIJ), and the other, dicentric (deficient for A and duplicated for the other region).

Individuals heterozygous for a large paracentric inversion are at a reproductive disadvantage, since crossing over within the inverted region results in genetically defective gametes. This reproductive disadvantage is sometimes avoided by a mechanism that prevents the dicentric produced by such a crossing over from entering a gamete.

Any such mechanism which causes the products of meiosis to occur in gametes in abnormal frequencies is said to produce a *meiotic drive* in favor of certain genotypes and against others. (The term "meiotic drive" is usually restricted to instances in which an *AA′* individual does not produce *A* and *A′* gametes in a 1 : 1 ratio.) A meiotic drive against the dicentric chromosome mentioned above is produced when the two meiotic divisions in a female occur in tandem, as they do in Drosophila.

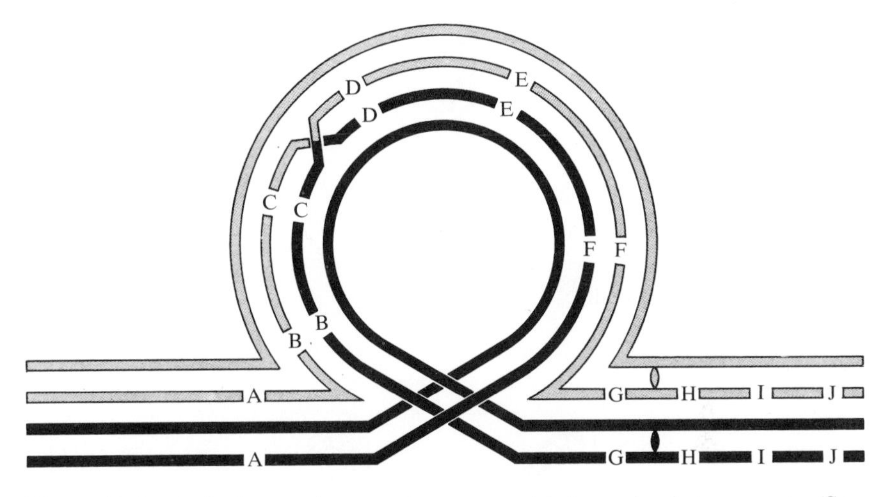

Figure 16-2. A single crossing over in a paracentric inversion heterozygote. (See text for explanation.)

In a Drosophila oocyte that is heterozygous for a paracentric inversion, a single crossing over within the inverted region likewise produces a dicentric chromosome at anaphase I (Figure 16-3). But this dicentric serves to hold the dyads at metaphase II so that the two eucentric monads, which did not undergo crossing over, proceed to the outermost two of the four poles at anaphase II. Therefore, at the end of telophase II the four meiotic products are arranged in a row: (1) one eucentric, (2) part of the dicentric, (3) the remainder of the dicentric, and (4) the other eucentric. Since one of the two end nuclei becomes the egg nucleus, the dicentric strand is prevented from entering the gametic nucleus. Consequently in Drosophila, paracentric inversions rarely give rise to aneuploid gametes of either sex type.

16·9 *Sexuality is under genetic control.*

In many organisms the sexes are of different genotypes. Both in Drosophila and man, the sexes are of the same ploidy; the balance between sex chromosomes and autosomes determines sexual type. The X chromosome of Drosophila causes development to proceed toward femaleness; the autosomes cause development toward maleness. When the ratio of number of X chromosomes to number of sets of autosomes is 1.0, the individual is female, whether it is diploid (2X + 2 sets of A), triploid (3X + 3 sets of A), or tetraploid (4X + 4 sets of A). In individuals with haploid tissues (1X + 1 set of A), these parts are female. When the chromosome ratio is 0.5 (1X + 2 sets of A), the result is male. More extreme ratios give rise to "supersexes": 0.33 (1X + 3 sets of A) results in sterile supermales; 1.5 (3X + 2 sets of A) sterile superfemales (Figure 16-4A, B). Intermedi-

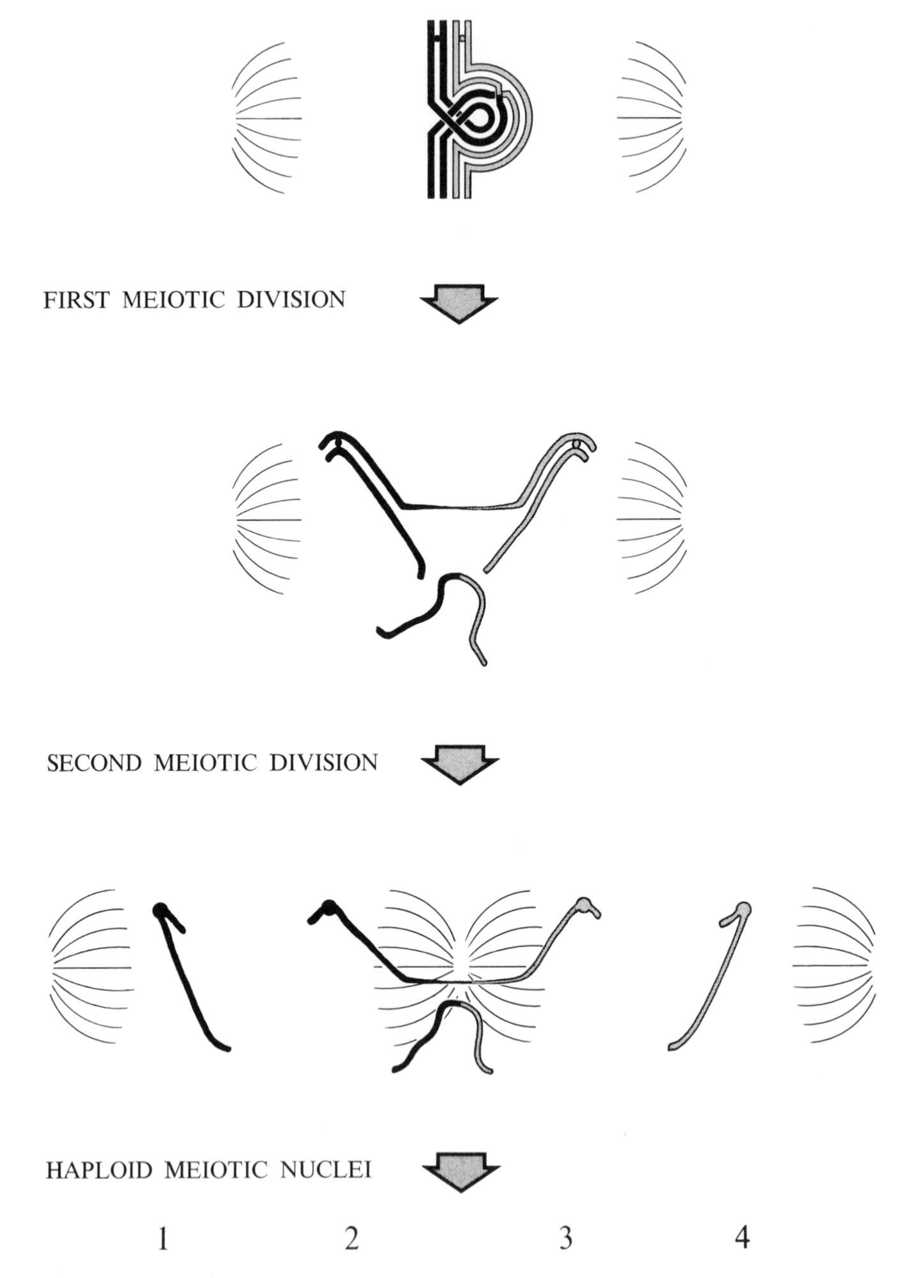

Figure 16-3. Distribution of strands during meiotic divisions after a single crossing over in a paracentric inversion heterozygote in Drosophila.

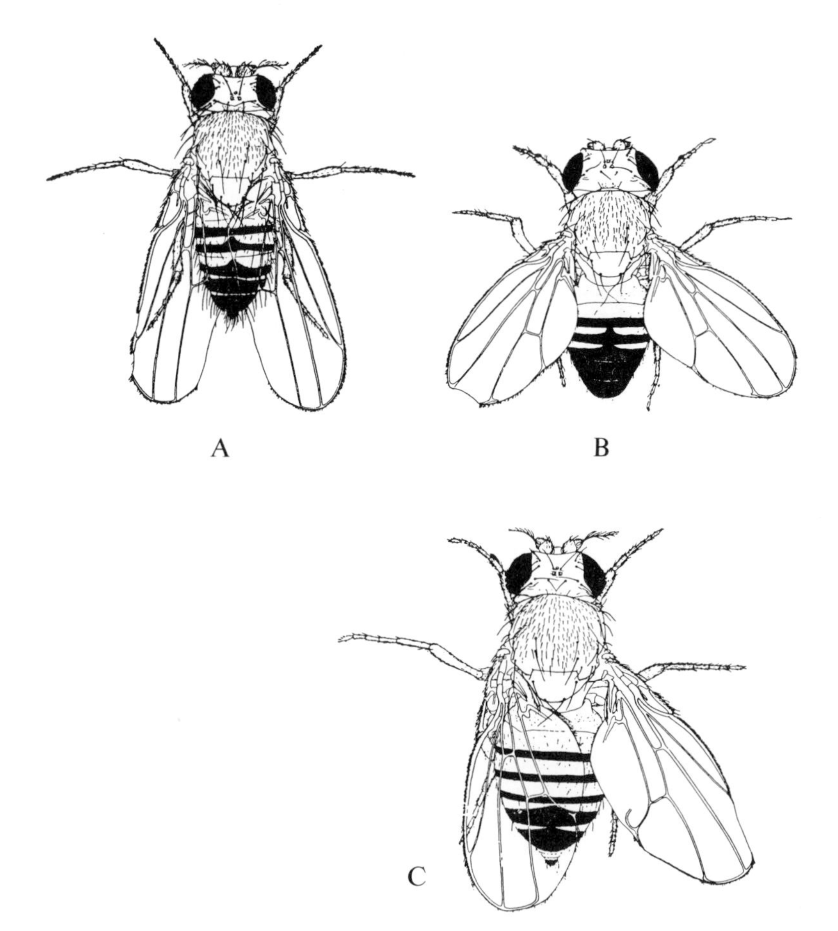

Figure 16-4. Some abnormal sex types in Drosophila: A = superfemale; B = supermale; C = intersex. (Drawn by E. M. Wallace) Compare with normal male and female in Figure 11-6.

ate chromosome ratios (*e.g.*, 0.67, due to 2X + 3 sets of A) give rise to sterile individuals of intermediate sex type, or intersexes (Figure 16-4C).

In man the Y chromosome is the main determinant of maleness, but the X chromosome also plays an important part in determining sex type, since the XXY male shows many feminine traits.

In other organisms, sexes may differ in ploidy. Unfertilized eggs of bees, ants, wasps, saw flies, and other Hymenoptera develop as haploid males, whereas fertilized eggs usually become diploid females. (Haploid males produce haploid sperm by means of a modified meiosis.) We should keep in mind, however, that details of sexual type in these and in other organisms are influenced by environmental factors.

16·10 *In organisms where a single genotype produces both kinds of gametes, the environment controls which of the sexes will be expressed.*

In many organisms the kinds of gametes and their formation are determined not by differences in genetic content but by differences in environment. For example, both eggs and sperm are produced in the same gonad in the snail Helix. In the earthworm, male and female gametes are made in separate gonads located in different segments of the body. And in some mosses, the two different gametes are also produced in separate sex organs (located on the same haploid gametophyte).

The marine annelid Ophryotrocha can produce male and female gametes, but not at the same time. The sex type of gametes is determined by the size of the organism. When the animal is small, because of youth or because it was obtained by amputation from a larger organism, it manufactures sperm. When larger, the same individual manufactures eggs. The environment of the gonad changes with the growth of the organism and thus regulates gamete formation.

The sexes of the marine worm Bonellia are radically different in appearance and activity. Females are walnut-sized and have a long proboscis, whereas males are microscopic, ciliated forms that live as parasites in the body of the female. Fertilized eggs grown in the absence of adult females develop as females. In the presence either of adult females or of an extract from the female's proboscis, such eggs develop as males. Thus, sexual differentiation seems to be determined by the environment of the eggs, that is, by the presence or absence of a substance made by the females.

Questions and Problems

16·1 Why do you expect the distribution of replicated genetic material to be under genetic control?

16·2 Compare the advantages and disadvantages of a ring vs. a rod chromosome with respect to the regulation of chromosome replication.

16·3 Do you expect ϕT4 to encode a phage-specific DNA-dependent RNA polymerase? Why?

16·4 DNA-dependent RNA polymerase can bind to duplex DNA even in the absence of RNA synthesis. What can you conclude from an electron microscope study (by Crawford, L. V., Crawford, E. M., Richardson, J. P., and Slayter, H. S., J. Mol. Biol., 14: 593–597, 1965), in which it is reported that polyoma DNA has about eight attachment sites for this enzyme?

16·5 In what specific ways do genetic nucleic acid polymerases regulate nucleic acid synthesis?

16·6 When homozygous, the mutant gene *claret-nondisjunctional* (ca^{nd}) in Drosophila causes nondisjunction of one or more chromosomes in meiosis but not in mitosis. What gene in corn acts like this mutant? How might you determine the similarity of these two genes?

16·7 Why can very small paracentric or pericentric inversions survive in populations even when they usually occur in heterozygous condition?

16·8 What are the meiotic products of a two-strand double crossing over within a heterozygous paracentric inversion such as shown in Figure 16-2?

16·9 Do you expect meiotic drive to occur in Neurospora, in which the meiotic divisions occur in tandem as they do in the Drosophila female? Explain.

16·10 Criticize the following statement: Corn chromosomes are normally polycentric.

16·11 In certain organisms that have several large and several small chromosomes, the smaller ones regularly are located in the center of the metaphase plate, the larger ones at the periphery. In what respect is this observation relevant to the present chapter?

16·12 Compare the genetic basis for sex type in man and Drosophila.

16·13 What is the role of the genotype when environmental factors determine sex type?

16·14 Why is further knowledge of the genetic basis for meiosis so desirable?

16·15 Litman, R. M., and Szybalski, W. (Biochem. Biophys. Res. Commun., 10: 473–481, 1963) have reported the enzymatic synthesis of transforming DNA *in vitro*. In what ways can the experimenter regulate the *in vitro* synthesis of genes?

16·16 What can you conclude about the time and place of phenotypic action of the mutant gene in corn, *polymitotic divisions*, which causes extra mitotic divisions of the haploid pollen grain when the diploid parent is homozygous, but not when it is heterozygous, for the mutant?

References

Bessman, M. J. 1963. The replication of DNA in cell-free systems, in *Molecular Genetics, Part I*, Taylor, J. H. (Editor), New York: Academic Press, Chap. 1, pp. 1–64. (Includes regulation of viral DNA synthesis.)

Green, M. H. 1964. Strand selective transcription of T4 DNA *in vitro*. Proc. Nat. Acad. Sci., U.S., 52: 1388–1395.

Hayashi, M., Hayashi, M. N., and Spiegelman, S. 1964. DNA circularity and the mechanism of strand selection in the generation of genetic messages. Proc. Nat. Acad. Sci., U.S., 51: 351–359.

Jacob, F. 1966. Genetics of the bacterial cell. Science, 152: 1470–1478. (Nobel Prize Lecture that discusses the replicon.)

Jacob, F., Brenner, S., and Cuzin, F. 1963. On the regulation of DNA replication in bacteria. Cold Spring Harb. Sympos. Quant. Biol., 28: 329–348. Reprinted in *Papers on Bacterial Genetics, Second Edition,* Adelberg, E. A. (Editor), Boston: Little, Brown and Co., 1966, pp. 403–436.

Lark, K. G., and Bird, R. E. 1965. Segregation of the conserved units of DNA in *Escherichia coli.* Proc. Nat. Acad. Sci., U.S., 54: 1444–1450.

Rhoades, M. M., and Dempsey, E. 1966. The effect of abnormal chromosome 10 on preferential segregation and crossing over in maize. Genetics, 53: 989–1020. (An example of meiotic drive.)

Rosenberg, P. H., and Cavalieri, L. F. 1965. Template deoxyribonucleic acid and the control of replication. Nature, Lond., 206: 999–1001.

Sandberg, A. A., Sofumi, T., Takagi, N., and Moore, G. E. 1966. Chronology and pattern of human chromosome replication, IV. Autoradiographic studies of binucleate cells. Proc. Nat. Acad. Sci., U.S., 56: 105–110.

Sandler, L., and Hiraizumi, Y. 1961. Meiotic drive in natural populations of *Drosophila melanogaster,* VIII. A heritable aging effect on the phenomenon of segregation-distortion. Canad. J. Genet. Cytol., 3: 34–46.

Subak-Sharpe, H., and Hay, J. 1965. An animal virus with DNA of high guanine and cytosine content which codes for sRNA. J. Mol. Biol., 12: 924–928. (About 1.2% of herpes simplex virus' double-stranded DNA codes for 10 to 20 molecular species of virus-specific sRNA.)

CHAPTER 17

Regulation of Gene Action – Operons

The regulation of replication and of distribution of genetic material entails the regulation of protein synthesis such that different polypeptides are made at different times and in different amounts. In this chapter we will see how this control of gene action depends upon different kinds of genes.

17·1 *The functioning of an enzyme often involves a feedback circuit in a synthetic pathway.*

In order for a cell to maintain its delicate metabolic balance, it must have some way to regulate its synthetic pathways. Since a particular metabolic product is often the result of a series of enzymatic reactions, its synthesis will be affected if any of the preceding steps is affected. In many instances the product itself inhibits the functioning of one of the first enzymes in the pathway. In other words, when the product reaches a certain level, it prevents any further synthesis. Such *end-product inhibition* of an enzyme provides immediate and sensitive control of the rate of synthesis of many metabolites. Enzyme inhibition by the end product (a widespread phenomenon in bacteria) is one example of a *feedback mechanism.*

17·2 *The production of a polypeptide encoded by one gene is often controlled by the product of another gene – a regulator gene.*

The polypeptide products of gene action can be controlled or regulated more directly than by end-product inhibition, at a stage prior to protein synthesis. Let us consider the *Lac* region of the *E. coli* genetic map, which contains four recombinationally separate genes: y^+ codes for β-galactoside permease, which helps lactose get into the bacterial cell; z^+ codes for β-galactosidase, which digests lactose (a β-galactoside) into galactose and glucose; another gene (not considered further here) codes for galactoside transacetylase; and i^+, the *regulator gene,* codes for a *repressor* substance (or, simply, a repressor) which prevents both y^+ and z^+ from producing permease and galactosidase. In the presence of lactose, however, the repressor substance made by i^+ is inactivated, so the formation of enzymes by y^+ and z^+ becomes possible. Lactose functions therefore as an *inducer.* In other words, *E. coli* of genotype $y^+ z^+ i^+$ can produce neither permease nor galactosidase *constitutively* (in the absence of lactose) but can produce both enzymes *inductively* (in the presence of lactose). Various studies indicate that the repressor substance is a protein that can diffuse throughout the cell and act at various places. The *Lac* region provides a model for the explanation of the genetic basis for many instances of induced enzyme formation. In contrast to end-product inhibition, the production (not the activity) of the enzymes is regulated by this mechanism.

17·3 *A functional gene, the operator, is located at one end of a series of structural genes. The functioning of the operator gene depends upon the repressor.*

The above model, which proposes the existence of a regulator gene, cannot account for all experimental observations of the functioning of the *Lac* region. A certain F-*Lac* particle containing y^+ and z^+ was found which could make both y^+ and z^+ products constitutively. We might think, therefore, that it produces no repressor substance and so does not have an i^+ gene. To check this possibility, the particle can be F-duced into a cell whose chromosome includes $y^+ z\, i$. By itself, this cell could produce permease and nonfunctional z protein (Cz) constitutively, but after F-duction, it no longer produces Cz constitutively. Evidently the F-*Lac* particle does contain an i^+ gene, whose product represses the z gene.

The apparent contradiction indicates that the model used above was not complete, and leads to a further understanding of the genetic make up of the *Lac* region. In order for a $y^+ z^+ i^+$ particle to be able to produce y^+ and z^+ products constitutively, the *Lac* region must also contain another locus whose gene o^c permits the y and z loci in the same chromosome to act constitutively regardless of the i alleles present in the cell. Let us hypothesize that in the example above the F-*Lac* particle includes $y^+ z^+ o^c i^+$ genes and the bacterial chromosome, $y^+ z\, o^+ i$ (without taking into account the order of the loci). In accordance with this hypothesis, the F-duced *E. coli* produces permease and galactosidase constitutively and Cz protein inductively. Results of studies involving other F-duced *E. coli* are summarized in Figure 17-1.

All these results confirm the hypothesized existence of an *operator gene,* o^+, which is sensitive to the repressor substance encoded by i^+. When the repressor is active, it interacts with o^+ and in some way prevents the formation of enzymes encoded by the y and z genes in the same region. When only the mutant allele i is present in the cell, no repressor is

Genotype		Non-Induced Bacteria			Induced Bacteria		
Chromosome	F-Lac	P	G	Cz	P	G	Cz
$y^+z\ o^+i^+$	$y^+z^+o^ci^+$	50	110	nd	100	330	100
$y\ z^+o^+i^+$	$y^+z\ o^ci^+$	–	<1	30	–	100	400
$y^+z\ o^+i^+$	$y\ z^+o^ci^+$	nd	60	–	100	300	–

P = Permease
G = Galactosidase
Cz = Cz Protein

Figure 17-1. Functioning of *Lac* genes in various hybrid *E. coli.* nd = not detectable, – = not tested.

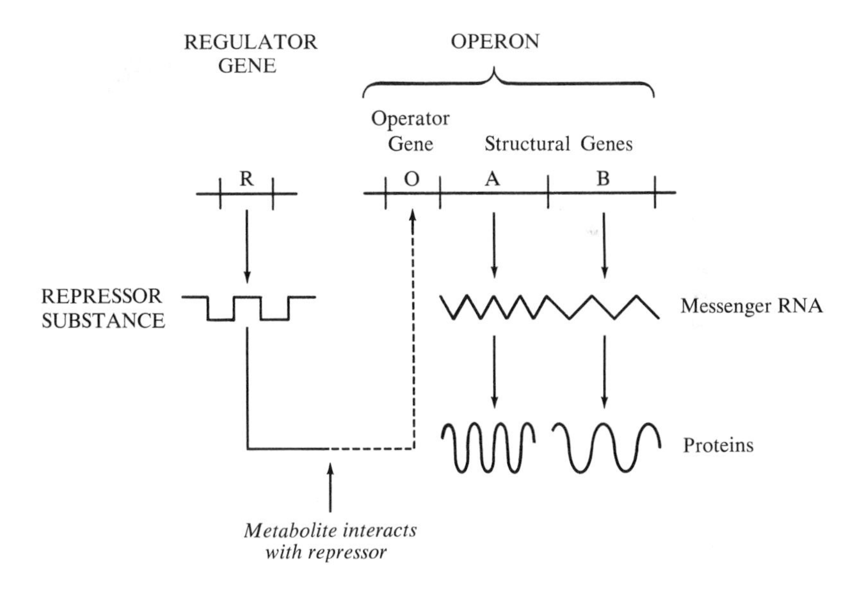

Figure 17-2. Relationships between a regulator gene and the operator and structural genes of an operon.

produced, o^+ is unaffected, and all alleles of *y* and *z* act constitutively. The mutant allele of o^+, namely o^c, is insensitive to the repressor substance; hence, regardless of whether or not the repressor is made, *y* and *z* alleles in the same chromosome act constitutively.

The operator gene does not produce any unique, detectable product. We can conclude, therefore, that its primary job is not to specify a chemical product (such as an amino acid sequence in a polypeptide) but to control the function of other genes. Consequently, operator genes are called *functional genes* in contrast to those which specify chemical structures and accordingly are called *structural genes* (Figure 17-2). Recombination studies show that the sequence of loci in the *Lac* region is *y z o i*, in which the functional gene, the operator, is at one end of the series of structural genes it controls, *y* and *z*.

17·4 *The operon is a unit of gene function. Some operons are normally inactive, others normally active; the action of both kinds can be changed by altering the repressor.*

The operator gene coordinates the expression of its neighboring structural genes by permitting or preventing the functioning of all of them. The genes of the *Lac* region in *E. coli* are further related functionally since they all involve a pathway of lactose utilization. Likewise, ten of the enzymes in the pathway of histidine biosynthesis in Salmonella are coordinately controlled and occur in the same gene cluster. As a matter of fact, both *E. coli* and Salmonella have many such closely linked groups of metabolically related genes. This relationship suggests that there is a unit of gene function intermediate in size between the gene that encodes a single polypeptide and the chromosome which encodes many polypeptides. Such a unit, called an *operon,* consists of a linear sequence of structural genes whose activity is coordinated by a functional gene, the operator, located at one end.

According to the mechanism described earlier, a regulator gene can control an operon in essentially two different ways. It can, as in the *Lac* system, produce an *active repressor* which must be inactivated to permit the operator gene (and hence the operon) to work. This inactivation occurs when a metabolite (lactose in the case of the *Lac* operon) combines with the repressor. Such systems as these, in which operon activity can be induced, often contain operons whose gene products are special structural proteins or enzymes needed for degradative (catabolic) reactions. Such operons are ordinarily inactive.

The other general method of control involves the production of an *inactive repressor* which must be activated in order to prevent the operator (and therefore the operon) from functioning. This kind of control is especially suitable for regulating synthetic (anabolic) reactions. In an environment which lacks a particular vital substance, the operon is allowed to function and direct the synthesis of this substance. If this metabolite is synthesized or taken into the cell, the repressor is activated and synthesis stops (as in the histidine operon in Salmonella). Subsequent withdrawal of the metabolite (derepression) causes the active repressor to become inactive, and allows the operon to function once again. Such operons are normally active.

17·5 *The structural genes in an operon are transcribed in a single strand of mRNA.*

Since an operon is a length of genetic material which is transcribed into a single strand of mRNA, it can be considered a unit of transcription. The mRNA transcript of a functional operon contains the codons for all the structural genes in the operon and is synthesized and translated starting at its 5′ end, apparently the operator end. A codon for N-formylmethionine apparently contains the information necessary for initiation of each polypeptide chain (at least in *E. coli;* see Section 6·10).

We would like to know what causes the termination of consecutive polypeptides encoded in an mRNA. Termination might be due to a nonsense triplet. Another possibility is that polypeptide termination is the result of an intramolecular base pairing to form double-stranded segments in single-stranded mRNA. Such segments would not have bases exposed for pairing with sRNA, and might, therefore, serve as terminators. Regardless of how polypeptides are terminated, we should keep in mind that an initiator codon, such as that for N-formylmethionine, ensures that consecutive polypeptides encoded in the same mRNA do not become linked.

17·6 *Sometimes chromosomal folding brings together metabolically-related genes which are not closely linked.*

We should not assume that all the enzymes involved in a sequence of biosynthetic activities are encoded within a single operon. In Neurospora, genes for metabolically-related enzymes are not always part of a single cluster but often are scattered widely throughout the genome. In *E. coli* another kind of relationship among metabolically-related genes is apparent – one which combines aspects both of scattered genes and the single operon.

Eight genes of the arginine synthetic pathway in *E. coli* are located in three different operons, all under the control of the same regulator gene. As we implied in Section 3·9, the circular *E. coli* chromosome is folded to attain a tertiary structure. This folding apparently brings together the genes of the three arginine operons so that, perhaps, their polypeptide products can interact in a manner that would not be possible otherwise. Evidence for this particular folding is that after UV-irradiation a significant number of bacteria are obtained with mutations in two not closely linked arginine genes. These double mutants might be the result of pyrimidine dimerization (induced by the UV light) between loci juxtaposed by the folding.

17·7 *Different operons within a chromosome are transcribed to mRNA in opposite directions. Some mRNA's are complementary to one strand of double-stranded DNA; others are complementary to the other strand.*

Not all operons in the circular chromosome of Salmonella or *E. coli* are transcribed to mRNA in the same direction; some operons run clockwise and others counterclockwise from their operator gene. Under certain conditions, it is possible to transpose the *Lac* operon of *E. coli* to a new chromosomal position. In some bacteria it becomes inserted in one direction; in others, the reverse. Let us assume that the double-stranded DNA of the *Lac* segment is composed of the single strands L_1 and L_2. Bacteria of type A have L_1 in the chromosome's + strand; B bacteria with *Lac* inverted must have L_1 in the − strand because polarity must be maintained. Since both A and B bacteria produce functional *Lac* enzymes, they must specify the same mRNA, which we will arbitrarily take to be a complement of L_1. Hence, to produce RNA complementary to L_1 in A bacteria, the complement of the + strand is made; likewise, in B bacteria, the complement of the − strand is made. Thus, some segments of a bacterial chromosome are transcribed to mRNA that is complementary to the + strand, and other segments are transcribed to mRNA complementary to the − strand (see Figure 4-3D).

17·8 *Operator genes in different operons seem to have similar nucleotide sequences. Part of the nucleotide sequences of different regulator genes also appear to be similar.*

Leucine synthesis in Salmonella is controlled by the leucine operon and its regulator gene. A certain mutation in the operator region (from o^+ to o^x), however, allows the operon to be irreversibly repressed, "superrepressed," by the product of a regulator gene which controls another operon. When the bacterial genome with o^x also contains a mutation in the foreign regulator gene, the leucine operon is no longer superrepressed. Since both the o^x and the foreign regulator gene mutations apparently are transitions of a single base pair only (as determined from reverse mutation studies), the regions of interaction between o^+ and its normal repressor and between o^x and the foreign repressor must be similar. These observations imply also that (1) there are relatively few nucleotide differences between the regions of different regulator genes that encode the functional portion of their repressor substances, and that (2) operator genes for different operons differ from each other by relatively few nucleotides.

17·9 *The functioning of an operon can be changed by various mutations. Regulation may take place at any stage between transcription and the release of polypeptides from the ribosome.*

The consequences of mutations in operons depend on whether structural genes or functional genes are affected. A structural gene in an operon can contain a sense, missense, or a nonsense mutation or a deletion. If sense, then there is no phenotypic effect. If missense, the resulting protein may be nonfunctional. If nonsense, only the codons between the operator and the mutation are read. Some nonsense mutations are, however, "polarity" mutations. These occur near the operator end of the operon, terminating translation at that point, and preventing translation of the codons for subsequent structural genes that are also near the operator end. Polarity mutations, however, do permit the translation of codons for structural genes close to the opposite end of the mRNA. The mechanism for this effect is not yet known. Deletions in structural genes also can give rise to the production of nonfunctional proteins. A large deletion between operons in *E. coli* has been found to cause the structural genes of one operon to be controlled by the operator of the other.

A mutation involving the operator or regulator loci can affect the functioning of an entire operon, as we saw in the preceding Section. The effects of such a mutation on regulation depend upon the nature of the operator gene. It is not yet known, however, whether the information in the operator gene sequence is (1) transcribed and translated, (2) transcribed but not translated, or (3) neither transcribed nor translated. Evidence indicates that at least for some operons, the operator gene is not transcribed to mRNA. In such instances, an active repressor acts at the level of DNA. If the operator information is transcribed and translated, then an active repressor has additional levels at which to act.

The functioning of an operon can be regulated or affected at the level of transcription. When the DNA of ϕX174 is a double-stranded, circular helix, RNA complementary to both single-stranded rods is made after the ring is broken (see Section 4·12). When, however, the duplex ring is intact, RNA complementary to only one strand of the DNA is made. We see, therefore, that one-complement transcription requires that the circular DNA duplex be intact. Other *in vitro* studies indicate that the double helical structure of DNA is necessary for one-complement transcription to RNA.

Regulation of gene action can take place after transcription. After the genome of phage T4 enters a host, apparently all genes are transcribed once, and only those genes whose mRNA's are translated continue to be transcribed to mRNA. The mechanism for this control is unknown. Just as the synthesis of mRNA is regulated, so is its degradation; some evidence indicates that the messenger is degraded from its operator end, that is, the end transcribed nearer to the operator gene. Regulation can also occur at the level of translation – depending, for example, on the presence or absence of specific sRNA's or the release of polypeptide products from the ribosome.

17·10 *In corn the regulator gene* Ac *controls the functioning of* Ds, *which acts like an operator gene. The presence of* Ds *can suppress the functioning of adjacent genes.*

The triploid endosperm (p. 141) in corn kernels can be white, colored, or white with colored speckles. The white phenotype results from the suppression of a normal allele for color by the closely-linked gene called *Dissociation* (*Ds*), which also causes chromosome breakage in regions near it. If *Ds* remains closely linked to the gene for color, the kernel will be white. If, however, *Ds* dissociates (that is, changes its position) before the kernel forms, the kernel and subsequent generations of plants will be completely colored. If *Ds* moves during kernel formation, the kernel will have colored dots or sectors on a white background. Large colored specks are due to the movement of *Ds* early in development; small ones are the result of shifting later in development, when relatively few successive cell divisions take place. We should note that the relocation of *Ds* by means of breakage is a genetic recombination and that the change in color is a phenotypic effect which depends upon the arrangement, or relative position, of genes. In other words, it is a *position effect* – a *Ds* gene near the gene for color prevents the latter from functioning; its absence permits the gene to function.

Ds can occur at many positions in the genome. At its various positions *Ds* often suppresses the phenotypic effect of a gene (not necessarily for color) located near it. So long as *Ds* remains in that position, the position effect produces a phenotype which often resembles that produced by a mutation of the gene. When *Ds* is moved from this locus, the suppressed gene is again functional. *Ds* can be transferred from one chromosomal position to another as a result of breakage or a mechanism which may involve contact with the locus to which *Ds* is relocated. It is possible to increase the number of *Ds* factors present in the endosperm by appropriate crosses. As the number of *Ds* genes in a given region of a chromosome increases, the region breaks with greater frequency.

The ability of *Ds* to cause chromosomal breakage is controlled by *Activator* (*Ac*) genes. *Ac* does not have to be in the same chromosome as

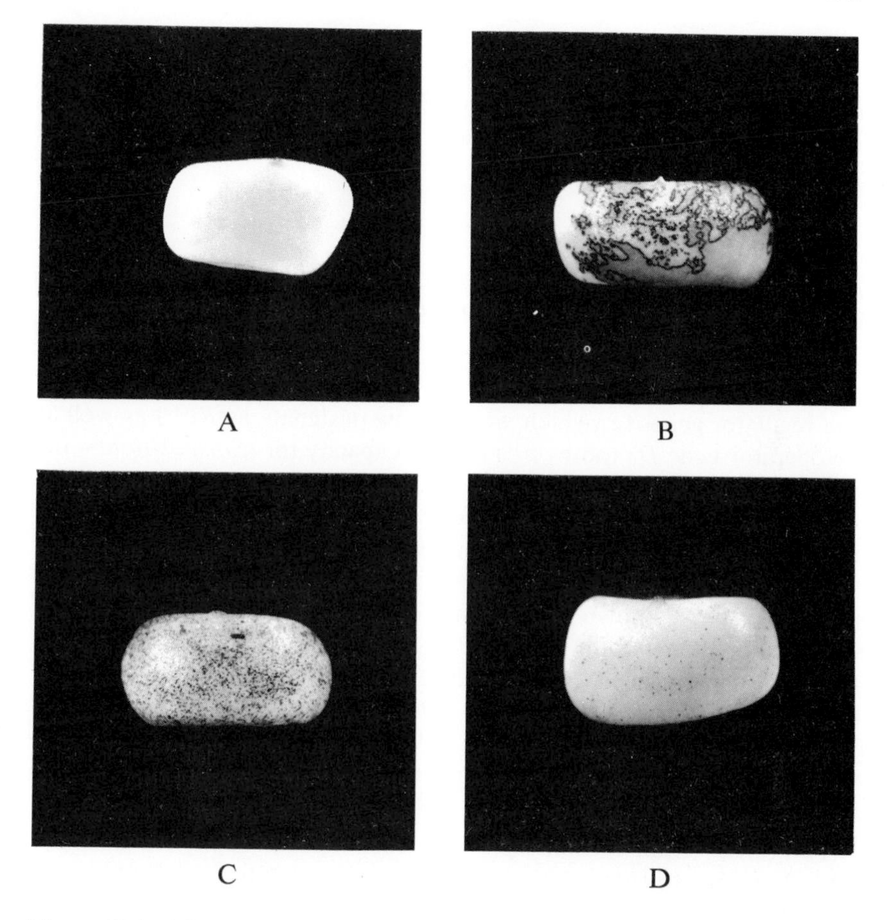

Figure 17-3. The effect of *Activator* on the action of *Dissociation.* (A) No *Ac* is present. The kernel is colorless due to the continued presence of *Ds,* which inhibits the action of a nearby pigment-producing gene. (B) One *Ac* gene is present. Breaks at *Ds* occur early in kernel development, leading to large colored sectors. (C) Two *Ac* genes are present. Time of *Ds* action is delayed, producing smaller sectors which appear as specks. (D) Three *Ac* genes are present. *Ds* action is so delayed that relatively few and tiny specks are produced. (Courtesy of B. McClintock and the Cold Spring Harbor Laboratory of Quantitative Biology)

Ds and, in fact, usually is not. By suitable crosses, kernels can be obtained whose endosperm contains one, two, or three *Ac* genes (or none) in addition to a single *Ds* gene located near a pigment-producing gene (Figure 17-3). In the absence of *Ac*, no specks are produced and the kernel is completely white. Hence, the *Ds* gene must not have moved. It appears that *Ds* cannot cause chromosomal breakage (nor can it be relocated in other ways) in the absence of *Ac*. In the presence of *Ac* colored spots are produced. Moreover, as the dosage of *Ac* increases from one to three, the colored spots become smaller and smaller. Thus, *Ac* also acts to delay the time at which *Ds* is relocated. *Ac* is clearly acting as a regulator gene, and *Ds* apparently as an operator gene. Genes like *Ac* may be important in cyclical metabolic processes as well as in embryonic development and cellular differentiation.

17·11 *Both* Ac *and* Ds *can move from one position to another and thus are sometimes near or adjacent to each other. Numerous operator-regulator, two-element control systems occur in corn and perhaps in other higher organisms.*

The regulator gene *Ac* (which we will now designate as Re^{Ac}) as well as the operator gene *Ds* (now op^{Ac}) has the capacity for *transposition* – the ability to move from one chromosomal locus to another. (Transposition is not a property of the usual regulator or operator gene in bacterial systems.) Consequently, we expect that both elements are sometimes adjacent or closely linked. Let us test the following general hypothesis: If a regulator gene is known to be near a structural gene whose function it affects, so is the operator gene.

The gene for bronze color in corn, *Bz*, is located in chromosome 9. The speckled-bronze coloration of one strain is known to be due to a regulator gene near *Bz*. If there is a two-element control system in this region (containing *Bz* op^{Ac} Re^{Ac}), three kinds of transpositional events are possible.

(1) Transposition of both op^{Ac} and Re^{Ac} should release *Bz* from the control system so that a uniform bronze color results; and Re^{Ac} should prove to be absent from the vicinity of *Bz*.

(2) Transposition of op^{Ac} only should likewise free the *Bz* gene from control by Re^{Ac}; but the latter should still be near *Bz* and be capable of regulating the op^{Ac} gene now located at another site in the genome.

(3) Transposition of Re^{Ac} only should leave the *Bz* op^{Ac} segment still under the control of Re^{Ac} at its new locus.

Experimental results confirm all these expectations. The first two kinds of results can be explained by a one-element control system; the third, however, requires that there be a two-element, operator-regulator, control system. Therefore, in some instances at least, both elements are closely linked.

Since other results show that many different *Re* genes occur in corn, each regulating a particular type of *op* gene, numerous *op-Re* systems must occur. Similar two-element control systems may also be involved in variegation in other flowering plants, ferns, and fungi.

Questions and Problems

17·1 Do you suppose that all genes in *E. coli* or man are part of operons? Explain.

17·2 Does the finding that some operons in Salmonella run clockwise and others counterclockwise prove that mRNA is the complement of one DNA strand at one place and of the other DNA strand at another? Explain.

17·3 An Hfr strain with z^+ i^+ is mated with an F^- of type z i in the absence of inducer. Assuming that i^+ product is not and that the *Lac* region is transferred, will any z^+ product be made? Explain.

17·4 How can Salmonella mutants whose histidine pathway is not repressed by histidine be selected? (Use a histidine analog.) Explain.

17·5 When Salmonella mutants selected by the procedure in Question 17·4 are mapped, they all involve changes in a short region of the DNA that encodes the first enzyme of the histidine pathway. What correlation can you make between the gene region mutated and the chemical nature of the enzyme?

17·6 *E. coli* grown in nutrient broth are infected with ϕT4. Soon after infection one sample is placed in minimal medium; another is left in nutrient medium. Explain why the bacteria in nutrient medium lyse first.

17·7 What evidence can you give that a genotype regulates its own mutability?

17·8 How is it possible that a given gene in corn can serve as the operator at a variety of previously uncontrolled loci?

17·9 What additional information would you seek with regard to *op-Re* systems in corn?

17·10 What metabolic advantage may chromosome folding provide?

17·11 What is meant by gene action?

17·12 How is gene action affected by recombination that involves genetic nucleic acid's
(a) primary structure?
(b) secondary structure?
(c) tertiary structure?
(d) quaternary structure?

References

Alpers, D. H., and Tomkins, G. M. 1965. The order of induction and deinduction of the enzymes of the lactose operon in *E. coli*. Proc. Nat. Acad. Sci., U.S., 53: 797–803.

Bautz, E. K. F., Kasai, T., Reilly, E., and Bautz, F. A. 1966. Gene-specific mRNA, II. Regulation of mRNA synthesis in *E. coli* after infection with bacteriophage T4. Proc. Nat. Acad. Sci., U.S., 55: 1081–1088.

Bourgeois, S., Cohn, M., and Orgel, L. E. 1965. Suppression of and complementation among mutants of the regulatory gene of the lactose operon of *Escherichia coli*. J. Mol. Biol., 14: 300–302. (Evidence that the regulator does and the operator probably does not code for a protein.)

Cellular Regulatory Mechanisms, Cold Spring Harb. Sympos. Quant. Biol., 26, 1962.

Doi, R. H., Kaneko, I., and Goehler, B. 1966. Regulation of a serine transfer RNA of *Bacillus subtilis* under two growth conditions. Proc. Nat. Acad. Sci., U.S., 56: 1548–1551. (Changes in the amount of one of three seryl-sRNA's.)

Gallant, J., and Spottswood, T. 1964. Measurement of the stability of the repressor of alkaline phosphatase synthesis in *Escherichia coli*. Proc. Nat. Acad. Sci., U.S., 52: 1591–1598.

Garen, A., and Otsuji, N. 1964. Isolation of a protein specified by a regulator gene. J. Mol. Biol., 8: 841–852.

Gilbert, W., and Müller-Hill, B. 1966. Isolation of the *Lac* repressor. Proc. Nat. Acad. Sci., U.S., 56: 1891–1898. (A protein.)

Jacob, F. 1966. Genetics of the bacterial cell. Science, 152: 1470–1478. (Nobel Prize Lecture that gives recent advances on the operon.)

Jacob, F., and Monod, J. 1961. Genetic regulatory mechanisms in the synthesis of proteins. J. Mol. Biol., 3: 318–356.

Jacob, F., and Monod, J. 1965. Genetic mapping of the elements of the lactose region in *Escherichia coli*. Biochem. Biophys. Res. Commun., 18: 693–701.

Jacob, F., Perrin, D., Sanchez, C., and Monod, J. 1960. The operon: a group of genes whose expression is coordinated by an operator. (In French) C. R. Acad. Sci. (Paris), 250: 1727–1729. Translated and reprinted in *Papers on Bacterial Genetics, Second Edition*. Adelberg, E. A. (Editor), Boston: Little, Brown and Co., 1966, pp. 198–200.

Margolin, P. 1965. Bipolarity of information transfer from the *Salmonella typhimurium* chromosome. Science, 147: 1456–1458.

Martin, R. G., and Ames, B. N. 1964. Biochemical aspects of genetics: the operon. Ann. Rev. Biochem., 33: 235–255.

McClintock, B. 1961. Some parallels between gene control systems in maize and bacteria. Amer. Nat., 95: 265–277.

McClintock, B. 1962. Topographical relations between elements of control systems in maize. Carnegie Inst. Wash. Yearb., 61: 448–461.

McClintock, B. 1965. The control of gene action in maize. Brookhaven Sympos. Biol., 18: 162–184.

Morris, D. W., and DeMoss, J. A. 1966. Polysome transitions and the regulation of ribonucleic acid synthesis in *Escherichia coli*. Proc. Nat. Acad. Sci., U.S., 56: 262–268.

Mukai, F. H., and Margolin, P. 1963. Analysis of unlinked suppressors of an o^0 mutation in Salmonella. Proc. Nat. Acad. Sci., U.S., 50: 140–148.

Newton, W. A., Beckwith, J. R., Zipser, D., and Brenner, S. 1965. Nonsense mutants and polarity in the Lac operon of *Escherichia coli*. J. Mol. Biol., 14: 290–296.

Ohtaka, Y., and Spiegelman, S. 1963. Translational control of protein synthesis in a cell-free system directed by a polycistronic viral RNA. Science, 142: 493–497.

Stent, G. S. 1964. The operon: on its third anniversary. Science, 144: 816–820.

Vogel, H. J., and Bacon, D. F. 1966. Gene aggregation: evidence for a coming together of functionally related, not closely linked genes. Proc. Nat. Acad. Sci., U.S., 55: 1456–1459.

CHAPTER 18

Regulation of Gene Action — Molecular Basis in Higher Organisms

In the preceding chapter we saw that particular kinds and sequences of genetic information serve to regulate gene action. We saw also how this regulatory information is used at various levels between the start of transcription and the end of translation in bacteria and phage. We shall now consider further the control of gene action in higher organisms and the molecular basis for such regulation.

18·1 *In order to be transcribed, the template material must be in an appropriate conformation and in the presence of suitable catalysts and precursor materials.*

It is obvious that for transcription to occur, the nucleic acid template must be available to the appropriate enzymes and substrate. If the template is double-stranded DNA with ten base pairs per complete turn, then several changes can take place to modify the template and make its major and minor grooves unavailable for transcription by DNA polymerase or DNA-dependent RNA polymerase. Undercoiling or overcoiling can prevent the proper copying of template information as can a substance which blocks one or both grooves. Molecules that complex with the DNA can also hinder local denaturation and strand separation. We should not assume, however, that a nucleic acid template in a suitable conformation is necessarily transcribed, since the appropriate enzymes and substrate may not be available.

18·2 *The puffs in polynemic chromosomes are sites of transcription.*

At various times during the development of certain Dipteran cells, different cross-bands of the highly polynemic chromosome "puff" and later "unpuff" in a regular sequence (Figure 18-1). The puffing sequence differs from one larval tissue to another. Puffing is thought to be a local unwinding or unclumping of the chromosome and its DNA so that the degree of

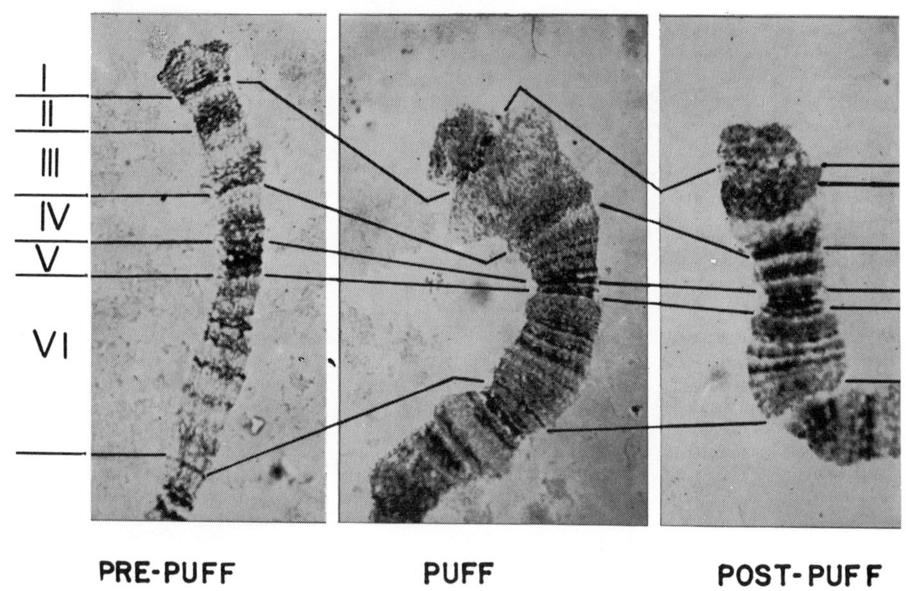

Figure 18-1. Puffing and unpuffing in a region of a salivary gland chromosome of Rhynchosciara. (Courtesy of G. Rudkin)

coiling is appropriate for transcription. In Drosophila and the midge Chironomus, a puff region synthesizes more RNA (probably mRNA) than an equivalent nonpuff region, thus indicating that puffs are sites for transcription.

Injection of Chironomus larvae with the pupation hormone *ecdysone* induces specific bands to puff. Later puffs seem to depend on the size and duration of earlier puffs. Apparently, then, this hormone is involved in the control of transcription. Since only about 20% of the bands are ever seen to puff in a Dipteran salivary gland cell, a great many genes in a tissue may not be transcribed to RNA.

In a certain species of Chironomus, granules occur in the cytoplasm of cells in one lobe of the larval salivary gland. The presence of these granules is associated with a gene as well as a puff near one end of chromosome IV. In cells without granules, this puff is not found. Larvae from a mating of individuals from species which differ in the ability to make these granules are cytogenetically hybrid; that is, one chromosome shows the characteristic puff, but its homolog does not. Moreover, the number of granules in a hybrid individual is approximately half the number in an individual with two puffing chromosomes. These findings correlate puffing with the activity of a specific gene.

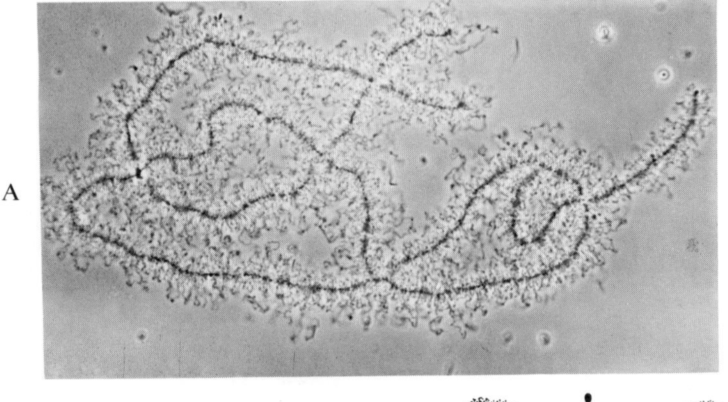

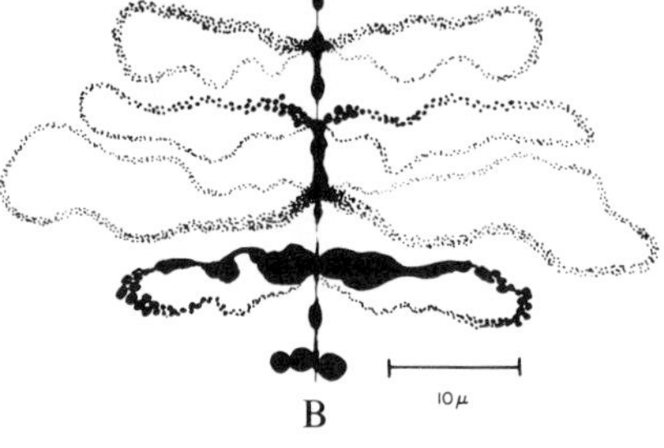

Figure 18-2. Giant "lampbrush" chromosomes of the amphibian oocyte. (A) Unfixed chromosomes of *Triturus viridescens* in saline solution, phase contrast, 540×. (B) Semidiagrammatic view of the central chromosome axis with paired lateral loops. (Courtesy of J. G. Gall)

18·3 *The loops of lampbrush chromosomes are sites of transcription to RNA. Chromosomal uncoiling allows this DNA to be used as a template.*

Amphibian oocytes have giant chromosomes that look like "lampbrushes" because of the lateral projection of many pairs of loops from the main chromosomal axis (Figure 18-2). Each loop is asymmetric, that is, thin at one point of attachment to the main axis and becoming thicker up to the other point of attachment. Some giant loops can be seen to contain a thin thread continuous with the main chromosomal axis (which contains DNA). Autoradiographs of newt lampbrush chromosomes exposed to radioactively-labeled uridine show that incorporation into a giant loop occurs in a definite sequence, starting at the thin end and proceeding around the loop in about ten days. Thus RNA is transcribed from different portions of the chromosome at different times.

It has also been found that (1) the loops contain DNA, (2) the RNA synthesis observed is DNA-dependent, and (3) agents such as actinomycin D which inhibit nuclear RNA synthesis lead to disappearance of the loops. From such results comes the hypothesis that a loop (like a puff) is a temporarily unwound portion of the chromosome. As the thick portion of a loop completes its synthetic activity, it is thought to wind up and form part of the nonsynthesizing, main chromosomal axis. At the same time, a wound part of the main axis unwinds to form the thin end of the loop, which proceeds to synthesize RNA. The presence of many loops in lampbrush chromosomes indicates that a large number of chromosomal sites are available for transcription to RNA. During the lampbrush stage, at which there is peak synthesis of RNA, about 98% of the RNA produced is rRNA and 2% is non-rRNA transcribed from roughly 2.7% of the genome.

The lampbrush type of chromosome structure has also been reported in the developing oocytes of various mollusks and mammals, as well as in the pigeon, the onion, and the Y chromosome of the Drosophila spermatocyte. (In T phages the DNA is not in lampbrush form, but is coiled within the phage head until infection. The DNA unwinds as it is injected into a host, where it is immediately used as a template.) In summary, then, chromosomal uncoiling seems to be necessary in a wide variety of organisms before DNA can be used as a template.

18·4 *The proteins that complex with DNA are likely to affect transcription.*

In contrast to phage DNA, the chromosomal DNA of most types of cells is complexed with basic proteins such as histone or protamine to form deoxyribonucleoproteins (p. 31). (A basic protein may be associated with *E. coli* DNA.) The histone in a nucleohistone apparently covers the DNA uniformly; it may be bound spirally around the DNA molecule and occupy one or both grooves of the double helix. Histones rich in arginine have been found in such associations with DNA. Other arrangements are also possible. Histones, especially those rich in lysine, may form a bridge between DNA duplexes or between tertiary coils of the same duplex. Because of their intimate association with genetic material, we can expect these basic proteins to influence the transcription of DNA.

18·5 *Different histones have different effects on the denaturation of DNA* in vitro.

Histone isolated from DNA in a nucleohistone can be separated into several subfractions, indicating that a cell probably contains a heterogeneous population of histone molecules. These molecules are relatively small – ranging in molecular weight from 3500 to 74,000 – and differ in amino acid composition. Three main classes exist: (1) *lysine-rich* (relatively very rich in lysine and proline and poor in arginine; (2) *moderately* (or *weakly*) *lysine-rich;* and (3) *arginine-rich* (relatively rich in arginine and poor in lysine). DNA can combine with these histone fractions to form reconstituted nucleohistones of about 35A in diameter, whose DNA seems to be as fully complexed with histone as the DNA in native nucleohistones.

When DNA is complexed with histones, its melting or denaturation temperature rises. In this respect, then, histones stabilize DNA. The suppression of DNA function as a template may be linked to this stabilizing effect, since it seems to involve the inhibition of strand separation. Lysine-rich histones in nucleohistones from peas increase the temperature required to melt half the DNA from 70°C to 81°C; half the DNA in arginine-rich nucleohistones melts at 71°C. An approximately linear relationship exists between the lysine content of histone and the melting temperature of DNA in a nucleohistone. DNA fully complexed with protamine, which is rich in arginine, melts at the same temperature as pure native DNA.

The types of basic proteins complexed with DNA vary in different organisms and in different tissues of the same organism. Many plant histones contain less of the arginine-rich fraction than animal histones. In chickens, the sperm contains protamine, and erythrocyte DNA is complexed with different histones than is liver DNA. In the snail and the squid, three different types of basic protein are associated with the same DNA at various stages in development.

The DNA of duck erythrocytes appears to be almost completely complexed with histone, but cells of other organisms have less of their DNA histone-complexed. In peas, for example, the fraction of the total DNA not complexed with histone is 5% for the developing cotyledon, 20% for the embryo, and 30% for the apices. These findings indicate that actively-growing, protein-synthesizing cells have more noncomplexed DNA than differentiated cells.

18·6 *Different histones differentially inhibit transcription of DNA* in vitro *and* in vivo.

Isolated nuclei can synthesize RNA by using their DNA as a template. Much of this synthesized RNA is mRNA; some is sRNA. In nuclei isolated from the calf thymus, arginine-rich histones added to the incubation medium not only reduce the uptake of thymidine into DNA but greatly inhibit the synthesis of RNA. Lysine-rich histones are much less inhibiting. Removal of certain histones from these nuclei results in a two- to four-fold increase in RNA synthesis (probably mRNA). Thus, transcription of DNA appears to be differentially inhibited by different histones. Furthermore, the removal of histones from DNA apparently can lead to the hitherto-repressed production of messenger RNA.

It appears that the control of genetic activity by histones *in vivo* is essentially preserved not only in isolated nuclei but in isolated chromatin as well, as indicated by the following experiments.

(1) Chromatin isolated from pea embryos, 20% of which is not complexed with histone, is able to carry out RNA synthesis with the four

usual ribonucleoside triphosphates and DNA-dependent RNA polymerase. Removal of histone increases RNA synthesis about 500%. Reconstituted nucleohistones either do not support DNA-dependent RNA synthesis at all or support it only to a small extent depending upon the histone involved. (DNA fully complexed with protamine, however, is fully active in DNA-dependent RNA synthesis.)

(2) Pea cotyledons synthesize a specific *pea seed reserve globulin* not produced in other tissues such as buds or roots. Chromatin isolated from pea cotyledons produces mRNA which can be used in a ribosomal system to manufacture this globulin, but chromatin isolated from pea buds does not make RNA coding for this protein. Removal of histones from pea bud chromatin, however, yields DNA which supports globulin synthesis. It therefore appears that the gene for globulin synthesis is normally suppressed in bud tissue by histones.

(3) Changing the amount of calf thymus histone in a rat tumor cell fraction that contains nucleoli and nucleolus organizers with adjacent DNA affects both the amount and the base ratio of the RNA transcripts produced by this fraction *in vitro*.

18·7 *The differential influence of histones on transcription may involve their amino, acetyl, phosphate, and methyl groups, and perhaps short RNA molecules complexed with them.*

Lysine-rich histones normally have more of their N-terminal ends acetylated than do arginine-rich histones. When some histones are further acetylated at their ends, they permit complementary RNA synthesis *in vitro,* although the same histones without further acetylation suppress RNA synthesis. It appears that histone acetylation also may be involved in controlling gene action *in vivo,* as shown by the findings that (1) nonfunctioning chromatin of calf thymus nuclei contains a smaller percentage of acetylated histones than functioning chromatin and that (2) acetylation of histones (as well as phosphorylation of proteins associated with chromosomes) appears to precede an increase in nuclear RNA synthesis.

Methylation of histones is expected to affect DNA template activity because it sterically hinders the binding between histone and DNA. RNA has been found complexed with histone in chromosomes, where it is insensitive to RNase. Such RNA (about forty nucleotides long, heterogeneous in base sequence and, apparently, rich in adenine and 5, 6-dihydrouracil) may function as an adapter molecule to help bind specific histones to DNA. Each unit of the histone-RNA complex includes, in addition to about 15 molecules of histone, 1 molecule of an RNA-binding protein (not a true histone) that is linked to the dihydrouracils of one molecule of RNA.

18·8 *Translation is inhibited by proteins which coat ribosomes during mitotic metaphase.*

Mammalian ribosomes isolated from interphase cells are translationally active *in vitro,* although ribosomes from metaphase cells are relatively inhibited. Treatment of metaphase ribosomes with trypsin restores almost full translational capacity. Likewise *in vivo,* viral RNA (hence RNA-dependent RNA polymerase) is synthesized when a mammalian cell is infected with an RNA virus during interphase but not during mitotic metaphase. These results suggest that at various stages of mitosis, protein coats ribosomes and thereby blocks translation.

Questions and Problems

18·1 What evidence would you accept as an indication that the RNA surrounding a puff in a salivary gland chromosome is not double-stranded?

18·2 How would you show that the RNA associated with a puff is a transcript of the puff DNA rather than an accumulation of RNA synthesized elsewhere?

18·3 Is the observation that only about 20% of all bands puff in a salivary gland cell in accord with your expectation? Explain.

18·4 Why are lampbrush chromosomes not seen in amphibian somatic cells or cells undergoing spermatogenesis?

18·5 Why might basic proteins be necessary for the regulation of transcription of human DNA but not of phage DNA?

18·6 Do you expect that each locus of DNA in higher organisms which encodes a different polypeptide is complexed with a unique histone? Explain.

18·7 Give one advantage of the inhibition of translation during mitosis.

18·8 How do you suppose that ribosomes inhibited from functioning during mitosis become uninhibited?

18·9 D. M. Fambrough and J. Bonner have found that the histones of pea buds and calf thymus are strikingly similar. What does this result suggest about
(a) the histones in all organisms?
(b) the number of genes coding for histones?
(c) the evolutionary origin of histones?
(d) the functioning of histones in different organisms?

References

Akinrimisi, E. O., Bonner, J., and Ts'o, P. O. P. 1965. Binding of basic proteins to DNA. J. Mol. Biol., 11: 128–136.

Allfrey, V. G., Faulkner, R., and Mirsky, A. E. 1964. Acetylation and methylation of histones and their possible role in the regulation of RNA synthesis. Proc. Nat. Acad. Sci., U.S., 51: 786–794.

Beermann, W., and Clever, U. 1964. Chromosome puffs. Scient. Amer., 210: 50–58, 156.

Benjamin, W., Levander, O. A., Gellhorn, A., and DeBellis, R. H. 1966. An RNA-histone complex in mammalian cells: the isolation and characterization of a new RNA species. Proc. Nat. Acad. Sci., U.S., 55: 858–865.

Bonner, J., Huang, R. C. C., and Gilden, R. V. 1963. Chromosomally directed protein synthesis. Proc. Nat. Acad. Sci., U.S., 50: 893–900.

Bonner, J., and Ts'o, P. O. P. (Editors) 1964. *Nucleohistones*. San Francisco: Holden-Day, Inc.

Busch, H. 1965. *Histones and Other Nuclear Proteins*. New York: Academic Press.

Davidson, E. H., Crippa, M., Kramer, F. R., and Mirsky, A. E. 1966. Genomic function during the lampbrush stage of amphibian oogenesis. Proc. Nat. Acad. Sci., U.S., 56: 856–863.

de Reuck, A. V. S., and Knight, J. (Editors) 1966. *Histones: Their role in the transfer of genetic information*. Boston: Little, Brown and Co.

Frenster, J. H., Allfrey, V. G., and Mirsky, A. E. 1963. Repressed and active chromatin isolated from interphase lymphocytes. Proc. Nat. Acad. Sci., U.S., 50: 1026–1032.

Gall, J. G., and Callan, H. G. 1962. H^3 uridine incorporation in lampbrush chromosomes. Proc. Nat. Acad. Sci., U.S., 48: 562–570.

Huang, R. C. C., and Bonner, J. 1962. Histone, a suppressor of chromosomal RNA synthesis. Proc. Nat. Acad. Sci., U.S., 48: 1216–1222.

Huang, R. C. C., and Bonner, J. 1965. Histone-bound RNA, a component of native nucleohistone. Proc. Nat. Acad. Sci., U.S., 54: 960–967.

Izawa, M., Allfrey, V. G., and Mirsky, A. E. 1963. The relationship between RNA synthesis and loop structure in lampbrush chromosomes. Proc. Nat. Acad. Sci., U.S., 49: 544–551.

Izawa, M., Allfrey, V. G., and Mirsky, A. E. 1963. Composition of the nucleus and chromosomes in the lampbrush stage of the newt oocyte. Proc. Nat. Acad. Sci., U.S., 59: 811–817.

Liau, M. C., Hnilica, L. S., and Hurlbert, R. B. 1965. Regulation of RNA synthesis in isolated nuclei by histones and nucleolar proteins. Proc. Nat. Acad. Sci., U.S., 53: 626–633.

Lin, H. J., Karkas, J. D., and Chargaff, E. 1966. Template functions in the enzymic formation of polynucleotides, II. Metaphase chromosomes as templates in the enzymic synthesis of ribonucleic acid. Proc. Nat. Acad. Sci., U.S., 56: 954–959.

Littau, V. C., Burdick, C. J., Allfrey, V. G., and Mirsky, A. E. 1965. The role of histones in the maintenance of chromatin structure. Proc. Nat. Acad. Sci., U.S., 54: 1204–1212.

Monroy, A., Maggio, R., and Rinaldi, A. M. 1965. Experimentally induced activation of the ribosomes of the unfertilized sea urchin egg. Proc. Nat. Acad. Sci., U.S., 54: 107–110.

Paul, J., and Gilmour, R. S. 1966. Restriction of deoxyribonucleic acid template activity in chromatin is organ-specific. Nature, Lond., 210: 992–993.

Pogo, B. G. T., Allfrey, V. G., and Mirsky, A. E. 1966. RNA synthesis and histone acetylation during the course of gene activation in lymphocytes. Proc. Nat. Acad. Sci., U.S., 55: 805–812.

Salb, J. M., and Marcus, P. I. 1965. Translational inhibition in mitotic HeLa cells. Proc. Nat. Acad. Sci., U.S., 54: 1353–1358.

Spalding, J., Kajiwara, K., and Mueller, G. C. 1966. The metabolism of basic proteins in HeLa cell nuclei. Proc. Nat. Acad. Sci., U.S., 56: 1535–1542.

Yamazaki, H., and Kaesberg, P. 1966. Analysis of products of protein synthesis directed by R17 viral RNA. Proc. Nat. Acad. Sci., U.S., 58: 624–631. (The main *in vitro* product is similar to lysine-rich histone, which may function *in vivo* to suppress host RNA synthesis.)

CHAPTER 19

Regulation of Gene Action — Position Effect and Dosage Compensation

As we noted in Chapter 17, any phenotypic effect which is dependent upon the relative positions of genes is called a *position effect.* Two different kinds of position effect were mentioned. (1) Folding of the *E. coli* chromosome apparently brings metabolically-related genes at widely separated loci near to each other so that their gene products can interact in a manner that would not otherwise be possible. (2) The functioning of structural genes in an operon depends upon the nearby operator gene and its regulator gene. In this chapter we will consider other position effects in higher organisms, their molecular basis, and their role in the regulation of gene action.

POSITION EFFECT

19·1 *In a position effect the functioning (not the primary structure) of a gene is changed by its gene neighbors.*

Chromosomal rearrangements in Drosophila often give rise to phenotypic effects which are expressed as mosaic or variegated characteristics. For example, the gene for dull-red eye color, w^+, is normally located in region 3C2 of the X chromosome, near the tip of the left arm. If a paracentric inversion brings this locus near to the centromere, a mottled eye color (white with dull-red speckles) results. It might be argued that the mottled eye color is caused by a change in the base sequence of the w^+ gene. Several observations, however, indicate that the primary structure of the w^+ gene is not changed. First, the relocated gene resumes its original function (to produce dull-red eye color) when placed by another inversion near its former gene neighbors in the chromosome. Secondly, a normal w^+ gene inserted by means of crossing over in the place of the "mottled" allele likewise becomes "mottled." Consequently, the change in phenotype brought about by the inversion seems to be the result of a position effect, in which the functioning of the w^+ gene is modified by its new linear gene neighbors.

19·2 *A position effect may be due to a change in a gene's coiling, and hence its capacity to act as a template, caused by a change in its linear gene neighbors.*

At any given stage of the life cycle of a cell, most chromosomal material reacts similarly to certain staining procedures and is called *euchromatin* ("truly" or "correctly colored" material). Some portions of chromosomes, however, stain either darker or lighter and thus are said to consist of *heterochromatin.* Differences in coiling are thought to account for these differences in staining. In Drosophila chromosomes the regions adjacent to centromeres are heterochromatic during mitotic prophase because they become condensed and stain darkly earlier than the other chromosomal regions. In the polynemic chromosome of larval salivary gland cells (which are permanently at interphase), the regions near the centromeres are heterochromatic because they stain more lightly (hence are less coiled) than the other regions of the chromosome.

We can expect that the arrangement of euchromatic and heterochromatic segments within a chromosome is of some advantage to the cell with respect to gene action (see Section 17·6). It is not surprising, therefore, that a shuffling of euchromatic and heterochromatic segments by breakage and reunion will give rise to position effects. For instance, a change in coiling caused by new gene neighbors might affect the ability of a gene to act as template for transcription and might be detectable cytologically.

19·3 *When a segment of euchromatin is moved near to heterochromatin, it becomes heterochromatized, and vice versa. Such cytological changes are correlated with changes in gene action.*

The degree of eye color mosaicism in Drosophila can be correlated with the cytological appearance of the 3C2 region of the X chromosome in larval salivary cells. In wild-type individuals this region is euchromatic. In two mutant strains which have a mosaic eye color (due to colorless ommatidia in a background of pigmented ommatidia), the 3C2 region (containing w^+) is inserted in heterochromatin or much closer to it than before, and sometimes appears heterochromatic. The frequency of *heterochromatization* differs in the two mutant strains: the 3C2 region of one strain, located near the heterochromatin of chromosome IV, is much more often heterochromatized (and has many more colorless ommatidia) than the one located in the heterochromatin of an X chromosome. It seems also that not only the location of the euchromatic segment but its size is of some importance, for the smaller the segment the greater the frequency of heterochromatization. These observations suggest that heterochromatization is associated here with limited template availability, perhaps caused by undercoiling of DNA.

In like manner, rearrangements in which a heterochromatic segment is inserted into a euchromatic region result in the *euchromatization* of the inserted fragment.

19·4 *The frequency of heterochromatization of a chromosomal segment depends upon its parental derivation as well as the other chromosomes present.*

The paracentric inversion *In* sc^8 of the Drosophila X chromosome places the normally euchromatic region containing the *y* (yellow body color) and *ac* (achaete bristles) loci next to a normally heterochromatic region. In relatively few males (16%) both loci become heterochromatic; whereas in homozygous females both loci are heterochromatic 39% of the time. When this sc^8 inversion is made heterozygous so that it has a noninverted homolog, a significant difference in heterochromatization can be seen in the nuclei of larval salivary gland cells, depending on which parent contributed the inverted chromosome. Both loci in the inverted chromosome are heterochromatized in only 20% of the nuclei when maternally-derived, but in 71% of the nuclei when paternally-derived. The meiotic events involving the sc^8 chromosome in one generation apparently affect its gene activity in the next generation.

The frequency of heterochromatization of a chromosomal segment also depends upon the other chromosomes present in the cell. Heterochromatization (and thus variegation of a trait) is reduced, for example, if an extra Y (or another heterochromatin-rich) chromosome is added to the genotype by breeding. The mechanism for this suppression of position effect is not yet clear.

As seen above, heterochromatization and euchromatization are reversible effects. The level of potential activity for a particular segment of chromatin, however, tends to remain fairly constant for several cell generations. (It should be noted that both op^{Ac} and Re^{Ac} genes in corn seem to be heterochromatic regions. Perhaps the position effect in such two-element control systems involves a change in chromatization.)

19·5 *Position effects can also be produced after crossing over. Such position effects are probably not due to a change in chromatization but rather to a change in gene action after transcription.*

The preceding sections describe position effects due to a shift in the relative positions of euchromatic and heterochromatic segments. Such position effects seem to involve a change in transcription brought about by the

$$\begin{array}{cc} \text{CIS} & \text{TRANS} \\ \dfrac{++}{\overline{\text{a b}}} & \dfrac{+\text{b}}{\overline{\text{a}+}} \end{array}$$

Figure 19-1. Cis and trans positions for dihybrid, linked genes.

action of a gene's linear neighbors. Another kind of position effect in Drosophila involves the arrangement of alleles at two closely-linked loci, for example, the X-limited loci for eye color *apr* (apricot) and *w* (white). A genotype of $apr^+ \, w \, / \, apr \, w^+$ yields pale apricot eye color; whereas one of $apr^+ \, w^+ \, / \, apr \, w$ obtained from the first genotype by crossing over yields dull-red eye color. Usually, the phenotype of a dihybrid is the same as the wild type whether the two + alleles are in the same chromosome (*cis position*) or in different homologs (*trans position*) (Figure 19-1). For the *apr* and *w* loci, however, we see that the cis and trans dihybrids are phenotypically different.

There is no reason to expect that this position effect is related to a change in chromatization, since both loci are part of a euchromatic segment. One explanation for the position effect is that the *apr* and *w* loci are transcribed in the same mRNA and code for two polypeptides which combine to form a unit of functional protein. One of the two proteins made from the cis dihybrid thus would be completely functional since the messenger transcribed from the DNA of one homolog contains correct information for both polypeptide chains. Proteins specified by either homolog of the trans dihybrid would each have one defective chain and so be less functional than the normal protein.

A position effect might also result when the different subunits are not encoded in the same mRNA. As before, the two subunits must combine to form functional protein. Hence, the subunits specified by the functional genes in the cis position, being closer to each other than the ones in trans, would be more likely to interact and form functional protein. Such *cis-trans position effects,* therefore, seem to be due to a difference in gene action after transcription.

DOSAGE COMPENSATION

19·6 *Many X-limited genes produce the same phenotypic effect whether in single or double dose.*

In diploid organisms with the heteromorphic sex chromosomes X and Y, X-limited genes not involved in sex determination or differentiation occur in single dose in one sex and in double dose in the other. It would seem advantageous for the organism to control these genes so that their level of activity is equal in both sexes. One method of regulation, called *dosage compensation,* is apparent in studies of the enzyme glucose-6-phosphate dehydrogenase (G-6-PD), which is encoded in human beings by an X-limited gene. Red blood corpuscles from males and from females have the same amount of G-6-PD activity, even though the female has twice the dose of the allele that the male has. Similarly in Drosophila, *apr*/Y males and *apr*/*apr* females produce the same amount of eye pigment. Many other X-limited loci in man and in Drosophila also show dosage compensation.

19·7 *Dosage compensation in man is effected by complete suppression of the action of one allele in the two-dose condition.*

In females heterozygous for a mutant gene which encodes defective G-6-PD, some red blood corpuscles have complete G-6-PD activity and others no activity at all; no corpuscles of intermediate activity are found. It appears that some of these red blood corpuscles are derived from cells in which the normal gene is nonfunctional, and the defective locus functional; others come from cells in which the mutant gene is nonfunctional and the normal locus functional. We conclude, therefore, that in a diploid female only one of the two G-6-PD alleles (sometimes the maternally-derived, sometimes the paternally-derived allele) is expressed in a given cell. Since the female heterozygote has some corpuscles with G-6-PD activity and some without, such an individual can be considered a *functional* (or *phenotypic*) *mosaic* for the G-6-PD locus. At least six other X-limited genes give rise to functional mosaicism in human beings, so it appears that dosage compensation is accomplished by completely suppressing the action of one of two alleles present.

19·8 *In man, clumped sex chromatin is cytological evidence for a mechanism of dosage compensation that probably involves preventing transcription to RNA.*

Many of the diploid interphase nuclei of human females have a large clump of chromatin which touches the nuclear membrane. These clumps are not found in males. This clumped material, called *sex chromatin* or the *Barr body* (after its discoverer), first appears at about the twelfth day of human development. The maximum number of Barr bodies in individuals with an abnormal number of sex chromosomes is 0 in X0 individuals; 1 in XXY and XXYY; 2 in XXX, XXXY; and 3 in XXXX. Cells with fewer than the maximum number have extra-large Barr bodies formed by the fusion of single Barr bodies. Since tetraploid cells (4 sets of A + 4X) of a female have two Barr bodies, it appears that the maximum number of Barr bodies depends on the balance between the number of X chromosomes and the number of sets of autosomes. Hence, one X chromosome is balanced by two sets of autosomes; and each X in excess of this balance clumps.

These cytological observations, which show that the X chromosomes are differentially affected, suggest a mechanism for dosage compensation in man and other mammals. In those organisms that contain Barr bodies, that is, one or more X chromosomes clumped during interphase, all inactivated loci are in the same homolog. The clumping apparently prevents these genes from being transcribed to RNA. Since dosage compensation appears to affect a whole chromosome, we can consider it to regulate gene activity at a "multi-operon" level.

19·9 *Dosage compensation in mammals seems to be a coordinated group of position effects.*

Although mice (unlike most other mammals) have no Barr bodies, one of the female's X chromosomes is heterochromatic. The condensation of this genetic material takes place early in mitosis. When loci in the X are heterozygous, a phenotypic mosaic is produced (for all loci tested but one) – as we might expect according to our earlier discussion. It thus appears that one X chromosome of the female is largely inactivated in interphase.

Female mice heterozygous for a reciprocal translocation between an X chromosome and an autosome have been useful in studying dosage compensation. These females are often phenotypic mosaics when the translocated autosome carries a particular normal allele, and its non-translocated homolog carries the mutant allele (Figure 19-2). (We should note that this variegation by rearrangement is a position effect.) In such reciprocal translocation heterozygotes, the normal trait is more often expressed when the distance between the locus of the normal allele and its attachment to the X is increased. In other words, the normal gene is more often inactivated the closer the attachment point is to the X. A translocated autosomal locus very far away from the X attachment point may not be inactivated at all.

In one reciprocal translocation with the X, no variegation resulted even though another one broken at almost the identical autosomal position did yield variegation. Perhaps this failure was due to the union of the autosomal segment with an X segment incapable of inactivating its neighbor. The X locus normally adjacent to this segment should also be unsuppressible and not show dosage compensation. One such locus was mentioned earlier in this section. The translocation results suggest therefore, that dosage compensation in mammals is essentially a coordinated group of position effects.

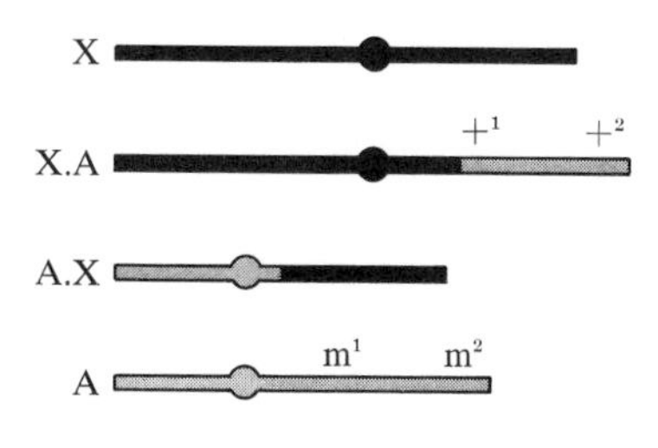

GENOTYPE
Heterozygote for X-Autosome
Reciprocal Translocation

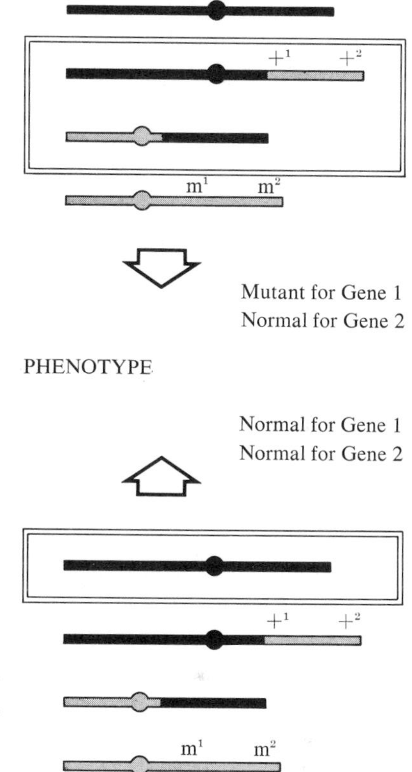

Figure 19-2. A position effect in the mouse. The X chromosome enclosed in a box is heterochromatized. Phenotypes refer to autosomal markers indicated.

19·10 *In mammals, groups of genes are permanently prevented from functioning as the result of dosage compensation.*

As noted earlier, the position effects in Drosophila involving changes in chromatization (often expressed in several successive cell generations) are reversible. In human beings, mice, and other mammals, the phenotypic mosaicism due to dosage compensation also involves changes in chromatization and, apparently, position effects. But in these organisms the position effect appears to be a permanent alteration in gene function. That is, once a chromosome segment is turned off (as in a Barr body) all descendent cells are similarly turned off, despite the intervening mitoses. The result is a phenotypically uniform patch of tissue – not patches within patches.

We should keep in mind, however, that even genes that are permanently turned off must be replicated once each mitotic cycle. Barr body chromosomes replicate last in interphase – indicating that before this time the clumped condition prevents transcription both to RNA and DNA.

In mice and in human beings, the turning off of one X occurs a little over a week after fertilization and seems to affect each X with equal probability. Sometimes, however, this turning off fails to occur in the germ line. For example, one of the two X's in an adult female rat is heterochromatic in somatic tissues, whereas both X's stain similarly in the oocyte.

19·11 *The mechanism of dosage compensation in Drosophila appears to be different from that in mammals; genes in the two-dose condition are apparently suppressed equally.*

Contrary to the situation in mammals, the alleles in both X chromosomes of the Drosophila female are apparently equally functional. We conclude this since (1) the somatically-synapsed polynemic X's in the nuclei of female larval salivary glands and other tissues appear identical; and (2) although the single polynemic X of the male and the paired polynemic X's of the female in salivary gland cells have the expected DNA ratio of 1:2, cells with the single X seem to contain just about as much RNA and protein as those with the double X.

When short segments from any part of the X except the *apr* region are added to the genotype of an *apr*/*apr* female, the eye color usually becomes lighter. These segments apparently contain genes which suppress the activity of the *apr* gene and thus bring about dosage compensation. Hence, they are called *dosage compensator genes.* (Note that the Drosophila female has twice the number of these genes as the male.) Dosage compensation in Drosophila thus seems to involve the equal suppression of genes in the two-dose condition. Perhaps the mRNA's (or the protein products) of the dosage compensator genes interact with RNA transcripts of genes to be compensated; or they could act directly upon these genes by interfering with their transcription to RNA.

Questions and Problems

19·1 How do you account for the finding that radiation-induced structural changes in chromosomes involve heterochromatic regions more frequently than euchromatic regions?

19·2 Construct a formula for the maximum number of Barr bodies in a cell nucleus in terms of x, the number of X chromosomes, and a, the number of sets of autosomes.

19·3 How can you explain that not all nuclei in a tissue of a human female contain a Barr body?

19·4 Compare human males and females with respect to functional X loci.

19·5 What evidence can you give that chromosomal rearrangements can produce position effects on genes some distance from the breakage point?

19·6 How do you know that the Y chromosome is not responsible for dosage compensation in man or Drosophila?

19·7 Drosophila males with or without a Y chromosome that are $X^{apr} X^{apr}$, having been genetically transformed from females by an autosomal mutant gene, have the same eye color as $X^{apr} Y$ males. What can you conclude from such individuals about the role of sex in dosage compensation?

19·8 Are you justified in considering an individual a mutant if it has the same phenotype as a known mutant? Explain.

19·9 Do you expect the *bobbed* (*bb*) gene, which has a locus in both the X and Y chromosomes of Drosophila, to show dosage compensation? Why?

19·10 Are all the loci in one X of a human female inactivated during all interphases? Explain.

19·11 How do you know it is the condensed X that is inactivated in the normal human female?

19·12 What eye color do you expect in Drosophila females that have the *apr* region deleted in one X and a single *apr* present in the other?

19·13 How much G-6-PD activity do you expect in cells that are X0, XX, XXXY, or XXXX in an otherwise diploid organism? Explain.

19·14 How can you explain the phenotype of a woman who is red-green colorblind in only one eye?

19·15 In corn, gene *R* produces anthocyanin pigment in the aleurone and other parts of the plant. In $R^{st} R$ individuals, pigmentation is suppressed and continues to be suppressed in all descendants which contain the *R* gene even if R^{st} is no longer present. R^{st} is said to be *paramutagenic,* and *R*, *paramutable.* How can you account for such a *paramutation* system?

19·16 Explain why in *Drosophila pseudoobscura,* which has a V-shaped X chromosome, more mutants show the same degree of phenotypic effect both in males and females in the arm homologous to the X of *D. melanogaster* than in the arm homologous to the left arm of chromosome III in *melanogaster?*

References

Barr, M. L. 1959. Sex chromatin and phenotype in man. Science, 130: 679–685.

Beutler, E., Yeh, M., and Fairbanks, V. F. 1962. The normal human female as a mosaic of X-chromosome activity; studies using the gene for G-6-PD-deficiency as a marker. Proc. Nat. Acad. Sci., U.S., 48: 9–16.

Brink, R. A. 1964. Genetic repression of *R* action in maize, in *The Role of Chromosomes in Development,* Locke, M. (Editor); New York: Academic Press, pp. 183–230. (Studies on paramutation, see Question 19·15.)

Cock, A. G. 1964. Dosage compensation and sex-chromatin in nonmammals. Genet. Res., Cambridge, 5: 354–365.

Coe, E. H., Jr. 1966. The properties, origin, and mechanism of conversion-type inheritance at the *B* locus in maize. Genetics, 53: 1035–1063. (A case of paramutation that seems to involve a transposable controlling element.)

Davidson, R. G., Nitowsky, H. M., and Childs, B. 1963. Demonstration of two populations of cells in the human female heterozygous for glucose-6-phosphate dehydrogenase variants. Proc. Nat. Acad. Sci., U.S., 50: 481–485.

DeMars, R. 1963. Sex chromatin patterns and the Lyon hypothesis. Science, 141: 649–650.

Evans, H. J., Ford, C. E., Lyon, M. F., and Gray, J. 1965. DNA replication and genetic expression in female mice with morphologically distinguishable X chromosomes. Nature, Lond., 206: 900–903.

Grumbach, M. M., Morishima, A., and Taylor, J. H. 1963. Human sex chromosome abnormalities in relation to DNA replication and heterochromatinization. Proc. Nat. Acad. Sci., U.S., 49: 581–589.

Human Genetics, Cold Spring Harb. Sympos. Quant. Biol., 29, 1965.

Lindsley, D. L. 1965. Chromosome function at the supragenic level. Nat. Cancer Inst. Monogr., 18: 275–290.

Lyon, M. F. 1962. Sex chromatin and gene action in the mammalian X-chromosome. Amer. J. Hum. Genet., 14: 135–148.

Mukherjee, A. S., and Beermann, W. 1965. Synthesis of ribonucleic acid by the X-chromosome of *Drosophila melanogaster* and the problem of dosage compensation. Nature, Lond., 207: 785–786.

Muller, H. J. 1950. Evidence of the precision of genetic adaptation. *The Harvey Lectures* (1947–1948), Ser. 43: 165–229, Springfield, Ill.: Charles C Thomas. Excerpted in *Studies in Genetics,* Muller, H. J., Bloomington, Ind.: Indiana University Press, 1962, pp. 152–171. (Dosage compensation in Drosophila.)

Muller, H. J., and Kaplan, W. D. 1966. The dosage compensation of Drosophila and mammals as showing the accuracy of the normal type. Genet. Res., Cambridge; 8: 41–59.

Ohno, S., Kaplan, W. D., and Kinosita, R. 1960. On isopycnotic behavior of the XX-bivalent in oocyte of *Rattus norvegicus.* Exp. Cell Res., 19: 637–639.

Prokofyeva-Belgovskaya, A. A. 1947. Heterochromatization as a change of chromosome cycle. J. Genet., 48: 80–98.

Russell, L. B. 1963. Mammalian X-chromosome action: inactivation limited in spread and in region of origin. Science, 140: 976–978.

Russell, L. B. 1964. Another look at the single-active-X hypothesis. Trans. N.Y. Acad. Sci., Ser. 2, 26: 726–736.

Russell, L. B. 1964. Genetic and functional mosaicism in the mouse. In *The role of chromosomes in development,* Locke, M. (Editor), New York: Academic Press, Inc., pp. 153–181.

Schwartz, D. 1965. Regulation of gene action in maize. *Genetics Today* (Proc. XI intern. Congr. Genet., The Hague, 1963), 2: 131–135. (Some maternally-contributed genes function in the endosperm while paternally-contributed alleles do not.)

CHAPTER 20

Genetic Regulation of Development

An understanding of the molecular mechanisms of cell differentiation and development is one of the most important goals of biology. A fundamental question to be answered is how cells derived from the same cell develop to perform different functions. For instance, brain cells, kidney cells, and muscle cells in an organism are functionally very different from each other, even though all are derived from the same zygote. Another basic question is how the different kinds of cells in an organism are coordinated. In this chapter we will discuss how such regulation depends upon genetic information.

20·1 *The development and differentiation of a cell is linked to the differential transcription of its genetic information.*

In both unicellular and multicellular organisms, the genetic material is differentially transcribed to RNA at various stages of development. For example, RNA-DNA hybridization studies of *Bacillus subtilis* show that the mRNA's from three different growth phases are derived from distinctly different groups of loci. Apparently, different parts of the genome are transcribed at different times in the bacterial growth cycle. Differential transcription is also indicated during the differentiation of tissue cells in multicellular organisms, since different regions in a chromosome puff at different times. Furthermore, the pattern of puffing during differentiation varies from tissue to tissue.

Cells which have completed differentiation also show differential transcription. In various somatic cells of the mouse, large differences are found among radioactively-labeled RNA molecules isolated from different organs, even though the cells contain the same DNA information. In these differentiated cells, identical DNA information is being read differentially.

From these results, we can see a general relationship between development and transcription. Let us now look at some examples of differentiation and development and consider how these processes depend upon the transcription and translation of genetic information.

20·2 *The amount and kinds of RNA change during oogenesis and early embryogeny. Protein synthesis, inhibited by protein in the unfertilized egg, starts after fertilization.*

Most of the RNA synthesized during oogenesis in toads and frogs is rRNA, which is incorporated into ribosomes that are conserved throughout oogenesis and early development. Although mature oocytes do not synthesize rRNA or sRNA, some sRNA is made after fertilization and during cleavage. Synthesis of mRNA and rRNA starts near the beginning of gastrulation, about the time at which nucleoli first appear. Newly synthesized rRNA is not incorporated into ribosomes, however, until later (after the tail bud is formed) when yolk utilization starts. These results provide a further example of differential transcription.

In the sea urchin, protein synthesis does not occur in the unfertilized egg, even though mRNA and ribosomes are present (see also Section 18·8). Recent evidence indicates that proteins complexed with these ribosomes prevent translation of the bound messenger. After fertilization, proteases (probably converted from an inactive to an active form) digest the protein from the mRNA-ribosome complex and thus permit translation.

20·3 *Various aspects of cell differentiation (competence, induction, and growth rate) are under genetic control.*

Embryological experiments have shown the following: (1) Specific regions of the early embryo (at the gastrula stage, for instance) will become specific kinds of tissues in the mature organism. (2) Cell type can be modified by transplantation of cells into different regions. (The cell type sometimes has been determined before the time of transplantation; such cells are said to have lost their *competence.*) (3) The differentiation of competent cells can be changed through interaction with other cells or cell layers, a process called *induction.* Genetic changes which affect these and other differentiating processes will have a profound effect on development, as we shall see in the examples that follow.

A. *Mutant genes can cause a tissue to lose its ability to respond to induction.* Mesoderm must be induced by presumptive notochordal tissue, that is, tissue which develops into the notochord, in order to differentiate. When the mesoderm from normal mouse embryos is wrapped around presumptive notochordal tissue from either normal embryos or embryos homozygous for the *Brachy* mutant, the mesoderm develops into cartilage and vertebral segments in tissue culture. Under similar conditions, however, mesoderm from homozygous *Brachy* embryos does not form cartilage or vertebrae when in contact with presumptive notochord from normal embryos. It appears, therefore, that the mesoderm of the mutant is unable to respond to the inductive stimuli of presumptive notochordal tissue.

B. *Mutant genes can cause a loss of inductive capacity.* In the mutant chick *wingless,* wing buds are made up of an inner core of mesoderm covered by ectoderm. After the buds develop somewhat, the ectodermal parts degenerate; and development of the wings stops. Even when normal ectoderm is placed around *wingless* mesoderm, the ectoderm soon degenerates. Hence, *wingless* mesoderm seems to have lost the inductive capacity to maintain the surrounding ectoderm.

C. *Mutant genes can prevent induction by preventing contact of the inducing and responding tissues.* A mutant gene in mice sometimes prevents the optic vesicle from making contact with the overlying ectoderm. Consequently, the ectoderm is not induced to form a lens. In mutant individuals in which the optic vesicle does contact the ectoderm, a lens is induced, indicating that the induction-response system is present but fails when the reactants are not in contact.

D. *Mutant genes can cause a general slowdown of growth.* In both homozygotes and heterozygotes for the chick mutant *Creeper* (*Cp*) the differentiation of cartilage is abnormal and their overall development is slower than in ++ individuals. The *Cp* in single or double dose apparently causes a general slowing-down in growth; the structures most affected seem to be those growing most rapidly at the time of the mutant gene's activity. Such a genetically-induced slowdown in growth rate causes a reduction in the size of the hind limbs and the long bones of fore limbs.

Dwarf mice homozygous for a particular mutant gene have all body parts proportionally reduced in size. During early development, both dwarf and normal mice grow at the same rate; later, however, the dwarf suddenly stops growing and never reaches sexual maturity. The anterior pituitary gland of the dwarf is considerably smaller than that of the normal mouse and lacks certain large cells normally present. Since dwarfs can grow to normal size after injection of an extract from a normal pituitary gland (Figure 20-1), it appears that dwarfs lack a growth hormone. Here, then, we are dealing with a chemical messenger, a pituitary hormone, which regulates growth in general, and whose presence is apparently determined by a single pair of genes.

20·4 *Hormones regulate gene action by affecting transcription and translation.*

Both protein and mRNA synthesis in various tissues can be stimulated by certain hormones; for example, in uterine tissue by estrogens, in the prostate gland by testosterone, and in plant buds by a flowering hormone. Experiments involving many different hormones have indicated several ways

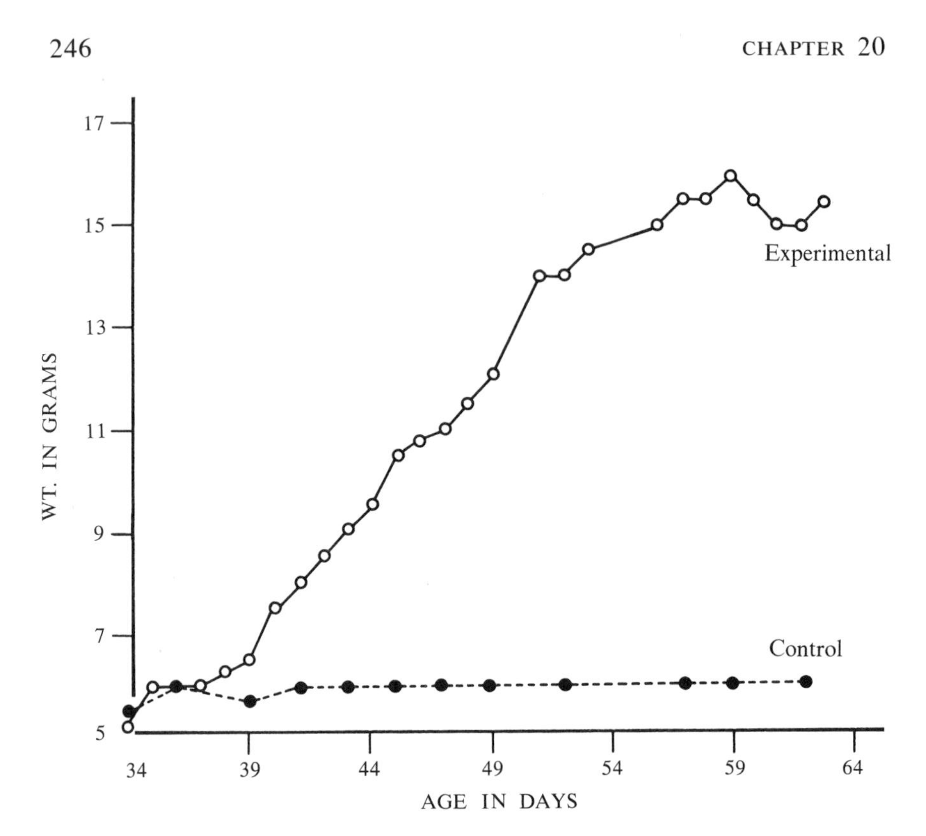

Figure 20-1. Effect of injecting pituitary gland extracts into dwarf mice. (See text for explanation.)

in which they might act at the molecular level. We should keep in mind that (1) although a number of hormones are proteins, many others are steroids or derivatives of a single amino acid (see Figure 20-2) – small molecules in comparison to proteins or nucleic acids – and that (2) since hormones act at low concentration, their metabolic effect must somehow be magnified.

The flowering hormone, which stimulates protein and mRNA synthesis in plant buds, is found to lower the ratio of histone to DNA. Perhaps this hormone enables the DNA to be used as template by causing the removal of histone. Several other types of hormone are known to change the melting profile of isolated mammalian DNA (but not bacterial DNA) in a manner which indicates that they promote strand separation of specific segments of DNA; hence, they also might promote the use of DNA as a template. Some hormones may affect operator or regulator genes or their products; for example, androgens appear to cause a differential transcription to RNA, which could be explained in these terms. It is possible that some hormones act to repress gene action and their antagonistic hormones to derepress gene action.

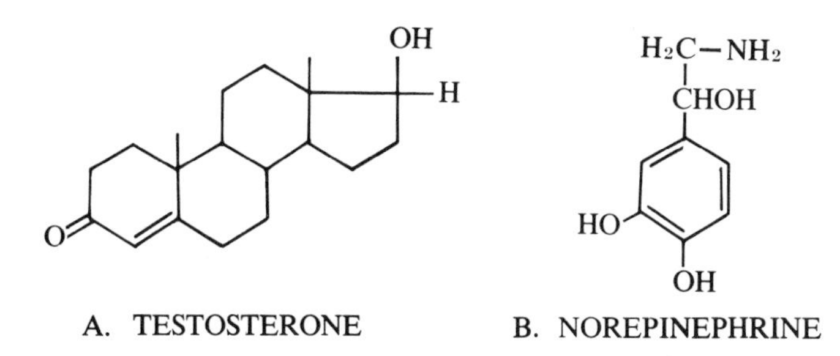

Figure 20-2. Structural formulas of a hormone of steroid (A) and amino acid derivative (B) types.

20·5 *The growth and differentiation of cells are modified when they are exposed to RNA or RNA-containing compounds or infected by viruses.*

Developmental changes can be induced in a growing cell by the introduction of RNA or RNA-containing compounds. For example, mouse ascites tumor cells ordinarily do not produce serum albumin *in vitro,* but can do so after exposure to RNA from the liver of a normal mouse or calf. In several strains of cancer cells, RNA introduced into the cell seems to function as mRNA for at least an hour. The enzymes synthesized (for example, tryptophan pyrrolase and glucose-6-phosphatase) apparently have much the same activity as the enzymes produced by the RNA-donor cell.

In a sense, viruses regulate the growth and differentiation of hosts by taking over their metabolic machinery. As we saw earlier, ϕT4 utilizes host materials for synthesis of its own DNA and protein. Temperate phages and various episomes can modify cellular growth and differentiation by turning host genes on or off. The cancer-inducing viruses polyoma and SV-40 are able permanently to alter properties of mouse fibroblast cells grown in tissue culture. Some of the characteristics acquired by the virus-infected cells appear to involve latent properties of the cell. For example, polyoma virus causes a marked increase in the synthesis of host DNA and enzymes involved in its synthesis; and certain virus-infected cells regain their ability to synthesize collagen, a protein whose production had been suppressed in the uninfected cells.

20·6 *Certain cells differentiate to produce a particular antibody.*

As we have seen above, a cell's interactions with its environment have an important effect on development and differentiation. Another important consequence of such interactions is antibody formation. *Antibodies* are specific proteins produced by cells upon exposure to certain macromolecular substances called *antigens,* which are often proteins but can also be carbohydrates or nucleic acids. The antibody is used by the cell to complex with the antigen that induced its formation.

Antibody formation in the rat involves the following sequence of events. After exposure to an antigen, certain cells called *plasmablasts* begin to synthesize ribosomes and mRNA at a high rate; their endoplasmic reticulum develops extensively. Each plasmablast then undergoes about nine divisions to form a colony of mature *plasma cells,* which do not divide again. Each of these cells produces protein (and a small amount of RNA) of which 90 to 95% is a single type of antibody. In antibody formation, then, an antigen causes a plasma cell to produce a specific protein almost exclusively. The mechanism by which an antigen causes specific antibody formation remains unclear.

20·7 *Some evidence indicates that the synthesis of specific types of RNA in nerve cells is associated with learning and memory. RNA synthesis likewise seems to play a role in the electrical activity of neurons.*

A number of observations suggest that the learning process involves the production of RNA in nerve cells. For instance, in Parkinson's disease, a nervous disorder, profound changes in RNA base ratios arise in nerve tissue. Interference with RNA synthesis in the brain of the rat sometimes impairs learning. Experiments such as the following seek to elucidate the relationship between RNA and learning. When rats are placed in a learning situation (involving balance), the amount of nuclear RNA in specific neurons and the A/U ratio increase; the relative amount of C decreases. When the responses do not involve learning, these neurons show the increase in RNA but not the change in base ratio. RNA content per cell and base ratios have also been studied in single cortical neurons of right-handed rats forced to use the left hand to obtain food. Neurons serving both sides of a single individual show an increase in RNA. Early in the learning period, however, the cortical neurons on the learning side synthesize small amounts of RNA rich in A and U; later in the learning period these neurons synthesize an increased amount of RNA with a base ratio like that of rRNA. These results suggest that, in an acute learning situation, select parts of the genome are transcribed in a first stage which may correspond to the labile period of short-term memory; a second stage, in which ribosomal-type RNA is formed, may constitute the period of fixation of long-term memory.

In the California sea hare, giant neurons in certain ganglia produce electrical discharges with characteristic patterns and frequencies even after removal from the organism. One particular neuron shows a burst of electrical activity at about the time of transition from dark to light (dawn).

Other neurons store information about the time of the light to dark transition. A change in the sea hare's light-dark schedule for half a dozen or so cycles causes the isolated cells to have a new discharge pattern. Injection of actinomycin D into these giant neurons sometimes gives rise to a phase advance and at other times to a phase delay. Such results indicate that DNA-dependent RNA synthesis is linked with the long-term electrical activity of neurons.

20·8 *Some cell differentiation is associated with a change in amount of genetic material.*

We noted earlier how the addition of viral DNA to a cell can affect the differentiation and development of the host. Furthermore, we saw that different cells in the same organism can contain different amounts of genetic information. For instance, the human liver contains cells whose nuclei are polyploid, and in corn the gametophyte generation is haploid, and the sporophyte, diploid. We expect such changes in DNA content to have various effects on differentiation.

In many organisms, the loss of genetic material is associated with development. Several examples of such losses are mentioned below.

1. The fungus gnat Sciara eliminates chromosomes from the nuclei of somatic and germinal cells in a systematic way.

2. Certain species of Ascaris lose a number of chromosome fragments when a polycentric chromosome breaks up into many smaller chromosomes in somatic cells.

3. Drosophila females extrude DNA from the nuclei of nurse cells in the ovary.

4. In the grasshopper *Melanoplus differentialis*, all the cells in certain testicular tubes normally disintegrate, and large quantities of DNA are liberated.

5. In the Dipteran Tipula, the oocyte nucleus has a body (containing 50% of all DNA present) which disappears at diplonema.

20·9 *DNA not used for transcription may be used as raw material for new DNA synthesis and possibly as messenger DNA.*

Nuclear DNA in the cytoplasm may serve as raw material for the synthesis of new DNA in the nucleus or other organelles. This function may be the fate of the DNA lost as described in the previous section. Other DNA may be supplied by sperm which enter an egg but do not fertilize it, since only one sperm per egg is used in fertilization. Such DNA may also act as a messenger in protein synthesis. The following examples lend some support to this hypothesis.

1. As the salivary gland cells of Rhynchosciara and of Sciara larvae differentiate, puffed regions of the chromosomes synthesize disproportionately more DNA than non-puffed regions. (Ordinary replication involves a proportional synthesis.)

2. The nucleoplasm of the newt oocyte contains about a thousand nucleoli, each of which is free of the main chromosomal body and appears to have a nucleolus organizer segment of DNA attached.

3. Germinating wheat seeds and growing roots of wheat and corn contain metabolically labile double-stranded DNA of low molecular weight (around 1×10^5) which has a higher G + C content than the high molecular weight DNA present.

4. Up to 41% of the DNA in *Aedes aegypti* mosquito larvae is double-stranded and has a molecular weight of about 5×10^5. This DNA, apparently nuclear in origin, is essentially absent in pupae and adults.

5. The DNA content of the salivary gland cell of the snail Helix decreases as a particular secretion product is made.

20·10 *Abnormal differentiation, as in cancer, may be due to changes in genetic information, transcription, or translation.*

We have seen in this chapter that normal differentiation requires the correct transcription and translation of a given amount of genetic information. Failure of differentiation to occur (or loss of accomplished differentiation – dedifferentiation) are clearly often due to changes in these normal components. Cancer cells result from the abnormal differentiation of normal cells and are characterized by an abnormally high rate of mitosis, the production of cancerous progeny cells, and a lesser response to the organism's mechanisms of regulation than the normal cells from which they arose.

The apparent permanency and transmissibility of a cancerous condition implies that there must be a permanent modification in gene content or action. It is not surprising, therefore, that the following can be carcinogenic: (1) exposure to mutagenic agents such as high-energy radiations and certain chemical substances, (2) various viral infections, and (3) exposure to certain nonmutagenic chemical substances. In no instance are we yet sure, however, whether a cancer is due to a mutation (say, by addition, subtraction, or relocation of genetic material), a change in transcription (by a permanent turning off or turning on of genes that are normally otherwise), or an alteration of the translational machinery (perhaps, a self-perpetuating change at the level of the ribosome and amino acyl-sRNA's). It is probable that different cancers arise by different means.

Questions and Problems

20·1 In what way does the genotype itself differentiate during a human life cycle?

20·2 Give experimental evidence that development of a mammal is not the result of the organism's genetic information alone.

20·3 In what general or specific ways do genetic factors affect developmental pathways?

20·4 What inferences can you make from the observations that the nucleus of a plasma cell is shrunken and dense, and seems to have no nucleolus? Formulate your answer in molecular terms.

20·5 What do you suppose happens to radioactively-labeled DNA taken in by mammalian cells in tissue culture? How would you test your hypotheses?

20·6 Tell how the following may be used by the cell:
(a) DNA excised in the repair of dimer formation and single-strand breaks;
(b) nonintegrated DNA transferred in transformation, conjugation, or transduction.

20·7 Such DNA-containing viruses as vaccinia and pseudorabies never stimulate but often inhibit host DNA synthesis. On the basis of this observation and information given in this chapter, propose a mechanism for the molecular basis of virus-induced cancer.

20·8 Certain cancer-inducing DNA viruses have such a small amount of genetic material that it is difficult to determine whether or not the cancer cells contain any viral DNA. Suggest a way to detect the presence of viral genes in these cells. (See reference to Fujinaga, K., and Green, M.)

20·9 In what way does the arrangement of the genes in the map of ϕT4D shown in Figure 8-3 suggest that viral gene action is regulated during phage development?

20·10 What general conclusions about genes and development are supported by the following observations of K. Marushige and H. Ozaki working with sea urchin embryos?
(a) Chromatin isolated from a later stage (pluteus) has twice the template activity for DNA-dependent RNA synthesis *in vitro* as chromatin isolated from an earlier stage (blastula).
(b) Removal of chromosomal proteins increases this template activity of the DNA and abolishes the difference in template activity between blastula and pluteus chromatin.
(c) They obtained results indicating that pluteus chromatin has twice the number of sites for binding DNA-dependent RNA polymerase as blastula chromatin.

20·11 Although the administration of hydrocortisone *in vivo* causes isolated rat liver chromatin to have an increased template activity for RNA synthesis *in vitro,* M. E. Dahmus found that the administration of hydrocortisone directly to liver chromatin isolated from untreated rats had no such effect on template activity. What can you conclude from these results about the mechanism of action of this hormone?

References

Bachvarova, R., Davidson, E. H., Allfrey, V. G., and Mirsky, A. E. 1966. Activation of RNA synthesis associated with gastrulation. Proc. Nat. Acad. Sci., U.S., 55: 358–365.

Bell, E. 1965. *Molecular and Cellular Aspects of Development.* New York: Harper & Row, Publishers.

Bonner, J. 1965. *The Molecular Biology of Development.* New York: Oxford University Press.

Dawid, I. B. 1966. Evidence for the mitochondrial origin of frog egg cytoplasmic DNA. Proc. Nat. Acad. Sci., U.S., 56: 269–276.

Differentiation and Development, 1964. Boston: Little, Brown and Co. and J. Exp. Zool., 157, No. 1.

Doi, R. H., and Igarashi, R. T. 1964. Genetic transcription during morphogenesis. Proc. Nat. Acad. Sci., U.S., 52: 755–762.

Dreyer, W. J., and Bennett, J. C. 1965. The molecular basis of antibody formation: a paradox. Proc. Nat. Acad. Sci., U.S. 54: 864–869.

Ebert, J. D. 1965. *Interacting Systems in Development.* New York: Holt, Rinehart & Winston, Inc.

Edgar, R. S., and Wood, W. B. 1966. Morphogenesis of bacteriophage T4 in extracts of mutant-infected cells. Proc. Nat. Acad. Sci., U.S., 55: 498–505.

Flexner, L. B., and Flexner, J. B. 1966. Effect of acetoxycycloheximide and of an acetoxycycloheximide-puromycin mixture on cerebral protein synthesis and memory in mice. Proc. Nat. Acad. Sci., U.S., 55: 369–374.

Fujinaga, K., and Green, M. 1966. The mechanism of viral carcinogenesis by DNA mammalian viruses: viral-specific RNA in polyribosomes of adenovirus tumor and transformed cells. Proc. Nat. Acad. Sci., U.S., 55: 1567–1574.

Gahan, P. B. 1962. The possible genetic significance of cytoplasmic deoxyribonucleic acid. (Abstr.) Heredity, 17: 603.

Gaito, J. (Editor) 1966. *Macromolecules and Behavior.* New York: Appleton-Century-Crofts, Inc. (The involvement of DNA, RNA, and other macromolecules in learning and memory.)

Genetic Control of Differentiation. 1965. Brookhaven Sympos. Biol. No. 18.

Goldberg, M. L., and Atchley, W. A. 1966. The effect of hormones on DNA. Proc. Nat. Acad. Sci., U.S., 55: 989–996.

Hanafusa, H., and Hanafusa, T. 1966. Determining factor in the capacity of Rous sarcoma virus to induce tumors in mammals. Proc. Nat. Acad. Sci., U.S., 55: 532–538. (Seems to be chiefly the viral envelope.)

Hood, L. E., Gray, W. R., and Dreyer, W. J. 1966. On the mechanism of antibody synthesis: a species comparison of L-chains. Proc. Nat. Acad. Sci., U.S., 55: 826–832.

Hormonal Control of Protein Biosynthesis, 1965. J. Cell Comp. Physiol., 66: Suppl. 1.

Hotta, Y., and Stern, H. 1963. Molecular facets of mitotic regulation, II. Factors underlying the removal of thymidine kinase. Proc. Nat. Acad. Sci., U.S., 49: 861–865.

Hydén, H., and Egyházi, E. 1964. Changes in RNA content and base composition in cortical neurons of rats in a learning experiment involving transfer of handedness. Proc. Nat. Acad. Sci., U.S., 52: 1030–1035.

Hydén, H., and Lange, P. W. 1965. A differentiation in RNA response in neurons early and late during learning. Proc. Nat. Acad. Sci., U.S., 53: 946–951.

Lang, C. A., and Meins, F., Jr. 1966. A soluble deoxyribonucleic acid in the mosquito *Aedes aegypti.* Proc. Nat. Acad. Sci., U.S., 55: 1525–1531.

Liao, S., Barton, R. W., and Lin, A. H. 1966. Differential synthesis of ribonucleic acid in prostatic nuclei: evidence for selective gene transcription induced by androgens. Proc. Nat. Acad. Sci., U.S., 55: 1593–1600.

Lima de Faria, A., and Moses, M. J. 1966. Ultrastructure and cytochemistry of metabolic DNA in *Tipula.* J. Cell Biol., 30: 177–192.

Lima de Faria, A., and Nordqvist, T. 1962. Disintegration of H^3-labelled spermatocytes in *Melanoplus differentialis.* Chromosoma, 13: 60–66.

Locke, M. (Editor) 1963. *Cytodifferentiation and Macromolecular Synthesis.* New York: Academic Press.

Locke, M. (Editor) 1964. *The Role of Chromosomes in Development.* New York: Academic Press.

Markert, C. L., and Ursprung, H. 1963. Production of replicable changes in zygote chromosomes of *Rana pipiens* by injected proteins from adult liver nuclei. Develop. Biol., 7: 560–577.

McCarthy, B. J., and Hoyer, B. H. 1964. Identity of DNA and diversity of messenger RNA molecules in normal mouse tissues. Proc. Nat. Acad. Sci., U.S., 52: 915–922.

McElroy, W. D., and Glass, B. (Editors) 1958. *A Symposium on the Chemical Basis of Development.* Baltimore: The Johns Hopkins Press.

Melander, Y. 1965. Mitotic events in animal embryogenesis and alterations of genetic activity. Hereditas, 52: 387–401.

Niu, M. C., Cordova, C. C., Niu, L. C., and Radbill, C. L. 1962. RNA-induced biosynthesis of specific enzymes. Proc. Nat. Acad. Sci., U.S., 48: 1964–1969.

Nossal, G. J. V. 1964. How cells make antibodies. Scient. Amer., 211: 106–115, 154, 156.

Sampson, M., Katoh, A., Hotta, Y., and Stern, H. 1963. Metabolically labile deoxyribonucleic acid. Proc. Nat. Acad. Sci., U.S., 50: 459–463.

Sanyal, S., and Niu, M. C. 1966. Effect of RNA on the developmental potentiality of the posterior primitive streak of the chick blastoderm. Proc. Nat. Acad. Sci., U.S., 55: 743–750.

Sonneborn, T. M. 1963. Does preformed cell structure play an essential role in cell heredity? In *The Nature of Biological Diversity,* Allen, J. M. (Editor), New York: McGraw-Hill Book Co., Inc. Chap. 7, pp. 165–221.

Sonneborn, T. M. 1964. The differentiation of cells. Proc. Nat. Acad. Sci., U.S., 51: 915–929.

Stern, H., and Hotta, Y. 1963. Regulated synthesis of RNA and protein in the control of cell division. Brookhaven Sympos. Biol., 16: 59–72.

Strumwasser, F. 1965. The demonstration and manipulation of a circadian rhythm in a single neuron, pp. 442–462. In: *Circadian Clocks,* J. Aschoff (Editor). Amsterdam: North Holland Publ. Co.

Sussman, M. 1964. *Growth and Development, Second Edition.* Englewood Cliffs, N.J.: Academic Press.

Symposium on Macromolecular Aspects of the Cell Cycle, J. Cell. Comp. Physiol., 62: Suppl. 1, 1963.

Tsutsui, E., Srinivasan, P. R., and Borek, E. 1966. tRNA methylases in tumors of animal and human origin. Proc. Nat. Acad. Sci., U.S., 56: 1003–1009.

Whiteley, A. H., McCarthy, B. J., and Whiteley, H. R. 1966. Changing populations of messenger RNA during sea urchin development. Proc. Nat. Acad. Sci., U.S., 55: 519–525.

CHAPTER 21

The Evolution of Proteins and Populations

By considering the proteins of present-day organisms, we can tell a great deal about their genetic material for the following reason: Such proteins are translations of genetic information according to a code which is essentially universal and whose degeneracy is limited. Furthermore, by considering the occurrence of these proteins among groups of organisms as well as individuals, we can learn much about the evolution of proteins, their genes, and populations.

THE EVOLUTION OF PROTEINS

21·1 *Hemoglobin is a tetrameric protein composed of two different dimers. Normal adults synthesize hemoglobin A and hemoglobin A_2.*

Human hemoglobin is a protein composed of two different dimers, each dimer consisting of identical polypeptide chains. These four chains, arranged approximately in the form of a tetrahedron, each contain about 140 amino acids and have a molecular weight of about 17,000. The chains are folded back on themselves and each has an iron-containing heme group that fits into a pocket on the strand's outer surface.

Hemoglobin isolated from normal adults is of three types: A(or A_1), A_2, and A_3. The A component, called *hemoglobin A* (*Hb-A*) makes up nearly 90% of the total hemoglobin; the A_2 component (Hb-A_2) about 2.5%. The rest is Hb-A_3, which is probably Hb-A that has become chemically altered during aging of the red blood corpuscles.

In vitro, Hb-A can dissociate into its two dimers, which can reassociate to form the Hb-A tetramer once again. If the monomers are represented as α^{A} and β^{A}, the reversible reaction can be symbolized as

$$\alpha_2^{A}\beta_2^{A} \rightleftharpoons \alpha_2^{A} + \beta_2^{A}.$$

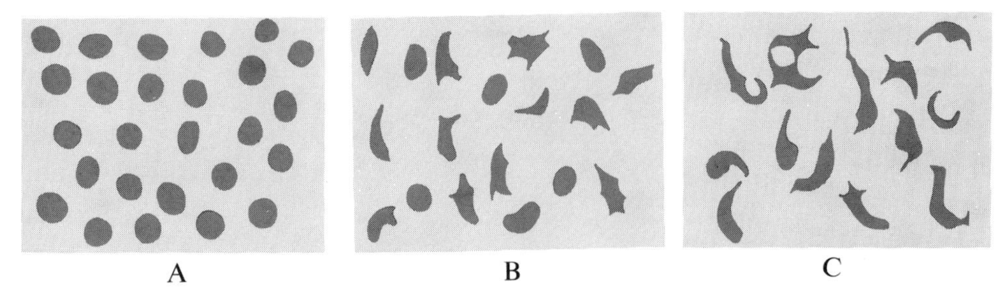

Figure 21-1. Silhouettes showing various types of human red blood corpuscles: (A) normal, in normal homozygote, (B) sickle cell trait, in mutant heterozygote, (C) sickle cell disease, in mutant homozygote.

21·2 *The α and β chains of Hb-A are encoded by different loci. Various mutant genes cause single amino acid substitutions in these chains.*

Sickle cell anemia occurs in individuals homozygous for a gene for sickling (Figure 21-1). The red blood corpuscles of such individuals assume a sickle-like shape when deoxygenated and are destroyed by the spleen, thus leading to a serious anemia. Persons heterozygous for this mutant gene have *sickle cell trait* but are only mildly anemic, if at all. The difference between normal and sickle cells is found in the hemoglobin they contain: the hemoglobin of the mutant homozygote differs from hemoglobin A (Figure 21-2) at only one amino acid position, number 6 in the β chain, where valine is present instead of glutamic acid. Cells heterozygous for the sickling gene produce both this abnormal type of hemoglobin, *hemoglobin S* ($\alpha_2^A\beta_2^S$), and the normal hemoglobin A ($\alpha_2^A\beta_2^A$).

Numerous other abnormal hemoglobins have been found (Figure 21-3). In some instances the alteration in the amino acid sequence occurs in the α chain, as in hemoglobin I (which has a substitution at position 16). These single amino acid substitutions can be explained as the result of the mutation of a single base in the gene encoding hemoglobin. It appears that two different genes must code for the two kinds of chains, since mutant genes that change the α chain produce no change in the β chain (and vice versa) and since the genes for defects of the α and β chains segregate independently. An adult homozygous for the hemoglobin A genes ($\alpha^A\alpha^A\beta^A\beta^A$) thus produces $\alpha_2^A\beta_2^A$ tetramers. A homozygote for the sickle cell gene ($\alpha^A\alpha^A\beta^S\beta^S$) produces $\alpha_2^A\beta_2^S$ hemoglobin, and one homozygous for hemoglobin I ($\alpha^I\alpha^I\beta^A\beta^A$) produces $\alpha_2^I\beta_2^A$. A dihybrid, $\alpha^A\alpha^I\beta^A\beta^S$, produces four types of globin: $\alpha_2^A\beta_2^A$, $\alpha_2^I\beta_2^A$, $\alpha_2^A\beta_2^S$, $\alpha_2^I\beta_2^S$, since either product of the two different α-specifying genes can join to either of the two different products of the β-specifying genes.

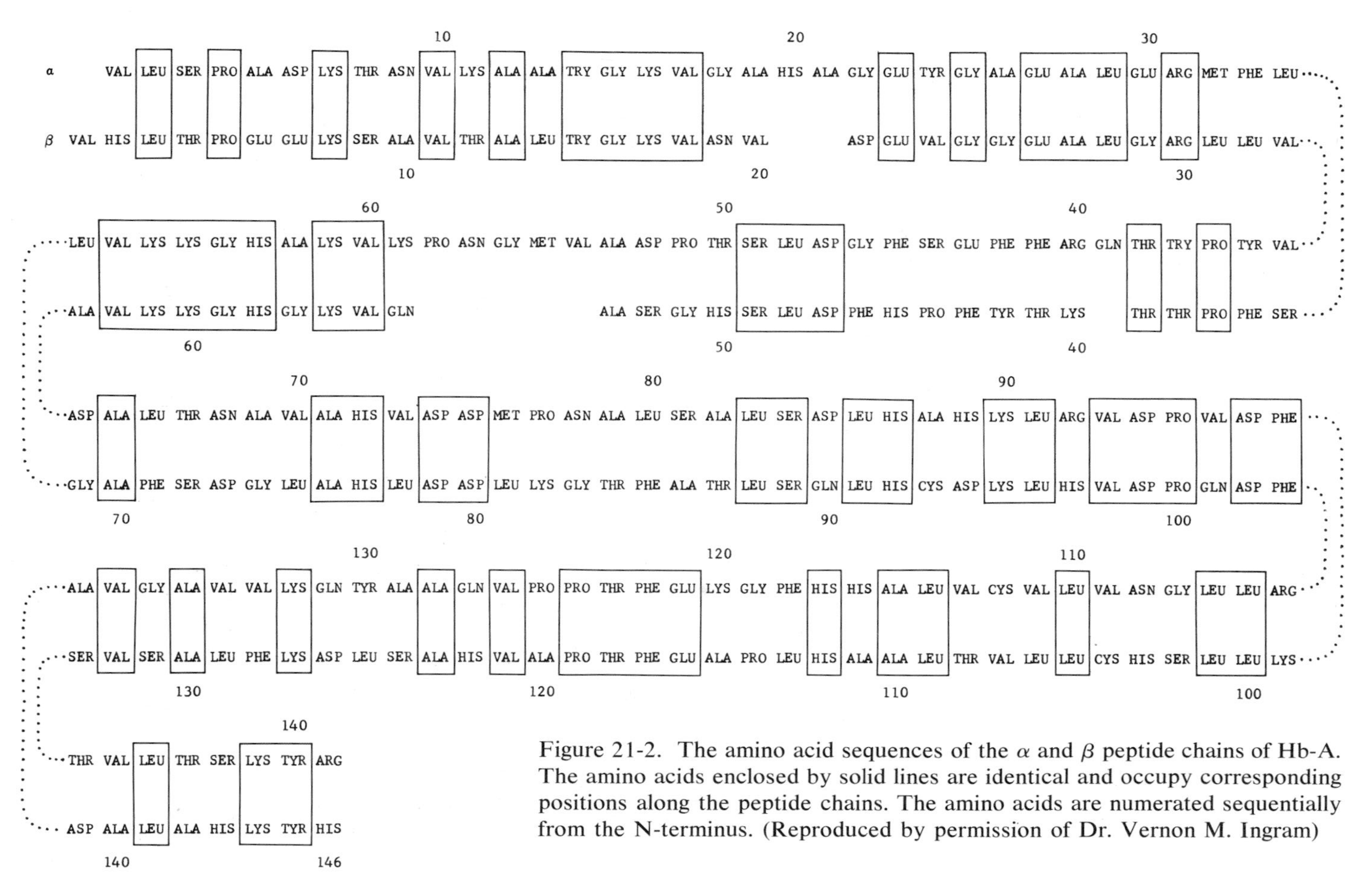

Figure 21-2. The amino acid sequences of the α and β peptide chains of Hb-A. The amino acids enclosed by solid lines are identical and occupy corresponding positions along the peptide chains. The amino acids are numerated sequentially from the N-terminus. (Reproduced by permission of Dr. Vernon M. Ingram)

Hb Type	Amino Acid Position	Change Involved
	β Chain	
S	6	Glu → Val
C	6	Glu → Lys
$G_{\text{San José}}$	7	Glu → Gly
E	26	Glu → Lys
$M_{\text{Saskatoon}}$	63	His → Tyr
Zürich	63	His → Arg
$M_{\text{Milwaukee-1}}$	67	Val → Glu
O_{Arabia}	121	Glu → Lys
D_{Punjab} (= D_{Cyprus})	121	Glu → Glu-NH_2
	α Chain	
I	16	Lys → Asp
G_{Honolulu}	30	Glu → Glu-NH_2
Norfolk	57	Gly → Asp
M_{Boston}	58	His → Tyr
$G_{\text{Philadelphia}}$ (= G_{Azakuoli})	68	Asp-NH_2 → Lys
$O_{\text{Indonesia}}$	116	Glu → Lys

Figure 21-3. Variants of Hemoglobin A.

21·3 *The Hb-A_2 tetramer contains an α dimer and a δ dimer. The latter is encoded by a gene δ, which has mutant alleles and is linked to gene β.*

The Hb-A_2 tetramer can also be dissociated into its two dimers; one is an α_2^A dimer, and the other is called a $\delta_2^{A_2}$ dimer, which is very similar to β_2^A, differing only by four (or perhaps eight) of 146 amino acids.

Some individuals produce only about half the normal amount of Hb-A_2. In place of the missing hemoglobin is an equal amount of another kind of hemoglobin, Hb-B_2, which consists of two α and two δ chains. The α chains are of the normal α^A type, but the δ chain appears to differ from the δ^{A_2} type by one amino acid: gly → arg at position 16.

The δ chain is specified by a gene, δ, which is neither an allele of α^A nor of β^A. Persons with both Hb-A_2 and Hb-B_2, therefore, have the hybrid genotype $\delta^{A_2}\delta^{B_2}$ with respect to the δ genes. The δ gene has been found to be linked to the β gene. Thus, the rare person who produces some Hb-S ($\alpha_2^A\beta_2^S$) and Hb-A and some Hb-B_2 ($\alpha_2^A\delta_2^{B_2}$) and Hb-A_2 has the genotype $\frac{\alpha^A}{\alpha^A}\frac{\beta^A\delta^{B_2}}{\beta^S\delta^{A_2}}$.

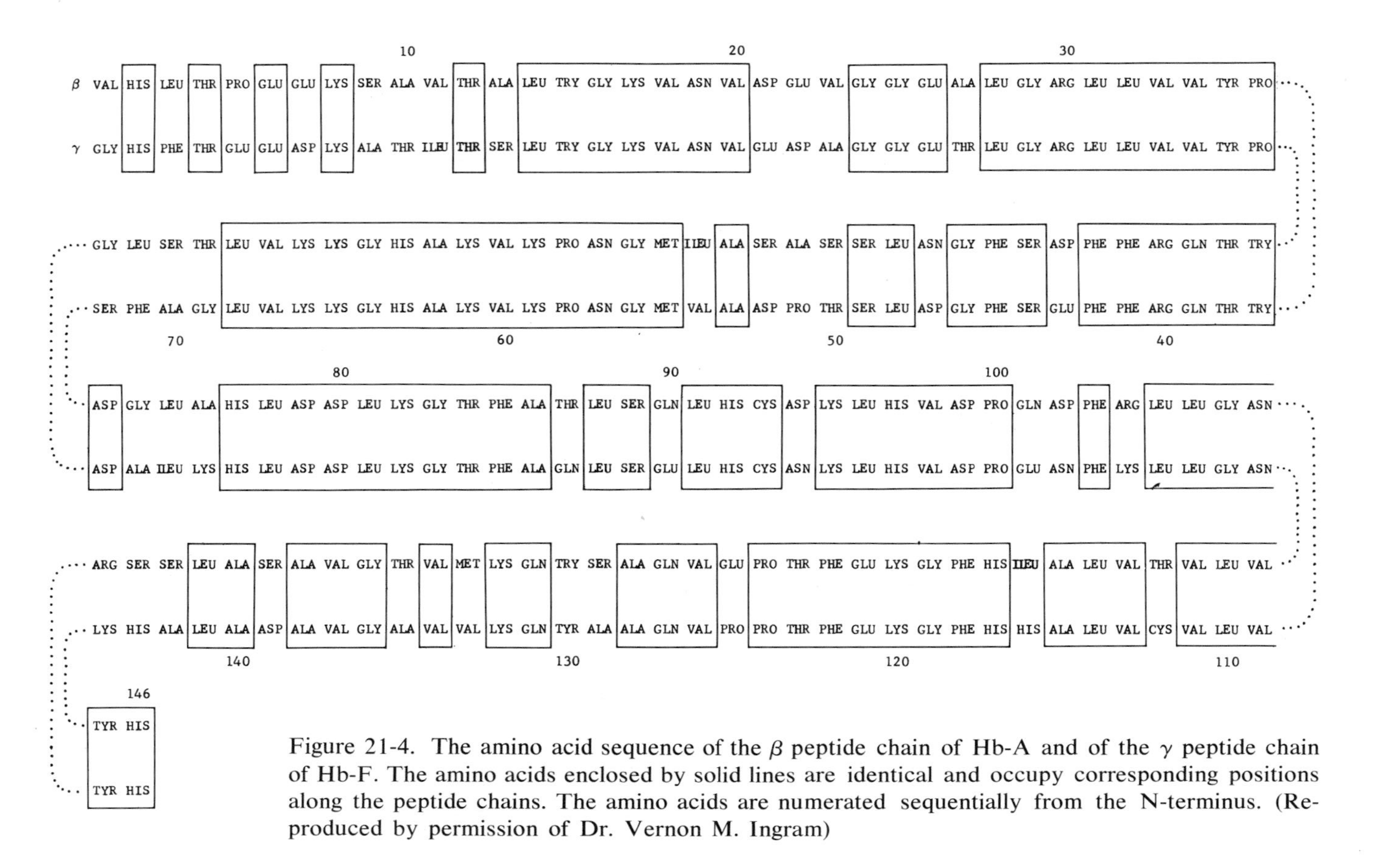

Figure 21-4. The amino acid sequence of the β peptide chain of Hb-A and of the γ peptide chain of Hb-F. The amino acids enclosed by solid lines are identical and occupy corresponding positions along the peptide chains. The amino acids are numerated sequentially from the N-terminus. (Reproduced by permission of Dr. Vernon M. Ingram)

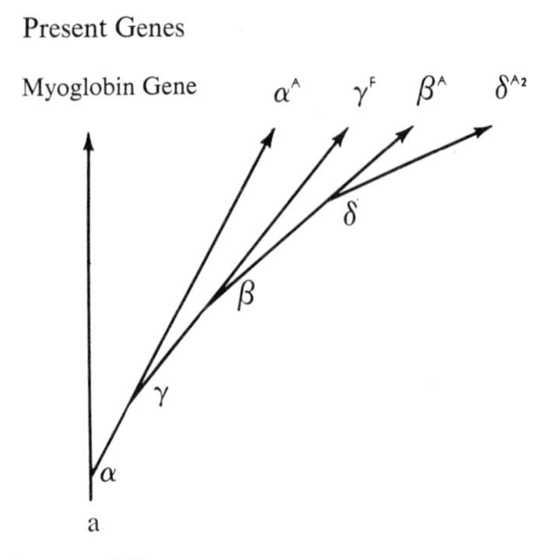

Figure 21-5. Hypothesized evolution of myoglobin and various hemoglobin chains from an ancestral gene.

21·4 *Fetal hemoglobin is $\alpha_2^A\gamma_2^F$. Its γ chains are encoded at a fourth locus, γ.*

The hemoglobin of a human fetus, *hemoglobin F*, contains two α chains identical to those in adult hemoglobin A. The other two chains in Hb-F differ from the α, β, and δ chains and are called γ chains (Figure 21-4). Normal hemoglobin F is thus $\alpha_2^A\gamma_2^F$. Homozygotes for the sickling gene make hemoglobin F which seems to be normal. Apparently, then, the gene for the mutant β chain has no effect on the γ chain. Some abnormal types of Hb-F, however, are thought to contain altered γ chains. It is likely, therefore, that a separate gene, γ^F, specifies γ^F chains.

Hb-A appears in the fetus as early as the twentieth week and gradually replaces Hb-F. Even at the time of birth, however, an infant has some Hb-F in its blood. This change from Hb-F to Hb-A indicates that during development the γ^F gene is turned off and gene β^A is turned on.

In summary, four genes seem to be involved in the manufacture of hemoglobin, namely α, β, δ, and γ, each of which code for a different polypeptide.

21·5 *By duplication and additional mutation, an ancestral gene may have given rise to the gene for myoglobin and the gene sequence, $\alpha \rightarrow \gamma \rightarrow \beta \rightarrow \delta$.*

Myoglobin, a protein in muscle, is similar in a number of ways to an α or β chain of hemoglobin. For example, it is approximately the same length, having 155 amino acids; it also has regions coiled right-handedly; and it contains a single heme group on its surface. Although the amino acid sequences of α and β hemoglobin chains differ considerably from myoglobin's, in a number of positions the same amino acid occurs on both the myoglobin chain and a hemoglobin chain. Their similar three-dimensional structures may be related to these similarities.

Let us postulate, then, that a single gene is the common ancestor for the myoglobin, α, and β chains (Figure 21-5). Since today's species have separate loci for the specification of myoglobin and hemoglobin, the ancestral gene, *a*, must have become duplicated in the genome. One of these *a* genes then led to the present gene for myoglobin, and of the other to the genes for hemoglobin chains. Some support for the common-origin hypothesis comes from the finding that the lamprey appears to have a rather primitive form of hemoglobin, a single polypeptide chain with a molecular weight of about 17,000.

Since all known hemoglobins of vertebrates (except the lamprey) have a chain that starts with Val-Leu-, they may all be derived from mutations of the α gene, whose encoded chain starts with Val-Leu-. The ancestral gene for hemoglobin may thus be α. It may later have mutated to an allele whose polypeptide product could form a dimer, thereby conferring a selective advantage, since by doubling the number of heme groups, the chain's efficiency as an oxygen carrier is increased. If the α locus became duplicated, and one of the loci mutated to form a gene which produced γ chains, dimerization might lead to a predecessor of fetal hemoglobin. Further dimerization to a tetramer would yield fetal-type hemoglobin, $\alpha_2\gamma_2$. The tetrameric hemoglobin is thought to be more efficient than dimeric hemoglobin in carrying oxygen.

Since the β^{A} chain is known to differ from both the α^{A} and γ^{F} chains by about twenty amino acids, we cannot by this knowledge alone determine which type of chain was the ancestor of the β chain. Although nearly as many mutants involving the α as the β chain have been discovered, only those affecting the β chain occur with any appreciable frequency. This finding, together with the similarities between vertebrate chains mentioned earlier, indicates that changes in the α dimer of a tetramer result in greater selective disadvantage than those in the β chain. Certain changes in the α chain may result in loss of ability to form tetramers. (The homotetramer of α^{A}, α_4^{A}, has never been observed, although β^{A} chains can form β_4^{A} and γ^{F} chains can form γ_4^{F}.) Moreover, a change in gene α^{A} modifies both fetal and adult hemoglobin, whereas a change in γ^{F} affects only fetal hemoglobin. It would seem more likely, therefore, that the ancestral β gene arose as product of a duplication of the γ gene.

As mentioned earlier, the β^{A} and δ^{A_2} chains differ in less than ten amino acids. Perhaps the β gene was duplicated in the genome, with one of the two genes subsequently mutating to become the δ gene. That this dupli-

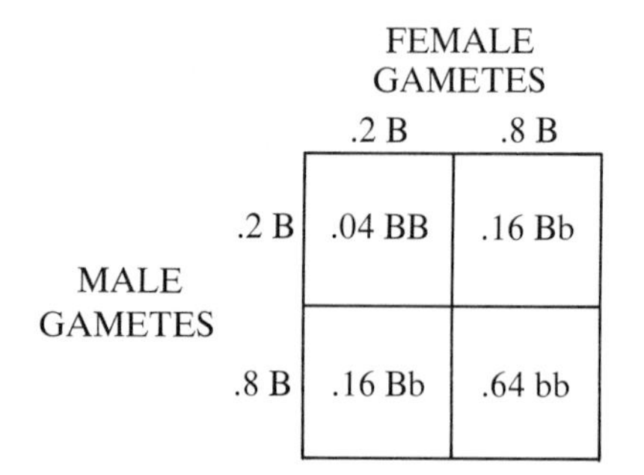

The F_1 Population
.04 BB + .32 Bb + .64 bb

The F_1 Gene Pool
B = .04 + .16 = .2
b = .16 + .64 = .8

Figure 21-6. F_1 genotypes and the gene pool they produce.

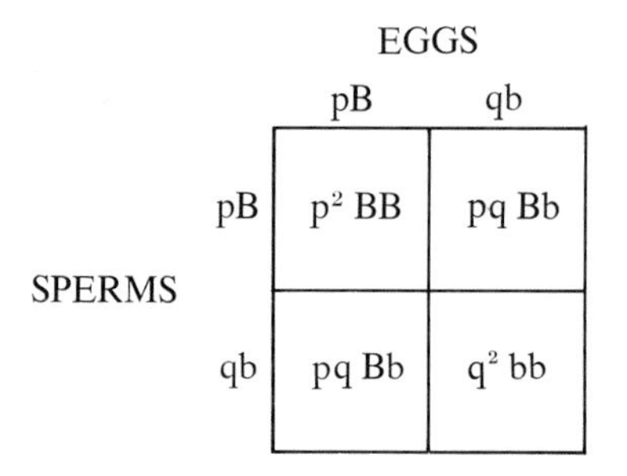

Figure 21-7. The types and frequencies of genotypes produced by a gene pool composed of p *B* and q *b*.

cation occurred "recently" is suggested by the small number of differences in amino acids between the β^A and δ^{A_2} chains, by the apparent persistence of linkage of the β^A and δ^{A_2} genes, and by the occurrence of A_2-like hemoglobin in primates only. In summary, it appears that the sequence of genetic evolution was $a \rightarrow \alpha \rightarrow \gamma \rightarrow \beta \rightarrow \delta$.

THE EVOLUTION OF POPULATIONS

21·6 *Cross-fertilizing populations that conform to the Hardy-Weinberg equilibrium principle have a static gene pool.*

A member of a *cross-fertilizing population* usually has the opportunity to choose a mate from a large number of the other members. The gametes of all mating individuals constitute a *gene pool* from which the genes of the next generation are drawn.

Let us consider a large cross-fertilizing population in whose gene pool the *B* and *b* alleles are present in the frequencies .2 and .8, respectively. Following random union of gametes (Figure 21-6), 4% of the resulting zygotes will be *BB*; 32%, *Bb*; and 64%, *bb*. From these calculations we can tell what the gene pool will be in the gametes of the F_1 (in the absence of mutation). *BB* individuals furnish 4% of all gametes; consequently, 4% carry *B*. *Bb* individuals supply 32% of all gametes, of which half carry *B* and the other half *b*. Therefore, 20% of the genes in the gene pool are *B*. And *b* gametes comprise 80% of the gene pool. The gene pool of the F_1 thus is identical to that of the P_1. Furthermore, the genotypes of the F_2 and all subsequent generations will remain in the same ratio, because the frequencies of *B* and *b* in the gene pool remain constant.

We can express the preceding analysis in more general terms by letting p equal the fraction of male and female gametes in the population which carry *B*, and q equal the fraction which carry *b*. For eggs, as well as for sperm, $p + q = 1$. Figure 21-7 gives the results of random union of these gametes. The offspring population, then, is $p^2\, BB + 2\, pq\, Bb + q^2\, bb$. And, the frequency of *B* and *b* among the gametes produced by the offspring population is

$$B = p^2 + pq = p(p + q) = p$$
$$b = q^2 + pq = q(q + p) = q.$$

Thus, the gene frequencies have remained the same as in the gametes of the previous generation. Likewise, all future generations will have the same gene pool and the same relative frequencies of diploid genotypes. This concept of a static gene pool is called the *Hardy-Weinberg equilibrium principle*.

21·7 *Mutation, selection, genetic drift, and migration (the principle causes of biological evolution) change the composition of a gene pool.*

If the Hardy-Weinberg equilibrium principle applied to all gene pools, gene frequencies would remain unchanged and the evolution of different genotypes and phenotypes would not occur. We recall, however, that certain conditions had to be fulfilled for the maintenance of a genetic equilibrium. We ruled out *mutation*, since it obviously can affect the frequency of the *B* and *b* alleles. The frequency of an allele will change if the mutation rates to it and from it are different. Whenever a gene frequency is changed, the genetic equilibrium is shifted until a new one is attained. This new equilibrium is maintained until the gene frequency is altered again.

In order for the Hardy-Weinberg principle to hold, the *reproductive potential,* or *biological fitness,* of each genotype must be the same. Otherwise, individuals with one genotype rather than another may be preferred as mates, in which case the reproductive potential of an individual will not be independent of the alleles under consideration. Moreover, if individuals of one genotype produce more offspring than those of another, the frequency of the genes responsible for this higher biological fitness will tend to increase. By operating on genotypes of different fitness, *selection* brings about changes in gene frequencies and, consequently, shifts in genotypic frequencies at equilibrium.

Gene frequencies will remain constant in successive generations only if the random sample of gametes drawn from the gene pool is infinitely large. The gametic sample, of course, is finite, so the gene frequencies will drift in accordance with the chance composition of the sample. This chance drift in gene frequencies is greater the smaller the sample drawn from the gene pool. In large populations *random genetic drift* produces only relatively minor, and, therefore, negligible changes in the composition of the gene pool.

Gene frequencies and genetic equilibrium can also be changed by *migration.* If the population is changed by individuals entering or leaving it, then the gene frequencies may change.

21·8 *Most species have arisen from races whose genetic differences increased until their gene pools became reproductively isolated from each other.*

Populations in different parts of the world differ both in types and frequencies of alleles in their gene pools. We can define a *race* as a population that has a characteristic gene pool. A species of cross-fertilizing organisms usually consists of several races, each adapted to a different environment. These races make up a genetic continuum through interracial breeding, so that the species as a whole has a single gene pool. On the other hand, different cross-fertilizing species are genetically discontinuous; and their gene pools are isolated from one another for genetic as well as environmental reasons.

Different species possess different gene pools. Formation of a species, or *speciation,* among cross-fertilizing individuals is thought to involve in most instances the genetic divergence of races, originally of the same species, to form separate and different gene pools. The usual inability of two species to mate with each other and the usual sterility of any interspecific hybrids are factors which make speciation an irreversible process. Once a gene pool has reached the species level, it can never lose its identity through crossbreeding with another species.

21·9 *Hybrid vigor is due to the adaptive superiority of the heterozygote over one or both types of homozygote.*

In cross-fertilizing species, inbreeding leads to increased homozygosis and, usually, to a loss of vigor. Heterozygotes usually have an adaptive superiority over such homozygotes. If, for instance, $A'A'$ is less vigorous than AA, the AA' heterozygote will be superior to one of the homozygotes. Sometimes, the heterozygote is of greater fitness than either homozygote. *Hybrid vigor,* or *heterosis,* is the condition in which the heterozygote is superior to one homozygote or both.

We can see the first type of heterosis by crossing two pure lines of corn homozygous for different detrimental mutants (represented by small letters): $AA\ bb\ CC\ dd \times aa\ bb\ CC\ DD$. With normal alleles at three loci rather than at two, as in each parent, the F_1 generation ($Aa\ bb\ CC\ Dd$) is superior.

The sickle cell trait is an example of the other type of heterosis, in which heterozygotes are superior to both homozygotes. Homozygotes for the sickle cell gene ($\beta^S\beta^S$) usually die from anemia before adolescence. Heterozygous individuals ($\beta^A\beta^S$), we recall, are either normal or have a slight anemia. In some places the frequency of β^S in the gene pool follows the Hardy-Weinberg principle, but in others, β^S is more frequent than expected. The reason for this difference is that the $\beta^A\beta^S$ heterozygote is more resistant to certain kinds of malaria than the $\beta^A\beta^A$ homozygote. Of course, in places where malaria does not occur, the β^S gene confers no advantage upon a person, so that the fitness of the heterozygote is lower than that of the normal homozygote, but higher than that of the $\beta^S\beta^S$ individual, whose fitness is zero. In such places, the genes for sickle cell anemia are removed from the gene pool and the incidence of the disease is lower. In other places, however, even though heterozygotes may be slightly anemic, their resistance to malaria makes them of greater overall fitness than $\beta^A\beta^A$ homozygotes. In other words, natural selection keeps the β^S gene in the gene pool even though it is lethal when homozygous.

We should notice that heterosis does not necessarily involve only a single pair of genes. It may also involve combinations of alleles and nonalleles.

21·10 *Protein analysis can be used to study the genetics of populations.*

The presence and relative amounts of certain proteins can be determined for individual fruit flies. A fly is homogenized and the resulting mixture is exposed to an electrical field to separate compounds of different molecular weight and electrical charge. Fractions can then be tested for enzymatic activity with different substrates. If different fractions digest the same substrate, we conclude that they contain different forms of the same enzyme – *isoenzymes,* or *isozymes*. They are thought to be encoded by different alleles at the same locus (or, perhaps, at duplicated loci).

If two parents each contain a different enzyme which acts on a given substrate, and each F_1 individual contains both enzymes, we can conclude that the parents are pure and their progeny are hybrids at a single locus. In some instances, an enzyme proves to be encoded at two or three different loci and to exist in a half a dozen allelic forms.

Related studies can determine not only the time of enzyme formation during development, but also genetic diversity, mutation frequencies, and changes in the gene pool with respect to time. Thus, the genetics of populations can be studied by analysis of the proteins they contain.

Questions and Problems

21·1 How many heme groups are present in hemoglobin A? A_2? Myoglobin?

21·2 What specific mutations in the β^A gene will give rise to its β^S allele?

21·3 What Hb-A_2 tetramers are found in individuals heterozygous for Hb-S? Hb-I?

21·4 Why is it extremely difficult to study by means of recombination techniques the position within the hemoglobin gene of mutant loci affecting the same polypeptide chain?

21·5 Give two explanations of why hemoglobin never contains heterodimers, even in heterozygotes.

21·6 Write the tetrameric formulas for the hemoglobins produced in the human fetus and adult of individuals with the following genotypes:

1. $\alpha^A\alpha^A$; $\beta^A\beta^A$, $\delta^{A_2}\delta^{A_2}$; $\gamma^F\gamma^F$
2. $\alpha^A\alpha^I$; $\beta^A\beta^A$, $\delta^{A_2}\delta^{A_2}$; $\gamma^F\gamma^F$
3. $\alpha^A\alpha^A$; $\beta^A\beta^S$, $\delta^{A_2}\delta^{A_2}$; $\gamma^F\gamma^F$
4. $\alpha^A\alpha^I$; $\beta^A\beta^A$, $\delta^{A_2}\delta^{B_2}$; $\gamma^F\gamma^F$

21·7 A woman that produces Hb-S marries a man who produces Hb-B_2. What are their most probable genotypes? What genotypes and what kinds of hemoglobin are expected in their children?

21·8 What kinds of mutations of gene *a*, the ancestor of today's hemoglobin and myoglobin genes, do you suppose were retained in the population?

21·9 In what way does the molecular evolution of proteins elucidate the molecular evolution of genes?

21·10 A population gene pool is composed of .6*A* and .4*a*. What are the diploid genotypes and their frequencies expected at Hardy-Weinberg equilibrium?

21·11 Suppose amylase occurs in two alternative forms, A and B, in a Drosophila population at Hardy-Weinberg equilibrium. If 49% of the population has only type A, what percentage of the population is expected to produce both A and B types?

21·12 What percentage of individuals in a population at Hardy-Weinberg equilibrium is heterozygous for B if its only allele, b, is homozygous in 9%, 16%, 36% of the individuals?

21·13 Assume a population gene pool at Hardy-Weinberg equilibrium contains three alleles a^1, a^2, and a^3 in the proportion of .6, .3, .1. For each allele give the proportion of individuals expected to be
(a) homozygotes.
(b) heterozygotes.

21·14 Which do you suppose has been more important in speciation, the accumulation of many mutations each of which produces a small change in protein composition, or the occurrence of relatively few mutations each of which produces gross changes in protein composition? Justify your answer.

21·15 Invent an explanation for heterosis in which the heterozygote is superior to either homozygote involving an enzyme encoded by a single locus.

21·16 How would you go about determining the mutation frequency of a locus from a population study of its protein product? What could you conclude from such work about the total mutation frequency at this locus?

21·17 Evidence has been obtained that a polysome active in protein synthesis in the reticulocyte has its ribosomes arranged in a closed ring rather than in an open chain. How may this evidence be related to the synthesis of hemoglobin?

References

Allison, A. C. 1956. Sickle cells and evolution. Scient. Amer., 195: 87–94.

Anfinsen, C. B. 1959. *The Molecular Basis of Evolution.* New York: J. Wiley & Sons, Inc.

Baglioni, C. 1963. Correlations between genetics and chemistry of human hemoglobins. In *Molecular Genetics, Part I,* Taylor, J. H. (Editor), New York: Academic Press, Chap. 9, pp. 405–475.

Bloom, B. 1966. A speculation relating the genetic code and the evolutionary process. Proc. Nat. Acad. Sci., U.S., 55: 375–376. (Use of amino acid sequences to detect genetic duplications.)

Cantor, C. R., and Jukes, T. H. 1966. The repetition of homologous sequences in the polypeptide chains of certain cytochromes and globins. Proc. Nat. Acad. Sci., U.S., 56: 177–184.

Fitch, W. M., and Margoliash, E. 1967. Construction of phylogenetic trees. Science, 155: 279–284. (Based on mutation distance—the minimal number of nucleotide substitutions required so that a gene coding for one protein can code for a similar one.)

Ingram, V. M. 1961. Gene evolution and the haemoglobins. Nature, Lond., 189: 704–708. Reprinted in *Papers on Human Genetics,* Boyer, S. H., IV (Editor), Englewood Cliffs, N.J.: Prentice-Hall, Inc., 1963, pp. 164–175.

Ingram, V. M. 1963. *The Hemoglobins in Genetics and Evolution.* New York: Columbia University Press.

Johnson, F. M., Kanapi, C. G., Richardson, R. H., Wheeler, M. R., and Stone, W. S. 1966. An analysis of polymorphisms among isozyme loci in dark and light *Drosophila ananassae* strains from American and Western Samoa. Proc. Nat. Acad. Sci., U.S., 56: 119–125.

Jukes, T. H. 1966. *Molecules and Evolution.* New York: Columbia University Press.

Lewontin, R. C., and Hubby, J. L. 1966. A molecular approach to the study of genic heterozygosity in natural populations, II. Analysis of geographical populations of *Drosophila pseudoobscura.* Genetics, 54: 595–609.

MacIntyre, R. J., and Wright, T. R. F. 1966. Responses of esterase 6 alleles of *Drosophila melanogaster* and *D. simulans* to selection in experimental populations. Genetics, 53: 371–387.

Nance, W. E. 1963. Genetic control of hemoglobin syntheses. Science, 141: 123–130.

Schwartz, D. 1966. The genetic control of alcohol dehydrogenase in maize: gene duplication and repression. Proc. Nat. Acad. Sci., U.S., 56: 1431–1436. (Possible role of repression in the evolution of duplicated genes.)

Spiess, E. B. (Editor) 1962. *Papers on Animal Population Genetics.* Boston: Little, Brown and Co.

Wallace, B. 1966. *Chromosomes, Giant Molecules, and Evolution.* New York: W. W. Norton & Company, Inc.

CHAPTER 22

The Origin and Evolution of Genetic Material

The organisms of today are intricate systems of macromolecules that have evolved from simpler macromolecular systems of preceding eras. In this chapter we will consider general aspects of chemical and biological evolution and, in particular, the origin and evolution of genetic material.

22·1 *The origin of genetic material was preceded by three stages: the origin of amino acids and organic bases, of polypeptides and nucleotides, and of polynucleotides.*

About four billion years ago the atmosphere of the Earth was rich in hydrogen, methane, ammonia, and water but poor in free oxygen and carbon dioxide. Laboratory experiments involving such an atmosphere have shown that large numbers of simple chemical radicals and organic molecules can be synthesized under certain conditions. With energy sources such as electrical discharges, heat, high-energy electrons, X rays, sunlight, and ultraviolet light, the following amino acids have been synthesized: glycine, alanine, aspartic acid, and glutamic acid. Other compounds formed include adenine, uracil, phosphoric acid, acetic acid, and succinic acid, as well as some sugars and fatty acids. Long ago, lightning might have been an important energy source for producing such molecules. Meteorites which caused some molecules to pass very rapidly through liquids and gases might also have promoted interactions among molecules. As more and more synthesis took place, especially in the oceans, the products accumulated to form an "organic soup."

The atmosphere changed as oxygen was released and converted to ozone, forming a layer above the Earth. Since ozone absorbs ultraviolet light, this layer prevented light of UV's wavelength (and energy) from reaching the Earth. Consequently, the main sources of energy from the sun thereafter were visible light and heat.

In the presence of excess aspartic and glutamic acids, a mixture of amino acids has been found to form peptide bonds and polymerize into *proteinoids* at temperatures of 200°C or less in a dry heat synthesis.

Nearly all amino acids common to proteins are included in these proteinoids. Linear polymers with a molecular weight of up to 10,000, proteinoids are very similar to natural proteins and polypeptides of corresponding size, and show some catalytic activity. The surface of proteinoid macromolecules may have provided a favorable site for various reactions to take place. Thus proteinoids may have served as rudimentary catalysts in the synthesis of more complex organic compounds from the organic soup, such as nucleotides, polyphosphates, porphyrins, and pigments.

By the action of certain dehydrating agents, nucleotides have been joined nonenzymatically to form polynucleotides of appreciable length. The rate of such a synthesis of polyuridylic acid has been found to increase more than tenfold in the presence of polyadenylic acid. The poly A apparently is used as a template in the synthesis of poly U. Such experiments may indicate steps in the natural origin of polynucleotides.

22·2 *Genetic material serves to maintain and replicate protein systems.*

In today's organisms, genetic material is closely linked to protein: its synthesis is directed by protein, and its information is translated into protein. The first interactions between protein and nucleic acid most probably were the result of chance collisions. From the principles of thermodynamics we know that if the interaction involves a large enough net decrease in energy, the protein and nucleic acid may form a complex with each other. For example, a complex between (one or more) nucleotides and (one or more) amino acids may be more stable than either compound separately. Because there is some kind of specificity between the parts of the complex, we might consider the amino acid portion to be a template for the nucleotide portion, or vice versa. We might even say that these two components code for each other in a primitive manner. Apparently because of the relatively greater chemical stability of nucleic acids, they assumed the role of template as chemical evolution continued, while the chemically more reactive and versatile proteins underwent an elaborate structural and functional evolution that produced increasingly complex organizations of molecules. This evolution eventually produced the first *organism,* essentially a system of proteins whose maintenance and continuity depended upon the use of information stored in nucleic acids.

As we saw in the last chapter, similarities between different types of hemoglobin suggested that the genes for the component polypeptides evolved from a common ancestral gene. The great similarities of DNA and RNA likewise strongly suggest a common precursor. We should not be surprised, then, if a "specialization of labor" has occurred so that DNA (more stable than RNA) has become the transcriptional template, and the less stable RNA the translational template. Another evolutionary advance took place when the organism became able to reproduce. Thereafter, the entire protein system could be replicated by means of nucleic acid information.

22·3 *Genetic material has undergone a quantitative evolution.*

The highly complex organisms of today are supermacromolecular systems whose organization is encoded in genetic nucleic acid. Although some organisms in the past may have evolved and persisted without replication, all those of the present are the progeny of similar predecessors that reproduced. A successful organism, therefore, must reproduce its genetic material. Since the complexity of organisms has increased during the course of evolution, the amount of information (hence, the amount of genetic material) needed to specify an organism has also increased. In some plants, increases in ploidy and subsequent differentiation of genomes have resulted in greater complexity, diversity, and adaptability. It has been estimated that about one quarter of the present species of flowering plants originated as allopolyploids. Autopolyploidy probably did not play as important a role in increasing the gene number of sexually-reproducing organisms, since the occurrence of multivalents (instead of bivalents) during meiosis results in numerous aneuploid gametes. Because of the genetic imbalance which it causes, the gain of whole chromosomes likewise does not seem to be a major mechanism for increasing the amount of genetic material. The relatively small increases in gene number which can occur after chromosome breakage and reunion, however, have played a major role in increasing gene number since they produce changes small enough to be tolerated by the organism.

22·4 *Genetic material has undergone a functional evolution.*

Mutation provides the raw materials for evolution; it is the process which enables organisms of superior genotypes to be produced. If, for instance, several kinds of wild-type organisms depended upon their environment for the same amino acid, the supply of that amino acid would determine the number of organisms that could live. Consequently, "abnormal" organisms that could synthesize this amino acid would be more likely to survive than the wild type. Also favored would be organisms in which a mistake permits another amino acid to be utilized in place of the scarcer one. Hence, the mutation allows the organism greater independence from its environment.

The number of possible different mutations is infinite; most are harmful to the organism. Consequently, certain mechanisms have evolved to counteract mutation. For example, the degeneracy of the amino acid code allows some mutant organisms to live, since a single base change does not necessarily cause the incorrect amino acid to be incorporated. Furthermore, repair systems prevent the expression of some mutations by removing the defective segment and inserting a functional one.

Genetic recombination (from the relatively simple event of breakage-and-reunion to the highly-specialized mechanisms of mitosis, meiosis, and fertilization) is also important in evolution, since it involves the shuffling of genetic material to form new, and possibly better, gene combinations.

In previous chapters, we have seen further evidence of a functional evolution of genetic material; for example, the occurrence of operator and regulator genes.

22·5 *A chemical and biological evolution similar to that of the earth is probably taking place on other planets.*

The universe is thought to be about ten billion years old, and the Earth roughly half this age. In it are an infinite number of stars, many of them, as is our sun, surrounded by planets. Surely, some of these planets are of nearly the same size as the one we live on, and are equally distant from their suns. Perhaps these suns are of similar size and age as ours. The possibility, then, that a chemical and biological evolution similar to ours has occurred elsewhere seems to depend upon the chemical composition of the planets themselves.

Most matter in the universe is either hydrogen or helium with some oxygen, nitrogen, and carbon. The universe is, in fact, richer than the Earth in carbon – the atom that has played such an important role in evolution on this planet. Since the Earth has supported a biological evolution even though it appears a relatively poor place for such a process, it is likely that the universe contains numerous planets on which a similar evolution is taking place.

Even in our own solar system, life may exist on planets other than our own. Venus is enshrouded by opaque, highly-reflecting clouds rich in carbon dioxide and water. From such an atmosphere (in conjunction with elements of the planet's surface) organic compounds might be synthesized. Evidence of organic compounds on Mars has been obtained. Seasonal variations in the color and texture of Mars suggest that some form of life may occur there. Our moon, with no atmosphere and probably no water, does not seem likely to contain any form of life. Analyses of the lunar surface, though, may reveal compounds formed before the satellite lost its atmosphere. It has even been suggested that the moon acts as a gravitational trap for spores drifting between planets and thus serves as an intermediary in an interplanetary gene flow.

If we can investigate planets on which chemical and biological evolution are at stages different from that here, we will be a long way toward answering important questions about evolution on this planet. In whatever ways we further clarify the principles of molecular genetics in the future, though, we can expect this science to continue its unification of the entire field of biology, and, hence, to play an increasingly important role in the modern world.

Questions and Problems

22·1 Why are missiles sterilized before they are sent beyond our atmosphere?

22·2 Give the evolutionary significance of the following observations about phage by J. W. Drake (see references to Chapter 7):
(a) Mutations occur in the absence of DNA replication.
(b) These mutations occur in G⋮C but not A:T base pairs.

22·3 The DNA of higher plants and animals is richer in A + T than in C + G. What advantage might such a base ratio confer upon an organism?

22·4 In what way does the table showing the DNA content of different organisms (Figure 2-11) support the view that biological evolution is closely parallel to the evolution of protein?

22·5 What enzymes were especially important in the first organisms? Justify your choices.

22·6 What effect did the release of oxygen into the atmosphere have on mutation rate?

22·7 Do you suppose some planets have more advanced civilizations than our own? Why?

22·8 How might we convert Venus biologically to an energy-storing planet?

22·9 Can organisms without protein or nucleic acid survive? Explain.

22·10 Why are most mutations harmful?

22·11 What are the evolutionary implications of the finding that amino acid attachment to sRNA is anomalous above 75°C?

22·12 Define genetic material.

References

Abelson, P. H. 1961. Extra-terrestrial life. Proc. Nat. Acad. Sci., U.S., 47: 575–581.

Abelson, P. H. 1966. Chemical events on the primitive earth. Proc. Nat. Acad. Sci., U.S., 55: 1365–1372.

Blum, H. F. 1961. On the origin and evolution of living machines. Amer. Sci., 49: 474–501.

Bryson, V., and Vogel, H. J. (Editors) 1965. *Evolving Genes and Proteins.* New York: Academic Press.

Calvin, M. 1961. The origin of life on earth and elsewhere. Ann. Int. Med., 54: 954–976.

Clark, F., and Synge, R. L. M. (Editors) 1959. *The Origin of Life on the Earth.* New York: Pergamon Press, Inc.

Dobzhansky, Th. 1966. Are naturalists old-fashioned? Amer. Nat., 100: 541–550.

Eakin, R. E. 1963. An approach to the evolution of metabolism. Proc. Nat. Acad. Sci., U.S., 49: 360–366.

Fitch, W. M. 1966. The relation between frequencies of amino acids and ordered trinucleotides. J. Mol. Biol., 16: 1–8. (Evolution of the genetic code.)

Fox, S. W. 1964. Experiments in molecular evolution and criteria of extraterrestrial life. Bio-Science, 14: 13–21.

Fox, S. W. (Editor) 1965. *The Origins of Prebiological Systems.* New York: Academic Press.

Green, D. E., and Hechter, O. 1965. Assembly of membrane subunits. Proc. Nat. Acad. Sci., U.S., 53: 318–325.

Hanson, E. A. 1966. Evolution of the cell from primordial living systems. Quart. Rev. Biol., 41: 1–12.

Hochstim, A. R. 1963. Hypersonic chemosynthesis and possible formation of organic compounds from impact of meteorites on water. Proc. Nat. Acad. Sci., U.S., 50: 200–208.

Horowitz, N. H. 1945. On the evolution of biochemical syntheses. Proc. Nat. Acad. Sci., U.S., 31: 153–157.

Huang, S.-S. 1960. Life outside the solar system. Scient. Amer., 202 (No. 4): 55–63.

Kasha, M., and Pullman, B. (Editors) 1962. *Horizons in Biochemistry.* New York: Academic Press.

Keosian, J. 1964. *The Origin of Life.* New York: Reinhold Publishing Corporation.

Keyl, H. G. 1964. Doubling of the DNA-content of small sections of chromosomes as a factor in evolution. Naturwissenschaften, 51: 46–47.

Lederberg, J. 1960. Exobiology: Approaches to life beyond the earth. Science, 132: 393–400.

Lederberg, J. 1966. Experimental genetics and human evolution. Amer. Nat., 100: 519–531.

Lederberg, J., and Cowie, D. B. 1958. Moondust. Science, 127: 1473–1475.

Matthews, C. N., and Moser, R. E. 1966. Prebiological protein synthesis. Proc. Nat. Acad. Sci., U.S., 56: 1087–1094.

Miller, S. L., and Urey, H. C. 1959. Organic compound synthesis on the primitive earth. Science, 130: 245–251.

Muller, H. J. 1966. The gene as the initiator and the organizing basis of life. Amer. Nat., 100: 493–517.

Oparin, A. I. 1957. *The Origin of Life on Earth, 3rd Edition,* New York: Academic Press.

Oparin, A. I. 1964. *The Chemical Origin of Life.* Springfield, Ill.: Charles C Thomas.

Ponnamperuma, C., Lemmon, R. M., Mariner, R., and Calvin, M. 1963. Formation of adenine by electron irradiation of methane, ammonia and water. Proc. Nat. Acad. Sci., U.S., 49: 737–740.

Sagan, C. 1961. On the origin and planetary distribution of life. Rad. Res., 15: 174–192.

Sinton, W. M. 1959. Further evidence of vegetation on Mars. Science, 130: 1234–1237.

Stahl, F. W., and Murray, N. E. 1966. The evolution of gene clusters and genetic circularity in microorganisms. Genetics, 53: 569–576.

Tax, S. (Editor) 1960. *The Evolution of Life,* (Vol. 1) *Evolution after Darwin.* Chicago: University of Chicago Press.

Urey, H. C. 1966. Some general problems relative to the origin of life on earth or elsewhere. Amer. Nat., 100: 285–288.

Woese, C. R., Dugre, D. H., Saxinger, W. C., and Dugre, S. A. 1966. The molecular basis for the genetic code. Proc. Nat. Acad. Sci., U.S., 55: 966–974. (The binding of organic bases to amino acids reveals a code.)

Yanofsky, C., Cox, E. C., and Horn, V. 1966. The unusual mutagenic specificity of an *E. coli* mutator gene. Proc. Nat. Acad. Sci., U.S., 55: 274–281. (Evolution of base-ratios.)

Zamenhof, S., Heldenmuth, L. H., and Zamenhof, P. J. 1966. Studies on mechanisms for the maintenance of constant mutability: mutability and the resistance to mutagens. Proc. Nat. Acad. Sci., U.S., 55: 50–58.

Author Index

Subject Index

Page numbers in bold face refer to figures.